Flight Training Manual

Transport Canada Air

Flight Traini

ng Manual

THIRD EDITION

gage PUBLISHING LIMITED TORONTO ONTARIO CANADA

Canadian Cataloguing in Publication Data

Canada Dept. of Transport.
  Flight Training Manual

"A revision of the Transport Canada Flying
Training Manual."

ISBN 0 7715 9552 2

1. Flight training — Canada — Handbooks, manuals,
etc. I. Title.

TL712.C35 1979   629.132'52   C79-094223-2

Photographs courtesy Aviation Training Systems Ltd.

Gage Publishing Limited
in association with Transport Canada and the
Canadian Government Publishing Centre,
Supply and Services Canada.

Catalogue No. T52-14/1981E

Fourth printing, 1983

Printed and bound in Canada

Contents

Preface

The aim of this manual is to provide basic, progressive study material for student pilots preparing for licensing, pilots improving their qualifications, and for the guidance of flight instructors. As such, it complements the Transport Canada Flight Instructor Guide.

This manual provides information and direction in the introduction and performance of flight training manoeuvres as well as basic information on aerodynamics and other subjects related to flight training courses. Thus, a working knowledge of the terms and the material in this manual which are relevant to the training being taken will enable the student to gain maximum benefit from the air exercises.

The contributions by many Canadian flight instructors to the material presented in this manual are gratefully acknowledged.

PART ONE

The Aircraft

CHAPTER ONE

Basic Principles of Flight

The Third Law of Motion

Heavier-than-air flight is possible because of certain laws of nature, expressed by various scientific laws and theorems. Of these, Newton's Third Law of Motion is possibly the fundamental one. "For every action there is an equal and opposite reaction." A propeller accelerates a mass of air backwards, and thereby receives an equal forward force. This forward force, called *thrust*, pulls the aircraft ahead.

As the aircraft is thrust forward by the propeller on take-off, the wing meeting the oncoming air commences to generate *lift* (Fig 1-1). As the forward speed of the aircraft increases, this lift force increases proportionately. When the lift force is equal to the weight of the aircraft, the aircraft begins to fly.

The Atmosphere

An aircraft operates in a world which is very near the earth, yet has vastly different properties. This world is the atmosphere, composed of air, which surrounds the earth. We must know something about this atmosphere to understand flight.

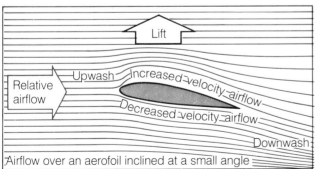

Figure 1-1   Lift Is Generated by Air Travelling Faster above the Aerofoil than below It

Density and Pressure

One property of air which is apt to mislead the novice student of flight is its *density*. Ask the weight of the air in an ordinary room and answers will vary from "almost nothing," to "about 10 pounds." Yet the answer is close to 300 pounds and in a large hall may be over a ton! Raise that half a mile above the earth, though, and the air in it will weigh far less. Its density — its mass per unit volume — has changed. These changes in density are measured as *air pressure*.

It is true, of course, that the density of air is low compared to that of water, yet it is this property of air that makes flight possible. Air being the medium in which flight occurs, as its properties change the properties of a particular flight will change.

The average pressure at sea level due to the weight of the atmosphere is 14.7 pounds per square inch, a pressure which causes the mercury in a barometer to rise 29.92 inches. In a standard situation the pressure drops from 14.7 pounds per square inch at sea level to 10.2 pounds per square inch at 10,000 feet, a drop of 4.5 pounds per square inch.

Temperature Changes (Lapse Rate)

With increase in height there is a decrease in air temperature. The reason for this is that the sun's heat passes through the atmosphere without appreciably raising the temperature. The earth, however, absorbs the heat. The temperature of the earth is raised and the air in contact with it absorbs some of the heat.

The Four Forces

An aircraft in flight is under the influence of four main forces: *lift, weight, thrust,* and *drag* (Fig 1-2).

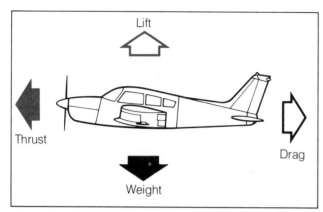

Figure 1-2   The Four Forces

Thrust and Drag Forces

In level flight two principal horizontal forces act on an aircraft — thrust and drag. Thrust is provided by the engine acting through the propeller, and drag by the resistance of the air to the passage through it of the aircraft and all its component parts.

Lift and Weight Forces

The vertical forces acting on an aircraft are lift and weight. Weight is the total weight of the aircraft and its contents; it is considered to act through a single point termed the *centre of gravity*. Lift acts vertically to the relative airflow (Fig 1-3). It does not act vertically to the horizon; in flight it may act at a considerable angle to the horizon. For computation purposes, the force of lift is considered to act through one point of the wing. This point is called the *centre of pressure* (Fig 1-4).

Angle of Incidence and Angle of Attack

Angle of incidence refers to the fixed angle between the plane of the wing chord and the longitudinal axis of the aircraft (Fig 1-5). It should not be confused with *angle of*

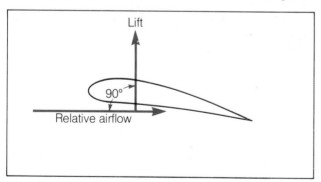

Figure 1-3   Lift Acts at 90 Degrees to the Relative Airflow

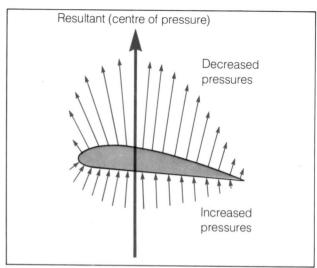

Figure 1-4   Pressure Distribution over an Aerofoil

attack, which varies according to the angle between the wing chord and the relative airflow. This angle can vary according to the direction of motion of the aircraft (Fig 1-6).

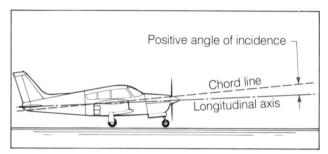

Figure 1-5   Angle of Incidence

Relative Airflow

Relative airflow is always parallel with, and opposite to, the flight path of the aircraft (Fig 1-7). The flight path angle is not necessarily the same as the angle of attack: an aircraft nearing the stall may have a very high angle of attack whereas its flight path may be the same as that of level flight.

Lift

Any flat object, such as a flat plate inclined upwards to the relative airflow, will provide lift (Fig 1-8). The kite is an example of this. The wings of the first aircraft may be likened to a flat plate in this respect. It was later discovered that much more lift could be produced by curving the upper wing surface, and the aerofoil evolved (Fig 1-9). The curved upper surface also provided for a thicker structure, which allowed for increased strength, fuel storage, and eventually the elimination of exterior structural members.

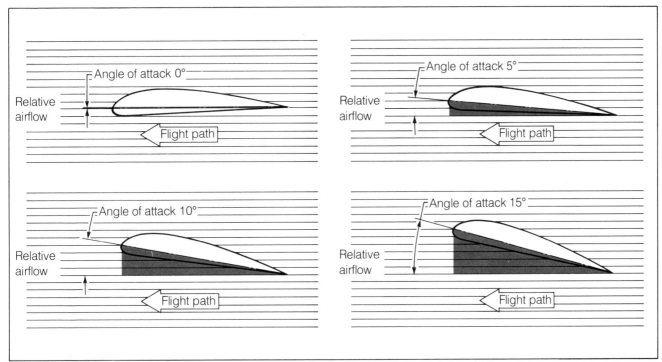

Figure 1-6   Angle of Attack: the Angle between the Chord Line and the Relative Airflow

A full description of the theory behind the production of lift would take many pages, and we do not intend to go into that amount of detail here. Simply stated, the wing generates lift by deflecting air downwards. It also derives lift from the pressure differential between the upper and lower surfaces.

The theoretical expression of this fact is found in *Bernouilli's Theorem*. Simply stated, this theorem means: "As the velocity of air increases, its pressure decreases."

Pressure Distribution over an Aerofoil

Pressure tests of an aerofoil in flight reveal that:

(1) There is a decrease in pressure on the top surface of the wing and an increase in pressure on the lower surface, but,
(2) The pressures are not distributed evenly. The decrease on the top surface and the increase on the bottom are most marked over the front portion of the aerofoil.

If all the pressures in (2) were replaced by a single resultant force, this single force would act less than half-way back from the leading edge of the aerofoil, along the chord. The position on the chord at which this resultant force acts is the *centre of pressure* (Fig 1-4).

Tests also show that as the angle of attack of an aerofoil in flight is increased, the centre of pressure moves gradually forward until at an acute angle (well beyond the ordinary flight angles), it begins to move back again. Since the centre of pressure is the "flight centre of gravity," when it moves back far enough the nose of the aircraft will pitch downwards suddenly as the wing enters a stalled condition (Fig 1-10).

The *boundary layer* is a thin layer of air flowing over the surface of a wing in flight, sometimes no more than a hundredth part of an inch thick. The boundary layer is divided into two parts: (1) the desirable *laminar* layer, and (2) the undesirable *turbulent* layer. Air flowing over the wing begins by conforming to its shape; at this stage the boundary layer is smooth and very thin. This is the laminar layer. There is a point of transition, which moves between the leading and trailing edges of the wing, where the boundary layer starts to become turbulent and increasingly thick. This is the turbulent layer (Fig 1-11).

In order to maintain a laminar flow over as much of the aerofoil surface as possible, the laminar flow-type wing was developed (Fig 1-12). This design is concerned with the transition point. The laminar flow wing is often thinner than the conventional aerofoil, the leading edge is more pointed and the section nearly symmetrical, but most important of all, the point of *maximum camber* (the point of greatest convexity of the aerofoil from its chord) is much further back than on the conventional wing. The pressure distribution on the laminar flow wing is much more even, since the airflow is speeded up very gradually from the leading edge to the point of maximum camber. As the stalling speed of a laminar flow wing is approached, the transition point will move forward much more rapidly than it will on a conventional aerofoil.

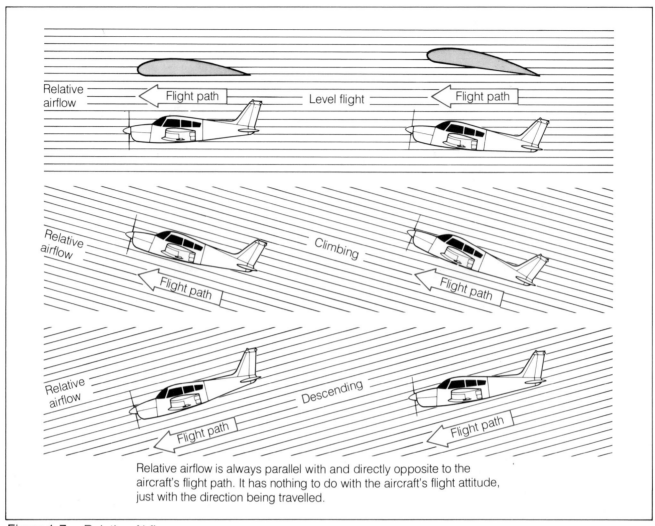

Relative airflow is always parallel with and directly opposite to the aircraft's flight path. It has nothing to do with the aircraft's flight attitude, just with the direction being travelled.

Figure 1-7   Relative Airflow

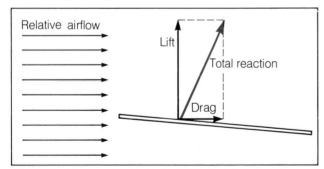

Figure 1-8   Horizontal Airflow

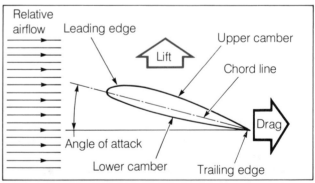

Figure 1-9   Aerofoil Terminology

Drag

For purposes of this text, drag will be divided into four types: *form, skin friction, induced,* and *parasite*.

Form Drag. The air imposes resistance on the very shape of the whole aircraft. Streamlining of the exterior components of the aircraft contributes to the reduction of this type of drag.

Skin Friction Drag. Air flowing over an aircraft tends to hold the aircraft back by grasping at its surfaces. A smooth, highly polished aircraft will be affected much less by this type of drag than the same aircraft dirty. Mud or ice that has accumulated on an aircraft contributes to skin friction. The boundary layer also contributes to skin friction since, as the speed increases, the transition point moves further forward. More of the boundary layer therefore becomes turbulent, with subsequent increase in skin friction.

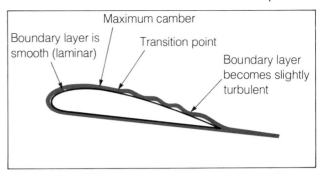

Figure 1-11 Boundary Layer of a Normal Aerofoil

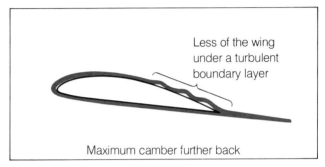

Figure 1-12 Laminar Flow-Type Aerofoil

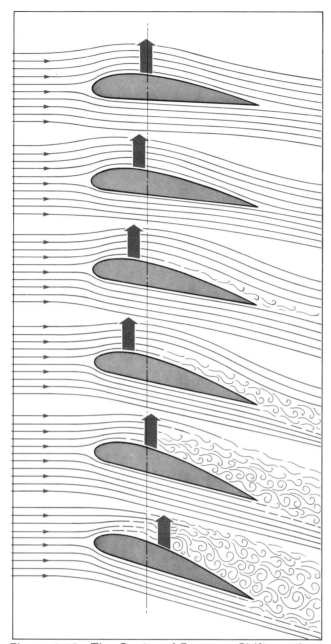

Figure 1-10 The Centre of Pressure Shifts as the Angle of Attack Changes

Induced Drag. This type of drag is a by-product of lift. The difference in pressure between the air flowing over the wing and the air flowing under the wing results in the air flowing from the high pressure to the low pressure area. The easiest way for it to do this is by flowing around the wing tips. This causes the air on the underside to flow towards the wing tips, where it quickly rotates and flows into the low pressure air on top of the wing; the meeting of the differing pressures causes a twisting, rotary motion which is very pronounced at the wing tips (wing tip vortices — Fig 1-13). This disturbed air exerts a retarding force on the wing, which is known as induced drag. *Aspect ratio* affects induced drag.

The aspect ratio is the ratio of the span to the mean chord (Fig 1-14). So long as there is lift there will be induced drag; however, the greater the span of an aerofoil in ratio to its chord, the less the induced drag. A long aerofoil with a relatively narrow width of chord is called a high aspect ratio wing.

Parasite Drag. Parasite drag is drag created by the resistance to airflow of such things as wheels, struts, radio masts, control balances, and hinges — in other words, all those parts of an aircraft which do not contribute toward lift.

Torque

Torque is the twisting action produced by an aircraft engine. The engine rotates the propeller in one direction, but in so doing and in obedience to Newton's Third Law, it also tries to rotate the whole aircraft in the opposite direction. In the case of most North American aircraft, the propeller rotates clockwise viewed from the cockpit, which means that a downward force is being exerted upon the left side of the aircraft. In the design of the aircraft this undesirable force is neutralized by giving the left wing slightly more angle of incidence (*wash in*) — and therefore slightly more lift — than the right wing.

Slipstream

The mass of air thrust backwards by the propeller is called the *slipstream*. It is roughly the size of a cylinder

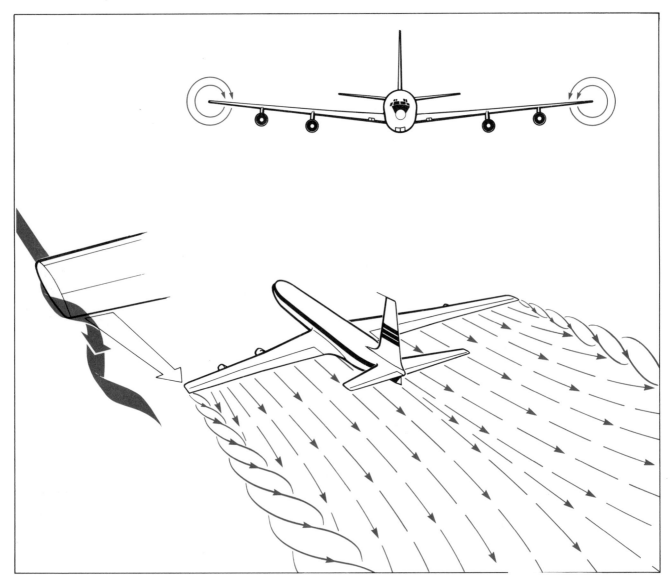

Figure 1-13   Wing Tip Vortices

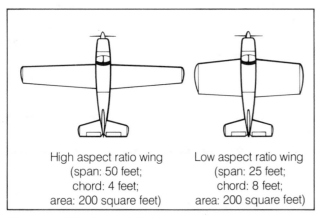

| High aspect ratio wing (span: 50 feet; chord: 4 feet; area: 200 square feet) | Low aspect ratio wing (span: 25 feet; chord: 8 feet; area: 200 square feet) |

Figure 1-14   Aspect Ratio

of the same diameter as the propeller.

The velocity of the slipstream is greater than that at which the aircraft is travelling through the air. This means that the velocity of the air flowing over those parts of the aircraft in the slipstream would be much more than that of the airflow over parts not in the slipstream.

The propeller imparts a rotary motion to the slipstream in the same direction as the propeller is turning. The result is that the slipstream strikes one side only of aircraft surfaces such as the fin and rudder, and affects the directional and lateral balance of the aircraft (Fig 1-15). To compensate for this, the fin is usually offset to balance the aircraft for normal cruising flight. This balance is upset when engine power is changed above or below cruise power settings (Fig 1-16).

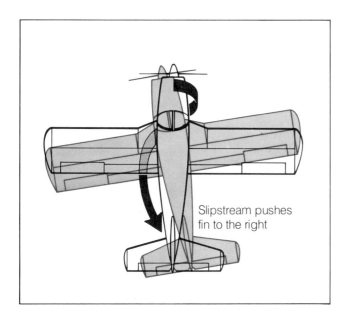

Slipstream pushes fin to the right

Figure 1-15   Slipstream Has a Rotational Velocity

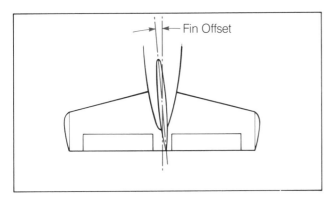

Fin Offset

Figure 1-16   Fin Offset

Equilibrium

An object which is neither accelerating nor decelerating is in *equilibrium*. A parked aircraft is in equilibrium; an aircraft in straight and level flight at a constant airspeed is in equilibrium; an aircraft in a straight descent or climb at a steady airspeed is in equilibrium. However, an aircraft in a turn at a constant height and airspeed is not in equilibrium, since during a co-ordinated turn the aircraft is always accelerating towards the centre of the turn.

Roll, Ailerons, Longitudinal Axis

When an aircraft is *rolled*, one aileron is depressed and the opposite one is raised. The "down" aileron increases the camber of the wing to which it is attached and causes it to produce more effective lift than the other wing, which, because the "up" aileron reduces its

camber, now produces less effective lift. As a result, the "down aileron" wing rises and the "up aileron" wing moves down. The total effect causes the aircraft to roll about its longitudinal axis. Aileron movement is controlled by left or right movement of the control column; when the control column is moved to the left (or the control wheel rotated to the left) the left aileron rises and vice versa.

Pitching, Elevators, Lateral Axis

Backward movement of the control column raises the elevators. In flight this changes the camber, producing a force which causes the tail to go down and the nose to rise. Forward movement of the control lowers the elevators; this produces the opposite reaction, raising the tail and lowering the nose. The elevators produce and control movement of the pitching plane about the lateral axis of the aircraft.

Yaw, Rudder, Normal (Vertical) Axis

The left or right movement of the nose of an aircraft in flight is controlled by the rudder, through the rudder pedals. The rudder is hinged to the trailing edge of the fin (vertical stabilizer). In straight flight the fin produces (for purposes of this subject) no aerodynamic reactions of its own. However, foot pressure on the left rudder pedal (for example), causes the rudder to move to the left and introduce camber to the fin; this causes a mass of air to be accelerated to the left which (Newton's Third Law) moves the tail of the aircraft to the right and causes the nose to move (yaw) to the left. Opposite reactions occur when pressure is applied to the right rudder pedal.

Aileron Drag (Adverse Yaw)

Flight controls are designed to be effective, well balanced, and highly responsive; however, the ailerons have an operating defect which should be explained. For example, if a turn to the left is desired, movement of the control column to the left causes the right aileron to move downward and increase the camber of the right wing, which in turn causes that wing to develop more lift and rise up (Fig 1-17). Conversely, the left aileron moves upward and decreases the camber of the left wing, causing that wing to develop less lift and drop. However, in developing more lift, the right wing is subjected to more induced drag, and in developing less lift the left wing is subjected to less induced drag. The whole effect causes a momentary yaw to the right, when the yaw to the left is what is desired. Hence the name *adverse yaw*. Adverse yaw is more noticeable in abrupt,

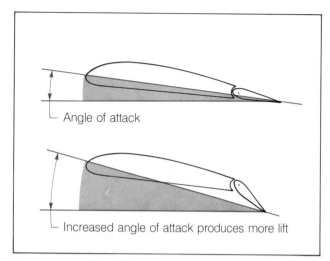

Figure 1-17   The Effect of the Aileron on the Angle of Attack

uncoordinated control movement. In a smooth, well co-ordinated turn, the effect is practically imperceptible.

Brakes (Differential)

On many aircraft each main landing wheel has its own independent braking system, to facilitate manoeuvring on the ground. Brakes of this type may be used to shorten a landing roll and give directional control on the ground at speeds where rudder control is inadequate. Pressure applied to the left brake pedal brakes the left wheel and turns the aircraft to the left; pressure applied to the right brake pedal turns the aircraft to the right. To bring an aircraft to a straight stop, equal or near equal pressure must be applied to each brake pedal.

Trim Tabs

To improve control and balance (trim) of an aircraft, small auxiliary control surfaces called trim tabs are fixed or hinged to the trailing edges of the ailerons, elevators, and rudder. Fixed tabs are pre-set on the ground to obtain a balanced control loading at the normal level cruising speed of particular aircraft. Hinged tabs are controlled by the pilot. Larger aircraft, for the most part, have hinged tabs fitted to all control surfaces to compensate for lateral shifts in loading and to provide additional rudder control in the event of an engine failure with a multi-engined aircraft. In the case of most small single-engined aircraft, such as those used for flight training, only the elevators have controllable trim. Elevator trim compensates for the constantly changing longitudinal stability resulting from varying attitudes of flight. Fixed trim tabs, if fitted, are normally adequate for the lateral (aileron) and directional (rudder) stability and control of this class of aircraft.

Variable Incidence Tail Planes (Horizontal Stabilizer)

On some aircraft the incidence of the tail plane can be varied in flight to trim the aircraft longitudinally. The effect is much the same as trimming the elevators on an aircraft with a fixed tail plane.

Flaps

Flaps are controlled by the pilot. They improve the lift and other characteristics of an aerofoil by increasing

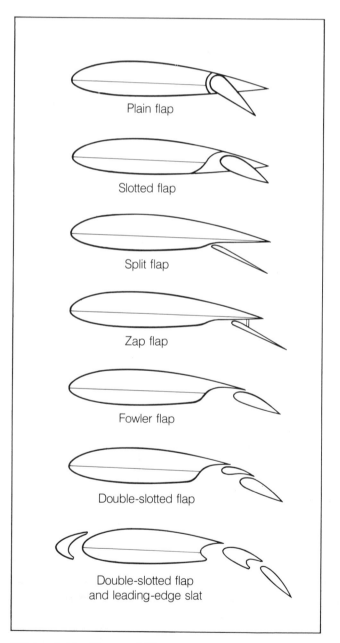

Figure 1-18   Types of Flaps

the camber of a large portion of the wing. Some of the operational advantages of flaps are:

(1) Stalling speed is decreased.
(2) A steeper approach to landing can be made without an increase in airspeed.
(3) Forward visibility is improved on approach to landing due to the lower position of the nose.
(4) Flaps assist in shortening the take-off run.

The plain flap, used on most light aircraft, is actually a portion of the main aerofoil, including upper and lower surfaces, which hinge downward into the relative airflow. However, in the case of more sophisticated articulated flap systems (Zap and Fowler are typical examples), there is an effective increase of the chord of the aerofoil, which up to a given point in their operation greatly increases lift while imposing minimum drag (Fig 1-18).

When the pilot selects a flap position, both flaps go down or up together. When flaps are fully retracted (up) they conform to the shape of the wing. Flaps must be used judiciously at all times but extreme care must be taken when retracting them in flight — especially near the ground — because of the resultant sudden loss of lift and change in the aircraft's balance.

Slots and Slats

Slots and slats (Fig 1-19) are devices along the leading edge of an aerofoil which, automatically or sometimes controllably, improve the airflow over the top surface of the aerofoil at low airspeeds, for the purpose of decreasing its stalling speed. Although quite common at one time on light aircraft, with improvements to the general lift characteristics of aerofoils these devices are now used almost exclusively for aircraft with special performance requirements.

Gyroscopic Effect

A balanced object spinning on a central axis has two special properties. The gyro wheels in aircraft flight instruments, such as turn-and-bank indicators, attitude indicators, and heading indicators, are examples of such spinning objects. Their properties, without which flight by instruments would be impossible, are:

(1) Rigidity in Space. A spinning gyro, pivoted on a platform, will keep its own attitude fixed even though the platform itself changes its attitude. Rigidity in space is the working principle of the attitude indicator. The horizon bar of the instrument is attached through a gimbal arrangement to the gyro wheel, and regardless of the aircraft's attitude, remains parallel to the earth's horizon. There are certain limits to the instrument's operation but for all normal flight attitudes these limits

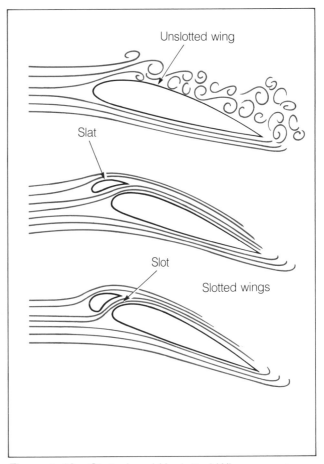

Figure 1-19 Slotted and Unslotted Wings

are seldom exceeded. The heading indicator, another gyro-operated flight instrument, also works on the principle of rigidity in space.

(2) Gyroscopic Precession. When a force is applied to a spinning object, the object will react as though the force had been applied at a point 90 degrees from where the force was actually applied. Gyroscopic precession forms the working principle of the turn indicator of the turn-and-bank indicator. When the aircraft is turned, since the instrument's gyro wheel remains "rigid in space," this is the same as applying a force to the gyro to tilt. By means of linkage, the amount of "tilt" is registered by the turn needle on the face of the instrument. The amount of "tilt" is actually the rate of turn. When the turn ceases, the gyro wheel is returned to its neutral position by means of a return spring.

The spinning mass of an aircraft engine and propeller is another example of a "gyro wheel" which endeavours to remain rigid in space and therefore susceptible to gyroscopic precession. Gyroscopic effect of this kind can sometimes be quite noticeable in a tail wheel-equipped aircraft, as the tail is raised in the take-off sequence (Fig 1-20). It is as though the pilot had reached out and applied the force to the propeller at the

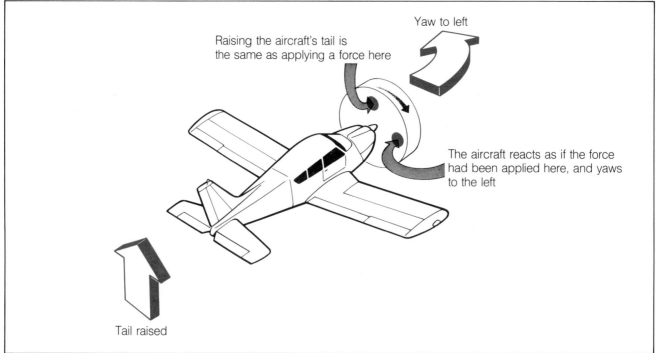

Raising the aircraft's tail is
the same as applying a force here

Yaw to left

The aircraft reacts as if the force
had been applied here, and yaws
to the left

Tail raised

Figure 1-20   The Effect of Raising the Aircraft's Tail

top of its arc. Since the engine rotates clockwise, gyroscopic effect changes the position of the force and applies it to the extreme right point of the propeller arc. This causes the aircraft to attempt to turn (yaw) to the left and requires appropriate application of rudder pressure to maintain the desired heading.

Wind

When the speed of an aircraft is referred to, what is meant is its speed relative to the air in which it is flying, or *airspeed*, as it is termed. Actually, what we know as "wind" is the bodily movement of a portion of the atmosphere and although the wind affects the speed of an aircraft relative to the earth (*ground speed*), it does not affect its speed relative to the air. Suppose an aircraft is flying from point A to point B (60 miles apart), and that its cruising airspeed is 100 mph. If there is a wind of 40 mph blowing directly from B toward A, the ground speed of the aircraft from A to B will be 60 mph and it will take one hour to reach B, but the airspeed will still be 100 mph. When the aircraft reaches B and flies back to A, the ground speed on the return journey will be 140 mph, but the airspeed will still be 100 mph.

CHAPTER TWO

Stability: Weight and Balance

A *stable* aircraft is one that tends to return to its original flight condition after being displaced by some outside force, such as an updraft or other like air disturbance. A stable aircraft is pleasant to fly. The stability of an aircraft concerns its three planes of rotation: (1) pitching, (2) yawing, and (3) rolling. Stability in the pitching and yawing planes is called *longitudinal* stability, and stability in the rolling plane is called *lateral* stability.

Lateral Stability. One design feature which provides stability in the rolling plane is *dihedral* design. This is a wing design feature in which the wing tips are higher than the centre section of the wing. When a wing is lowered due to an outside influence, such as turbulent air, the aircraft starts slipping towards the "down" wing; the "down" wing is now exposed to more airflow (than the "up" wing), and as a result of its higher angle of attack produces more lift and returns to its former level state (Fig 1-21).

Longitudinal Stability. Of all the characteristics which affect the balance and controllability of an aircraft longitudinal stability is the most important, since it can be influenced by both aerodynamic and physical factors, including human error.

The position of the centre of gravity of an aircraft has the greatest influence on its longitudinal stability, but this stability is also influenced by changes of speed, power, and attitude. It is difficult to obtain the right degree of longitudinal stability to meet all conditions of flight, but it is essential to achieve an acceptable compromise if the aircraft is to be safe and pleasant to handle. Turbulent air, operation of the flaps, etc., all disturb the balance of the aircraft.

This problem is primarily resolved by the horizontal stabilizer (tail plane), aided by the vertical stabilizer (fin). Purposely placed at a considerable distance behind the wing, these stabilizers aerodynamically provide the basic forces necessary to counteract the effect of outside forces. Because of its distance from the centre of gravity, which gives it great leverage, even a small force on the tail plane will produce a large correcting moment.

Much like the tail feathers on an arrow, the tail plane will resist outside influences altering the aircraft's selected longitudinal flight path. Outside influences and forces may be likened to uncoordinated use of the flight controls, to which a stable properly trimmed aircraft will also offer resistance. A stable aircraft will not attempt to counteract forces intentionally introduced by co-ordinated use of the flight controls and throttle.

Directional Stability. Directional stability concerns the motion of the aircraft about the normal axis, or the yawing motion of the aircraft. An automobile has a directional stability which can be seen every time the car turns a corner. After the turn is made and the steering wheel released, the wheels straighten and the car moves in a straight direction. This is directional stability. The vertical stabilizer contributes to the directional stability of an aircraft.

Centre of Gravity

The basic centre of gravity of an aircraft is determined mathematically on the presumption that ideally an aircraft at its empty weight presents a properly balanced unit, within acceptable tolerances. It is the responsibility of the pilot-in-command to disperse the proposed useful load fore and aft of the centre of gravity to maintain this balance within the tolerance set out in the authorized weight and balance report.

To simplify loading problems, most manufacturers of light aircraft supply pre-calculated graphs, charts, or loading examples for specific aircraft that are adequate for the use of the average private pilot. However, you should have a working knowledge of the basic principles behind these calculations.

13

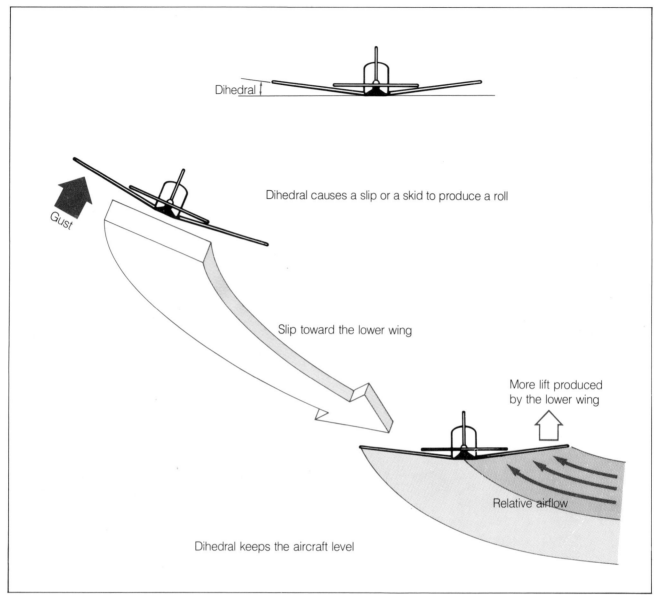

Dihedral

Dihedral causes a slip or a skid to produce a roll

Gust

Slip toward the lower wing

More lift produced by the lower wing

Relative airflow

Dihedral keeps the aircraft level

Figure 1-21   Dihedral Keeps the Aircraft Level

The centre of gravity for each aircraft is calculated at the factory and recorded on the weight and balance report. The method used to find the centre of gravity for an empty aircraft is also used to calculate the shift of the centre of gravity caused by loading of fuel, pilot, passengers, baggage, etc.

It is imperative, for optimum control response and stability, that the centre of gravity of an aircraft be maintained within its permissible design limitations. You can seriously affect the controllability of your aircraft by disposing the load incorrectly. If the centre of gravity loading limitations as outlined in the aircraft flight manual are followed carefully, you will have a stable aircraft and predictable response to the controls. If the centre of gravity is permitted to go beyond the forward limitations, the aircraft will become too stable, less responsive to the controls, and very difficult to trim.

However, in the average light aircraft there is considerably more scope for error in exceeding the *aft* centre of gravity limitations. Careless aft loading can lead to very hazardous balance and control problems, even though the maximum permissible overall weight is not exceeded. Say, for example, the fuel load of a four place aircraft is reduced to remain within maximum permissible take-off weight, then two relatively light-weight people are placed in the forward seats, two very heavy people are placed in the rear seats, and the aft luggage compartment is loaded to its maximum allowable weight. An aircraft so loaded could have such an excessive aft centre of gravity that the pilot would have control problems beginning from take-off, and the normal stall characteristics might change drastically. Should an aircraft with excessive aft loading be permitted to enter a spin, there is every possibility that recovery would be extremely difficult if not impossible to execute.

Useful Load

Of prime interest to the pilot-in-command is the *useful load* that the aircraft about to be flown is permitted to carry. In light aircraft, useful load consists of crew, passengers, baggage, usable fuel and oil, and other non-fixed items. It may be calculated by subtracting empty weight from maximum permissible weight. These weights are generally defined as:

(1) Empty Weight. The weight of the basic aircraft, including its fixed equipment and unusable fuel and oil.

(2) Maximum Permissible Weight. The maximum permissible gross take-off weight specified in the aircraft's certificate of airworthiness.

Passengers. Although airlines use average passenger weights as determined by actual survey for main line route weight and balance computations, actual passenger weights must be used for aircraft with limited seating capacity. Light aircraft can easily be loaded outside limits when estimates or average weights are used, particularly when winter clothing is worn. If in doubt, ask passengers how much they weigh and make appropriate allowances for clothing.

Weight and Balance

The maximum permissible gross take-off weight must never be exceeded. If you carry additional fuel to give the aircraft more range, you must in many cases balance it by reducing the number of passengers or baggage, freight, or other such weight, so as not to exceed the maximum permissible weight.

The pilot-in-command must know all the loading information about the aircraft to be flown, and be able to determine permissible loading and its correct disposition. Current weight and balance data must be carried as part of the aircraft documentation; unless loaded in accordance with this information, the aircraft cannot be considered airworthy. In addition, it may bear a placard concerning operational loading, such as the seat to be occupied in solo flight or a fuel tank to be emptied first. The information on these placards must be observed scrupulously.

Weight and balance limitations are imposed for the following principal reasons:

(1) The effect of the disposition of weight (and subsequently balance) on the flight characteristics of the aircraft, particularly on stall and spin recoveries, slow flight, and stability.

(2) The effect of the weight on primary and secondary structures of the aircraft.
(3) The effect of weight on take-off and landing performance.

Computing Weight and Balance

The weight and balance calculations for individual flights are computed by using information in the aircraft's Weight and Balance Report, and the weights and disposition within the aircraft of each passenger and/or item of the load proposed for the flight. The items of information available on the Weight and Balance Report are:

(1) Empty weight, in pounds.
(2) Balance Datum. This is the reference point from which all weight and balance calculations are made. It could be anywhere on the aircraft, preferably somewhere forward of the centre of gravity. It could even be a point in open space several feet in front of the nose. To avoid calculations of minus quantities, most aircraft balance datums are situated so that all useful loads are positioned aft of the balance datum.
(3) Centre of gravity (empty), in inches from the balance datum.
(4) Moment arm. The distance in inches from the balance datum to the centre of gravity of the aircraft or centre of gravity of an item of load.

Concerning the proposed load, the pilot-in-command must be aware of:

(1) The weight in pounds of each passenger and/or item.
(2) The location of each passenger and/or item within the aircraft.

Weight and balance factors may be computed as follows:

(1) The balance moment of the empty aircraft is found by multiplying the empty weight by the moment arm of the aircraft.
(2) The balance moment of each item of load is found by multiplying its weight by its respective moment arm.
(3) The new centre of gravity is found by dividing the total balance moment by the total weight of the aircraft.

Sample Computations. A sample weight and balance calculation for a typical light aircraft, with a centre of gravity 30 inches aft of its datum when empty, using the foregoing items and factors, might look like this:

	Weight (lbs.)	Moment Arm (inches)	Balance Moment (inch/lbs.)
Aircraft empty	1,000	30	30,000
Pilot	170	20	3,400
Passenger	170	20	3,400
Fuel	50	30	1,500
Oil	10	20	200
	1,400		38,500

The new centre of gravity is (38,500 divided by 1,400) 27.5 inches aft of the balance datum.

The following is an example of a weight and balance computation for a more sophisticated aircraft:

	Weight (lbs.)	Moment Arm (inches)	Balance Moment (inch/lbs.)
Aircraft empty	1,552	37	57,424
Pilot and passenger at 170 lbs.	340	36	12,240
One passenger in rear seat	170	70	11,900
Baggage	120	95	11,400
Fuel, 46 gals. at 7.2 lbs.	331.2	48	15,897.6
Oil, 1.8 gals. at 9 lbs.	16.2	-15	-243
	2,529.4		108,618.6

In this case the loaded centre of gravity (loaded moment divided by loaded weight) is 42.9 inches aft of the datum point. The example above uses a balance datum somewhere aft of the nose to illustrate a minus item; in this aircraft the oil reservoir is forward of the balance datum and therefore must be shown as a minus quantity on the total scale of balance.

The pilot-in-command of this particular aircraft must now refer to the current aircraft documentation and verify that the loaded weight of 2,529.4 pounds and the loaded centre of gravity of 42.9 inches are both within the prescribed tolerances. If they are not, the aircraft should not be considered airworthy until satisfactory adjustments are made.

CHAPTER THREE

Engine Handling

A typical four cylinder engine in a single-engined light aircraft has over 250 moving and 70 non-moving parts, the failure of any of which may result in a complete loss of power, or such power loss as to require an immediate landing. However, because of compulsory testing of material and parts, a high degree of quality control is achieved, resulting in the aircraft engine being one of the most reliable mechanical components in use today. Whether or not this high level of reliability is sustained depends to a great extent on the pilot-in-command's handling of the engine. Besides its flight operation, the handling of an engine includes the use of recommended fuels and oils, pre-flight inspections, and a basic knowledge of how an engine and its ancillary components work. Since it represents the majority of training aircraft power plants in use today, the engine we will consider is air cooled, has horizontally opposed cylinders, and is unsupercharged. The propeller may be made of wood, composition material, or metal, and has a fixed pitch.

Inspection

Before any flight the pertinent log books are studied to check the engine hours, what inspections, repairs or modifications have been made, whether any reported defects are outstanding, and whether the aircraft has been currently signed out by the appropriate authority.

Never inspect an aircraft engine and propeller until the ignition (magneto) switches have been checked and are off, and even then always treat the propeller as if it were "live." There is not a great deal that a pilot can do in the way of mechanically inspecting an engine prior to flight, but the few things that can be done are extremely important. The engine oil can be checked for acceptable level and the caburettor air filter checked for obstructions. Actuate the fuel strainer drain and, using a suitable glass container, make sure that the fuel is free of water and sediment. Look for oil and fuel leaks. Physically check components on the engine to see if there are any loose items, misplaced wires, etc. Check the propeller and spinner for nicks and see that they are properly secured.

Prior to starting an engine there are several things that can be done to ensure that it will perform properly:

(1) Verify the fuel supply by a physical check of the fuel tanks.

(2) Fuel tank air vents must be open and clear of foreign material, to ensure that fuel may flow at recommended rates.

(3) Check all fuel tank caps for security. In most cases, if a cap comes off in flight, the contents of the tank may empty rapidly through the filler neck, due to the syphoning action of the airflow.

(4) Check the propeller for nicks and other damage which may cause imbalance, and undesirable and often dangerous engine vibration.

(5) Engine oil. Never add a detergent oil to an engine which uses a non-detergent oil as its regular lubricant. Add non-detergent oil to an engine which uses detergent oil as its regular lubricant in an emergency only.

(6) Cold oil. The oil used in the engine of an aircraft is of higher viscosity than that used in most other engines, and becomes very thick when cold. With the ignition switch off and mixture control in idle cut-off position, turn the propeller by hand for several revolutions to help break the drag created by cold oil between the piston and the cylinder wall. This will ease starting and reduce the load on the starting mechanism and battery.

(7) Drum fuelling. Refuelling an aircraft from gasoline drums is not a preferred method if regular fuelling facilities are available, because condensation and

flakes of rust are often present in the drums. Since most of the foreign material settles to the bottom of the drum, make sure that the suction tube on the pump being used has at least an inch clearance from the bottom of the drum. A chamois strainer should be used, since it not only removes solids but also resists the passage of water.

(8) Ensure that the fuel is of the octane rating specified for the engine. Never use a lower grade; in an emergency use the next higher grade.

Starting

The engine is started (and operated) as specified in the aircraft flight manual or as specified by a particular operator to meet the requirements of non-standard conditions, such as temperature and elevation extremes. We will not attempt to outline a standard method engine starting here, since it would not satisfy the requirements of all aircraft. Instead we propose to accent those points which are generally common to all.

Nearly all engines will start more readily with a degree of throttle opening larger than specified, but avoid this in all but emergency situations, because of the stresses that such starts impose upon the engine and its components plus the possibility of a dangerous leap forward against the brakes. Once started, avoid too high or too low an RPM for engine warm-up. Too low an RPM results in inadequate distribution of the sluggish engine oil; too high an RPM can cause excessive wear of parts which depend on gradually acquiring heat to expand to operating clearances. If, after starting, an oil pressure indication as specified in the aircraft flight manual is not evident, shut down the engine.

To ensure that there are no fuel blockages between the fuel tanks and the engine, it is a good practice to start the engine and taxi out on one tank, then select another tank (before engine run-up) for the take-off.

Warm-up

There are two warm-up phases, the first being before taxiing, to ensure that oil pressure is within the operating range and that other engine instruments are beginning to register somewhere in the lower portion of the operating range before applying "break-away" power. This warm-up is important during seasons when relatively more engine power may be required to pull the aircraft through snow or loose soil. Avoid starting and running an engine where the propeller may pick up loose stones, blow them back, and possibly damage the aircraft or other property behind it.

The second phase, prior to take-off, ensures that engine temperatures and pressures are within the specified limits. At this point the RPM may be increased to hasten the warm-up. The ground running of the engine must be consistent with good judgment, and should be carried out with the aircraft headed into wind or as close to it as possible. Since an aircraft engine is closely cowled for efficient in-flight cooling, take care to avoid overheating it on the ground.

Run-up

If there is to be a change in fuel tanks before take-off, change them before the run-up. Should a fuel system malfunction occur as a result of changing tanks, let this show itself during the run-up, not during the take-off.

Carburettor Heat Check

Set the engine RPM as recommended in the flight manual; if there is no recommended RPM available use the setting recommended for the magneto check. Then:

(1) Select "full cold" position of carburettor heat and note RPM.
(2) Select "full hot" position and note decrease in RPM; allow RPM to stabilize in this position.
(3) Select "cold" position again and note increase in RPM to confirm that the unit and its controls are functioning through their full range. If, on returning the control to "cold," the RPM shows an increase over the initial RPM reading, carburettor icing conditions exist and additional care will be necessary.

The engine air intake filter is usually bypassed when "hot" is selected, so use the "cold" position while taxiing or during sustained ground operation of the engine.

The decrease in RPM in the "hot" position varies with engine types; verify this point by consulting the flight manual or other reliable source of information. If there is no decrease in RPM, suspect a malfunction. Should you suspect that an in-flight power loss is due to an engine air intake filter clogged with snow or ice, apply full carburettor heat to obtain an alternate source of intake air.

Magneto Check

The primary purpose of dual ignition in aircraft engines is safety. The reason for the magneto check is to test this feature, and also to ensure that the ignition is actually off when the magneto switch is selected to the "off" position. When the magneto switch is selected to "left," the engine is operating on the left magneto only; when the "right" position is selected, the engine is operating on the right magneto only. By selecting one or the other, you can test the proper functioning of each. (The magnetos are operating simultaneously when the magneto switch is selected to the "both" position).

The first check should be made at low RPM (idle or slightly above). After checking the operation of both magnetos separately for even firing, select the "off" position momentarily to verify that the engine ceases firing. The next check, carried out at the RPM recommended in the flight manual, is to check the performance of one ignition system against the other for even firing and "drop" in RPM. Consult the aircraft flight manual for acceptable RPM drop.

Carry out the magneto check at precisely the RPM specified in the aircraft flight manual. Ignition systems operate properly up to the point of maximum compression stroke pressure in the engine cylinders. This high pressure point is in the high RPM range but may be well below maximum RPM. When an ignition system operates satisfactorily at maximum pressure, proper operation at lower pressures is ensured; therefore, when other than specified RPM is used, the check may not prove what it is supposed to prove.

Most light aircraft engine run-up procedures no longer include a static full power check, but unless this is carried out nothing in the normal check will ensure that full power is actually available. Under ideal conditions this check is usually carried out during the take-off roll, but in a short field take-off do a full power check before allowing the aircraft to move.

Climbing

Most light aircraft climb at full throttle; with this power setting the engine generates excessive heat. Since the engine is dependent upon the flow of outside air for cooling, the higher the airspeed the more effective the cooling. The normal climbing speed specified for an aircraft takes into account, among other things, the need for adequate cooling. However, two other climbing speeds are generally specified for an individual aircraft:

(1) best angle of climb speed, and
(2) best rate of climb speed.

Since both of these climb speeds are often lower than normal climb speed, with resultant higher engine temperatures, their use should be limited to the period of time they are necessary, with normal climbing speed resumed as soon as possible.

In the case of engines designed to climb at full throttle until cruising altitude is reached, you gain no advantage by reducing power on climb with the thought of "sparing the engine," provided the specified climbing speed is strictly adhered to. One of the important reasons for maintaining the recommended speed concerns adequate cooling, which has already been discussed. Another reason is that with a fixed pitch propeller an airspeed higher than normal may cause engine RPM to exceed the limitations for sustained full throttle operation.

Unless otherwise specified, the procedure for aircraft equipped with a mixture control is to take off and climb with the control in the "full rich" position. Within certain bounds an aircraft engine runs cooler with a rich mixture, and since a power setting greater than that of normal cruise power generates much more undesirable heat, the enriched mixture contributes greatly to the welfare of the engine.

Cruise Power

Most of the time the average light aircraft is operated in the normal cruising range. In determining the cruise power setting of an engine for a particular aircraft, the manufacturer strives for the best choice in consideration of reliability, performance, economy of operation, and engine life. Of these, engine reliability is the overriding factor. It goes without saying, therefore, that a sustained power setting in excess of that recommended for normal cruising may threaten a most important factor of safe flight — i.e., engine reliability.

General

When descending with low power settings or practically no use of power, as in the case of a glide, an engine will cool rapidly even in relatively warm weather. A sudden application of power, such as for a pull-up, can damage a cold engine and/or result in a momentary engine malfunction. Therefore, it is good practice in a sustained descent to apply power periodically to retain engine operating temperatures.

Avoid gunning an aircraft engine. Power should be increased and decreased by prompt but smooth operation of the throttle; this eliminates backfiring and the possibility of an abrupt loss of power at a crucial moment.

Following a landing, with normal use an engine will cool enough during the approach and taxiing period to permit shutting it off without further idling. However, if there has been an excessive amount of power used while taxiing, allow the engine to run two or three minutes at just above the idling speed, before you shut it off.

CHAPTER FOUR

Load Factor

Principles

Any force applied to an aircraft to deflect its flight from a straight line produces a stress on its structure, the amount of which is termed a *load factor*. Simply stated, load factor is the ratio of the total aerodynamic load acting on an aircraft to its gross weight.

A load factor of 3 means that the total load on an aircraft's structure is 3 times its gross weight. Load factors are generally expressed in terms of G. A load factor of 3 is usually spoken of as 3 G's. When an aircraft is subjected to 3 G's, say, for an example, in an abrupt pull-up, the pilot will be pressed down into his seat with a force equal to 3 times his own weight. Thus, a rough estimate of the load factor obtained in a manoeuvre can be made by considering the degree to which a person is pressed down in his seat.

Load factors are important for two distinct reasons: (1) the dangerous structural overload that it is possible to impose upon an aircraft; (2) the fact that an increased load factor increases the stalling speed alarmingly and makes dangerous stalls possible at seemingly safe flight speeds.

In a level co-ordinated turn, the load factor is the result of two forces: centrifugal force and weight. In any aircraft at any airspeed, holding a constant altitude, the load factor for a given degree of bank is the resultant of centrifugal force and weight. The rate of turn does vary with the airspeed; the higher the speed the slower the rate of turn for a given degree of bank. Because of this fact, there is no change in the centrifugal force; therefore, the load factor remains the same. For example, the load factor for any aircraft in a 60 degree bank at any airspeed, executing a level co-ordinated turn is 2 G's.

Figure 1-22 shows an aircraft banked to 60 degrees. Note that the line representing the resultant load factor

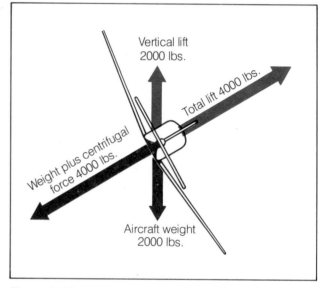

Figure 1-22 Load Factor in 60 Degree Banked Turn

is twice the length of the line representing weight.

Figure 1-23 reveals an important fact about turns — the load factor increases at a tremendous rate after the bank has reached 50 degrees. It is important to remember that the wing must produce lift equal to the load factor, otherwise it will be impossible to maintain altitude. Notice how rapidly the line representing load factor rises as it approaches the 90 degree bank line (which it reaches only at infinity). Although an aircraft may be banked to 90 degrees, a constant altitude turn with this amount of bank is mathematically impossible for conventional aircraft. At slightly more than 80 degrees the load factor exceeds 6 G's, which is, in general, the flight load factor limit of aircraft structurally designed for acrobatic flight. For conventional light aircraft, the approximate maximum bank, in a sustained level co-ordinated turn, is 60 degrees. An additional 10

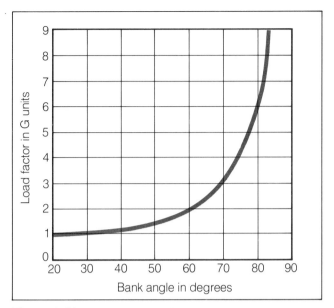

Figure 1-23   Load Factors Produced at Varying Degrees of Bank at Constant Altitude

degrees of bank will increase the load factor by approximately 1 G, bringing the loading dangerously close to the point at which structural damage may occur.

Stalling Speeds

When the angle of attack of the wing exceeds the stalling angle, the relatively smooth flow of air over the wing breaks up and tears away, producing the sudden change of flight characteristics and loss of lift known as a *stall*. Within the limits of its structure and the physical strength of the pilot, any aircraft may be stalled at any airspeed.

The stalling speed of an aircraft increases in proportion to the load factor. An aircraft with a normal stalling speed of 50 mph can be stalled at 100 mph by imposing a load factor of 4 G's upon it. If it were possible to impose a load factor of 9 G's upon this aircraft, it could be stalled at 150 mph. This knowledge must be applied from two points of view: (1) the danger of unintentionally stalling an aircraft by increasing the load factor, as in a steep turn or a spiral; (2) the tremendous load factor imposed upon an aircraft when it is intentionally stalled above its manoeuvring speed. This may be done by an abrupt pull-up, or any other manoeuvre producing a load factor beyond 1 G, and can result in a hazardous and sudden loss of control.

Abrupt or excessive deflection of the flight controls can impose severe structural loads upon an aircraft, and these load factors are directly proportionate to the aircraft's speed. This type of loading may occur when executing certain flight manoeuvres or during flight in turbulent air. For this reason each aircraft type has a design manoeuvring speed, which is defined as "the maximum speed at which the flight controls may be fully deflected without causing structural damage." This speed limitation may be found in the aircraft flight manual of a particular aircraft.

Since leverage in control systems varies from aircraft to aircraft, the pressure required on controls cannot be accepted as an index of the load factors produced by the various manoeuvres of any particular aircraft. Load factors can be measured by certain instruments, but since these instruments are not common in conventional training aircraft, it is important to develop the ability to judge load factors from their effect on the body.

Load Factors and Flight Manoeuvres

Load factors apply to all flight manoeuvres. In level cruising flight a load factor of 1 G is always present, but certain manoeuvres are known to involve relatively high load factors.

Stalls

A stall entered from straight and level flight, or an unaccelerated straight climb, will not produce added load factors beyond 1 G. As the stall occurs, this load factor may reduce towards zero (the factor at which nothing seems to have weight) and the pilot experiences a feeling of "floating free."

If recovery is effected by snapping the elevator control forward, negative load factors, which impose a down load on the wings and raise the pilot from his seat, may be produced. Except in aggravated cases, this negative load factor is so small as to be of little significance structurally.

During the pull-up following the recovery from a stall, significant load factors are often encountered. These may be induced by excessive diving (and consequent high speed), and abrupt pull-ups to regain level flight. An abrupt pull-up at high speed, besides producing undesirable structural loading, may cause a secondary high-speed stall when, due to an excessive load factor, the stalling speed increases rapidly to the point where it equals the seemingly safe and relatively high airspeed. Generally, the load factor will be less than 1.5 or 2 G's if good stall recovery technique is used, since the airspeed is normally well below cruising speed at the completion of the recovery. A higher load factor should never be necessary unless recovery is carried out at extremely low altitudes.

Spins

The load factor during a spin varies with the spin characteristics of each individual aircraft, but is usually very near the 1 G of level cruising flight. This relatively low factor is because: (a) the airspeed in a spin is very low, since the aircraft is stalled; and (b) the aircraft is mainly pivoting, rather than turning, while it is in a spin. The only essential difference between a spin and a stall is the element of rotation. Therefore the same load factor considerations apply as in the case of recovery from a stall. Spin recoveries, however, usually begin with the nose of the aircraft much lower than in recovery from a stall, so that higher airspeeds and load factors are to be expected. During the pull-ups, load factors in spin recoveries are usually about 2.5 G's.

Turbulence

Aircraft are designed to take *gust loads* of considerable intensity. Gust loads represent loading imposed upon an aircraft, particularly the wings, as a result of the aircraft being flown into vertical or horizontal air currents, the latter being more commonly referred to as "turbulence." By definition, gust load factor is an acceleration imposed upon an aircraft flown into a gust. Gust load factors increase as airspeed increases: in moderate or extreme turbulence, such as may be encountered near thunderstorms or frontal weather conditions, it is wise to reduce airspeed to the manoeuvring speed specified for the aircraft. This is the speed least likely to permit structural damage to the aircraft, yet it allows a sufficient margin of safety above the normal stalling speed if abrupt control movements must be made. "Maximum dive" or "never exceed" speeds for a particular aircraft are determined for smooth air only. Abrupt manoeuvring or high diving speeds in turbulent air at airspeeds above the specified manoeuvring speed can place damaging stresses on the whole structure of an aircraft.

Structural Damage

Many people have a mistaken tendency to consider load factors only in terms of their immediate effect upon aircraft components. The cumulative effect of load factor excesses over a long period of time may loosen and weaken vital parts so that a structural failure may occur later, when the aircraft is being operated normally.

CHAPTER FIVE

Aircraft Documentation

On your student pilot permit it states that, subject to certain conditions, the holder of the permit may, for the purpose of his own flight training and under supervision, act as pilot-in-command of any aircraft not carrying passengers. "Pilot-in-command" means just what it says: the person responsible for the successful completion of a safe flight. The pilot-in-command of any aircraft must be familiar with, and conform to, all the regulations and administrative requirements about the aircraft he is to fly, particularly the conditions under which it must be flown. In many respects, these are governed by the documents which must be carried on board an aircraft during its flight.

Flight Time and Air Time

Since documentation and other similar requirements are applicable only if the aircraft is operated in contemplation of flight or is flown, it is important to differentiate between *flight time* and *air time*. Flight time is the total period of time from the moment the aircraft first moves under its own power for the purpose of taking off until the moment it comes to rest at the end of a flight. Air time is the time elapsed between an aircraft's leaving the surface on take-off and touching the surface again on its next landing.

Documents Carried on Board

Responsibility. It is the responsibility of the pilot-in-command to ensure that all documentation required for an aircraft and its crew is on board and/or current and valid for the flight contemplated.

(1) Pilot Licence or Permit of the pilot-in-command. This and the licences of all crew members must be on board an aircraft during flight time. They must be valid in all respects and properly endorsed for the aircraft and type of operation being carried out. If the pilot-in-command (or any other crew member) does not have his licence aboard, though validly licensed in other respects, it can be construed that he is carrying out flight duties without a licence. The regulation states that an aircraft crew member shall produce his licence for inspection on demand by certain designated officials.

(2) Certificate of Registration. It must bear the same nationality and registration marks as the aircraft. Check also to see that the name and address of the owner are properly inscribed.

(3) Certificate of Airworthiness. Check that the registration marks on this document compare with those on the aircraft, that the aircraft is properly described, and that the certificate is valid according to the appropriate Air Navigation Order.

(4) Licence for the radio apparatus installed in the aircraft.

(5) Certificate of Proficiency. The pilot-in-command is required to have a certificate of proficiency to operate the aircraft's radio apparatus, except in the case of a holder of a valid student pilot permit, or of a pilot's licence that is appropriately certified.

(6) Aircraft Journey Log. Ensure that the journey log is the correct one for the aircraft, and that the appropriate airworthiness entries and certifications have been made, in accordance with the appropriate Air Navigation Order. Remember that irregularities in the journey log may invalidate the Certificate of Airworthiness. (Carrying this document may be waived under special circumstances.)

(7) Aircraft Flight Manual. Aircraft manufactured prior to the requirement for flight manuals may not be equipped with this document. In such cases the

JOURNEY – ROUTE		CREW – ÉQUIPAGE	RECORD OF TIME – FICHE DE TEMPS					NUMBER OF PERSONS ON BOARD	
1. DATE	2. FROM PREVIOUS LINE DE LA LIGNE PRÉCÉDENTE	3. NAMES – NOMS	4. UP QUITTE LE SOL À	5. DOWN PRISE DE CONTACT	6. AIR TIME TEMPS DANS LES AIRS	FLIGHT TIME TEMPS DE VOL	7. TOTAL AIR TIME SINCE MANUFACTURE TEMPS AIR TOTAL DEPUIS SA CONSTRUCTION	8. NOMBRE DE PERSONNES À BORD	
								NUMBER NOMBRE	WEIGHT POIDS
BROUGHT FORWARD REPORTÉ							►		
6 July 75	Ottawa	Carter	1115	1215	1.0	1.2	1844.5	1	165
12 July 75	Sherbrooke	MacDonald	1305	1505	2.0	2.2	1846.5	2	330
12 July 75	Charlottetown	Carter	1845	2330	3.8	4.0	1850.3	2	330
16 July 75	Charlottetown	MacDonald	1715	1915	2.0	2.2	1852.3	4	700
21 July 75	Saint John	Carter	0800	0930	1.5	1.8	1853.8	2	330
21 July 75	Sherbrooke	MacDonald	1200	1458	3.0	3.2	1856.8	2	330
22 July 75	Ottawa	Carter	1000	1230	2.5	2.6	1859.3	4	616
1 Aug 75	Ottawa	MacDonald	0900	1000	1.0	1.2	1860.3	1	165
2 Aug. 75	Toronto	Thomas	0900	1230	3.5	3.7	1863.8	1	143
3 Aug. 75	Ottawa	Thomas	1310	1650	3.7	3.9	1867.5	2	187
TOTAL THIS PAGE TOTAL DE CETTE PAGE			►						

Figure 1-24A   Aircraft Documentation: Sample Page from Aircraft Journey Log Book

aircraft's operating limitations must be conspicuously placarded in the cockpit.

Documents Not Carried on Board

(1) Aircraft Technical Log. Every aircraft must have a technical log in which the overhaul and maintenance history of the aircraft's airframe, engine, propeller, and accessories is recorded.

(2) Pilot Log Book. When enrolled in an approved course of pilot training, you must maintain a pilot log-book of recognized form, with accurate, legible, certified entries. This is a personal document in other respects, but it is recognized practice to maintain a pilot log-book in the manner mentioned. This is in fact a basic requirement as proof of experience for the issue of licences and licence endorsements throughout a pilot's career.

Log-Book Entries (A.N.O. VIII, No. 2 & 3)

It is the responsibility of the pilot-in-command to make and sign entries in the journey log, in the prescribed

RECORD OF QUANTITY – *FICHE DE QUANTITÉ*				REMARKS *REMARQUES*	SIGNATURE
9. FUEL CARBURANT	10. OIL HUILE	11. EQUIPMENT BAGGAGE CARGO *ÉQUIPEMENT BAGAGE MARCHANDISE*	12. TOTAL WEIGHT AT T/O *POIDS TOTAL AU DÉCOLLAGE*	13. DEFECTS AND AIRWORTHINESS CERTIFICATION *DÉFECTUOSITÉS ET CERTIFICATION DE NAVIGABILITÉ*	14. PILOT OR ENGINEER MAKING ENTRY AND LICENCE NUMBER *LE PILOTE OU MÉCANICIEN AUTEUR DE L'INSCRIPTION ET SON NUMÉRO DE LICENCE*
		WEIGHT – *POIDS*			
30	2	20	1893		*F. Carter* QMA-820
				I hereby certify that all applicable requirements stated in the Engineering and Mechanical Manual have been met and the aircraft is determined to be airworthy. Signature of AME *W.Dibbs* Licence No. QMM-286 Date 10 July 75	
30	2	30	2068		*J. MacDonald* QMA-761
30	2	30	2068		*F. Carter* QMA-820
20	2	20	2353		*J. MacDonald* QMA-761
30	2	50	2088		*F. Carter* QMA-820
30	2	50	2088		*J. MacDonald* QMA-761
30	2	50	2374		*F. Carter* QMA-820
				I hereby certify I have inspected this aircraft in compliance with the Condition and Conformity Inspection procedure prescribed in the Engineering and Inspection Manual and it is airworthy. *W.Dibbs* QMM-286	
30	2	20	1893		*J. MacDonald* QMA-761
				I hereby certify I have flown this aircraft and its performance, flying qualities, function of controls, power plant, and landing gear, etc., were equivalent to the standard of this type. *J. MacDonald* QMA-761	
30	2	20	1871		*D. Thomas* Y2P-5512
30	2	35	1930		*D. Thomas* Y2P-5512

Figure 1-24B   Aircraft Documentation: Sample Page from Aircraft Journey Log Book

manner, to record the events of a flight. Each period between a take-off and a landing is generally considered a flight, requiring a separate log entry. Exceptions to this general rule are included in the subject Air Navigation Order. Entries must be made in *ink,* by a competent person, as soon as possible after the events recorded. Should an error be made in an entry it is an offence to erase or alter the log, or to remove a page. Draw a single line in ink through the full length of the incorrect entry, initial it, and insert the correct entry in the next space. (Special privileges concerning log entries may be granted to certain training establishments.)

See Figures 1-24A and 1-24B for samples of correct aircraft journey log entries.

Except as otherwise defined by the Air Regulations it is an offence to fly an aircraft that has not been certified or recertified airworthy by a qualified person. A "qualified person" is the holder of a valid and appropriately endorsed Aircraft Maintenance Engineer Licence, issued under authority of the Air Regulations.

CHAPTER SIX

Operational Procedures and Considerations

Airport is the customary designation of an area used expressly for the taking off, landing, and surface manoeuvring of aircraft. However, simply stated, an airport is a licensed aerodrome; therefore, all airports are first aerodromes, and in this text the term "airport" may often be used even though "aerodrome" might be more correct technically.

In Canada the majority of controlled civil airports (airports with control towers) are operated by Transport Canada, with the remainder operated by municipalities. The majority of uncontrolled civil airports are operated by municipalities, corporations, and private citizens. Airports are divided into two classes for licence purposes. A public licence qualifies an airport for use by the general public. A private licence is usually issued when the airport owners desire that its use be restricted to purposes compatible with their own operations.

NOTAM: Field Condition Reports

At all Transport Canada airports and many other airports the NOTAM ("NOtice To AirMen") office provides NOTAM and NOTAM summaries concerning operations which may affect an aircraft in flight at or in the vicinity of certain airports.

These NOTAM also contain field condition reports on various airports and should be reviewed very carefully by pilots prior to carrying out local or cross-country flights. For the most part the airport NOTAM office is located in or adjacent to the Flight Service Station (FSS). Transport Canada's flight information publication the *VFR Supplement* provides information on those aerodromes where NOTAM service can be obtained and the telephone number of the operator where applicable.

When approaching an airport to land, never hesitate to ask the control tower (or Flight Service Station) for a field condition report if you have any doubts about it, especially when winter airport maintenance is being carried out.

Charts

It is recognized as good practice for aircraft to fly equipped with all the charts and publications required for the proper navigation of the flight. No VFR flight should leave the ground, regardless of how short its duration, without current aeronautical charts on board covering the area in which the flight will be conducted.

Emergency Locator Transmitter (ELT)

Full details concerning the requirement, testing, and operation of the ELT may be found in Transport Canada's *Aeronautical Information Publication* (A.I.P. Canada).

Taxi Clearance

VICTOR HOTEL /WINNIPEG GROUND /RUNWAY 36 /WIND 340 AT 10 /CLEARED TO TAXI VIA TAXIWAYS HOTEL AND CHARLEY /HOLD SHORT OF RUNWAY 31. This is a clearance that could be received by an aircraft intending to take off from a controlled airport. (A controlled airport is one at which an airport control tower is in operation.) The control tower not only keeps a pilot informed but also issues instructions which must be adhered to so as to afford an efficient and safe operating environment for all aircraft using the airport. In Canada, control towers at civil airports are operated by Transport Canada, regardless of airport ownership.

Advisory Service

Civil airports that do not have control towers are called uncontrolled airports. These sites may be operated by municipalities, corporations, individuals, or Transport Canada. At many uncontrolled airports Transport

Canada operates Flight Service Stations, which offer an advisory service to aircraft operating into and out of the airport. An aircraft initiating a call to a Flight Service Station might receive the following reply:

VICTOR HOTEL / BROMONT UNICOM / WIND 240 AT 10 / ALTIMETER 3011 / WIND IS FAVOURING RUNWAY 23 / AIR CANADA FLIGHT 166 REPORTS ON APPROACH TO RUNWAY 23 / NO OTHER REPORTED TRAFFIC / TAXI AND TAKE OFF AT YOUR DISCRETION.

A Flight Service Station does not exercise control of air traffic; an aircraft receiving the above message is free to taxi and take off at will. In fact, an aircraft may taxi and take off without any communication with the Flight Service Station at all. However, no pilot should make any flight, no matter of what duration, without obtaining all possible information to ensure the maximum safety of that flight.

Responsibility

Regardless of whether an airport is controlled or uncontrolled, nothing relieves the pilot-in-command of the responsibility for exercising good judgment and adhering to the Rules of the Air when an aircraft is being manoeuvred on or in the vicinity of an airport.. At a controlled airport the pilot-in-command has another pair of eyes helping to ensure the safety of his operation, but this does not mean he may close his own eyes. When a control tower clears an aircraft across a runway or through any active area, the pilot-in-command must reassure himself that no hazards exist before proceeding as cleared. A pilot-in-command must never presume that he may hand over the responsibility for the safe operation of his aircraft to any other agency.

Surface Winds

Control towers (and Flight Service Stations with voice facilities) broadcast surface winds for the airport at which they are located, in knots and in degrees magnetic. However, when a Flight Service Station broadcasts surface winds for sites other than for the airport at which the Flight Service Station is located, the winds are given in degrees true.

Manoeuvring Surfaces

An aircraft should not be operated upon the aircraft manoeuvring surfaces at a controlled airport without a clearance to do so from the control tower. Even if the aircraft is being moved for purposes other than intended flight, the control tower must be advised by radio, telephone, or other means.

Taxiway centre-line markings and holding point markings are readily distinguished from runway markings. The colour used is yellow instead of white and they are a relatively narrow width of 6 inches. Taxiway holding point markings consist of solid and broken lines across the taxiway (or holding bay), parallel to the runway (Fig 1-25).

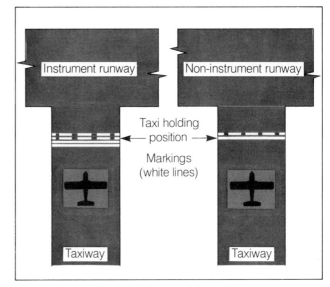

Figure 1-25   Taxi Holding Position

Taxi Holding Positions

Taxi holding positions are established at many airports, but at airports where they have not been established an aircraft should be held at least 150 feet from the edge of the runway in use. Where this is not possible, aircraft should be held at a distance that does not create a hazard to arriving or departing aircraft.

Runway Button

The term "button" has no official definition. It normally means the point at the end of a runway where an aircraft is positioned for take-off with the intention of having the full length of the runway available.

Radio Frequencies (Control Tower)

When an aircraft equipped with radio receives taxiing instructions on the ground control frequency at a controlled airport, unless otherwise advised it should remain on the frequency until ready for take-off. When all take-off checks are complete and you may take off without delay, switch to the control tower frequency to obtain permission to take off. It is not necessary to advise ground control of the change of frequency.

Clearances and Instructions

If the pilot-in-command of an aircraft accepts a clearance or instruction to taxi, take off, taxi fast, take off immediately, etc., he must do everything possible to execute the clearance as stated. But if there is the remotest possibility that the clearance may jeopardize the safety of the operation, he must not hesitate in asking the tower for an alternate clearance. Avoid taking off in response to the tower's "Cleared for immediate take-off" if the pre-take-off check is incomplete, if there is some concern about disturbed air behind a heavy aircraft which has just taken off, etc.

Do not request take-off clearance until all pre-take-off checks have been completed, because once the tower has given the clearance a presumption is made that there will be no undue delay in vacating the active runway.

Similar pre-take-off practices apply at uncontrolled airports and controlled airports; engine run-up and take-off checks are completed well clear of any runway and prior to entering the runway to be used. Turn the aircraft so that a full view of all angles of the approach may be scanned for other traffic; also inspect approaches to all other runways in case an aircraft has arbitrarily selected a different runway for landing or take-off. Once you are positive that all is clear, proceed onto the runway and take off without delay.

Air Filing

Although the filing of a flight plan after becoming airborne is not encouraged when it is possible to file before take-off, do not hesitate to "air file" when it appears to be the prudent thing to do. To speed up the procedure, always carry a sample copy of the approved flight plan or flight notification form so that you can read the flight plan to ATC rather than having them ask for information item by item.

Keep Alert

The necessity for keeping a sharp look-out for other aircraft while in an airport traffic pattern or en route cannot be overemphasized. It is a good idea to remember that if another aircraft or object appears within the normal view from the cockpit, remains in view, and appears to increase in size, a risk of collision exists.

Visibility

The visual flight rules (VFR) state that the ground visibility when flying within control zones, control areas, and aerodrome traffic zones shall be a minimum of 3 miles and, outside of these areas, that the flight visibility be a minimum of 1 mile. There are reasons for these minima; probably the most important one is the risk of collision. Two light aircraft approaching head-on, with an airspeed of 120 mph each, have a closing speed of 240 mph. If they become visible to each other at the 3 mile range, they will have only 45 seconds to determine and execute the appropriate evading action. With a visibility of only 1 mile, the period of time in which decision and action must be taken is only 15 seconds. These times are based on a pilot-in-command actually sighting another aircraft at the exact point of visibility; in normal practice another aircraft may not be sighted until well into visibility range, which further reduces the time available for whatever action may be necessary.

Advice of Conflicting Traffic

In many areas of controlled airspace, air traffic is monitored by radar, and when aircraft appear to be getting too close to each other, ATC may advise of this apparent conflict by using the clock position system outlined in Transport Canada's *Aeronautical Information Publication*. When advised of other traffic, do not merely acknowledge the advice if the other traffic has not been sighted. Instead, acknowledge and state, "Traffic not sighted." ATC will then continue with advice until either you sight the other traffic or a risk of collision no longer exists.

Avoiding a Collision

When you meet another aircraft head-on at the same altitude and it appears that evasive action is necessary, turn right. In some situations a diving or climbing right turn may assist in avoiding other aircraft. The right turn is a requirement of the Air Regulations when meeting an aircraft head-on or near head-on.

When uncertain whether the other aircraft is above or below your altitude, look for the following. If any underparts of the wings or fuselage of the other aircraft show, go down and turn right; if any part of the top surfaces of the other aircraft is visible, climb and turn right. In the latter case the other aircraft becomes lost to view, but you were already above it. Therefore, your climb is increasing the separation.

A stationary target — that is, one that remains in the same position in your vision and appears to grow larger — is one that may result in a mid-air collision.

Formation Flying

Due to the high risk of mid-air collision, pilots who have not been properly trained in formation flying should not attempt it. An extensive course of ground and air training is required to produce a pilot who is qualified to fly in formation with another aircraft, and continuous practice is necessary to maintain that skill at a safe level.

Vectors

During flight training you will become familiar with terms involved with direction, such as magnetic heading, track, compass heading, etc. But when an ATC unit requests that you fly on a certain heading, do not become involved in any calculations; merely fly your aircraft on the requested heading as indicated by the magnetic compass or the direction indicator. Most likely ATC is observing you on radar and will be providing guidance by manoeuvring the aircraft by means of vectors. (*Vector*, simply stated, is another way of saying "heading.")

VHF Direction-finding Assistance (DF Steer)

A pilot who is unsure of his position and is able to contact a VHF/DF equipped control tower or FSS, on frequencies listed in the *VFR Supplement*, may be provided with headings to reach the airport concerned. Details of this service are outlined in Transport Canada's *Aeronautical Information Publication*.

Encountering IFR Weather

If you are qualified for flight under the Visual Flight Rules (VFR) only, always plan your flight so that there is no risk of encountering Instrument Flight Rules (IFR) weather, but at the same time have an alternate plan should the weather deteriorate. One alternate plan is to turn 180 degrees and fly a reciprocal track (see Exercise 23 in Part 2, "Pilot Navigation"). However, when no alternate appears available and the weather continues to deteriorate, contact ATC, who will do all that is possible to:

(1) Provide information concerning an alternate route and radar navigation assistance if this will enable the flight to be continued in VFR weather conditions; or
(2) If action in (1) is not practicable, provide radar navigation or radar approach guidance, provided you declare an emergency. You must not declare an emergency lightly, but if you have any doubt

about the safety of your flight don't allow a doubtful situation to develop into a bad one. Ask for assistance.

Right-Hand Circuits

The standard direction of any airport traffic circuit is left-hand, whether the airport is controlled, licensed, municipal, military, or anything else. There are exceptions to this rule, however, where traffic conflict with other airports or hazardous terrain necessitate the adoption of a right-hand pattern, for an entire airport or for specific runways. The exceptions are listed in Transport Canada's VFR Supplement.

Uncontrolled Airports

A great number of uncontrolled airports have a mandatory or advisory radio frequency to assist pilots in determining the runway in use and to inform them of other known traffic. Advising the ground station and other aircraft of your position in the traffic pattern at an uncontrolled airport becomes very important. Even though the airport advisory service does not reply to a call, do not hesitate to broadcast position, landing, or take-off intentions.

When approaching an uncontrolled airport for a landing, first fly over the airport well above circuit height to determine wind direction and to inspect the airport for runway conditions, surface traffic, and other information. When the runway in use, or to be used, has been established, return to the upwind (dead side) of the traffic pattern, descend to circuit height, and then join the downwind leg by crossing the airport over the upwind end of the runway in use, at 90 degrees to it.

During the winter be highly suspicious of an aerodrome not being used by other aircraft in the same landing configuration (i.e., skis or wheels). If you are in doubt, do a low approach over the entire length of the landing surface to inspect it for snow depth, icy patches, puddles, slush, etc., then pull up and execute another circuit at the normal height.

Landing

Hazards

When an aircraft has been cleared to land by a control tower it does not mean the runway is clear of all hazards.

Any known hazards will be mentioned at the time of the clearance; however, at times of restricted visibility or at night, when a view of the runway from the tower may be limited, unauthorized vehicles or animals may have moved onto the runway without the controller's knowledge. As the pilot, it is your final responsibility to keep a look-out for hazards on the landing and manoeuvring area, and you alone must decide whether it is acceptable for your aircraft and level of flying skill.

VASIS

To enable pilots to maintain a specific angle of approach during final descent to a runway where it has been determined that there may be difficulty in judging the approach due to inadequate visual guidance, a visual aid known as Visual Approach Slope Indicator System (VASIS) has been installed at major airports (see Transport Canada's *Aeronautical Information Publication*).

Runway Numbering

To standardize runway identification in Canada, a system of numbering runway ends by utilizing the reciprocal of their magnetic bearings is used. A runway running east and west (magnetic) would have the number 27 on the east end, representing the magnetic bearing of 270 degrees with the last digit of the 270 removed. The number nearest the even 10 degrees division is used; i.e., a runway bearing 134 degrees is numbered 13 at one end and 31 at the other. If an aircraft on a compass heading of between 136 degrees and 144 degrees has a runway directly ahead of it, the number on the runway should be 14 (Fig 1-26).

Runway Threshold Markings

The markings for runway thresholds consist of a group of lines displaced across the width of the runway at the threshold ends. The lines are parallel with the runway centre-line: they are 100 feet long, 5 feet 6 inches wide, and have varying lateral spacing (Fig 1-26).

Displaced Threshold

The threshold of a runway may be temporarily or permanently displaced to take a poor surface out of service or to bring the runway within zoning standards. Under certain conditions there may be a temptation to land on the wrong side of the displacement marking because the displaced part looks reasonably

serviceable. This should be avoided, as the area may not receive regular maintenance and could contain hazards not readily visible, especially during the winter when ice-hardened windrows of snow may be left by snow plows.

The markings that indicate a temporarily displaced threshold consist of a white line placed across the width of the runway to indicate its new end, and four white arrowheads equally spaced across the width of the runway on the approach side of the runway end with their points indicating the new end. A permanently displaced threshold will have a white line across the width of the runway and two white arrows on the approach side, one following the other on the former centre-line, leading up to and pointing towards the new runway end.

Centre-Line Markings

Centre-line markings of a runway, besides being an excellent directional guide, are very useful as an aid to depth perception because of the "broken" line presentation. The marks are 100 feet long and longitudinally spaced 100 feet apart at airports under Transport Canada's jurisdiction.

Ground Control Frequency

After landing, remain on the control tower frequency until advised to change to ground control by the tower. More often than not this will occur after the aircraft has cleared the runway, but on occasion instructions may be given during the landing roll. The tower does not expect an acknowledgment from a pilot who is still busy with the landing roll.

Taxiing on a Runway in Use (Uncontrolled Airports)

It is sometimes necessary to turn 180 degrees and taxi back down the runway just landed upon in order to clear the runway. Do this as quickly as possible consistent with safety, remembering that until the runway is cleared no other traffic has landing priority. However, should another aircraft inadvertently execute a take-off or landing before the runway is clear, the aircraft taxiing back should immediately obey the Rules of the Air. To avoid a collision, turn right and vacate the runway; if it is not possible to vacate the runway, crowd to the edge, remaining in line with the runway edge to present the least obstruction to the oncoming aircraft. The major reason for making a right turn is to place the aircraft on

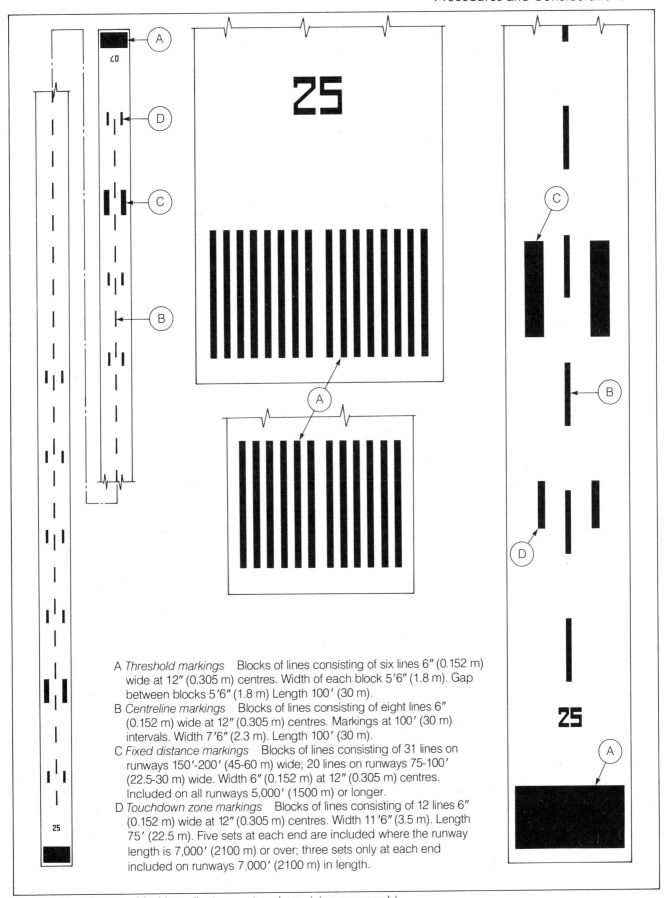

A *Threshold markings*   Blocks of lines consisting of six lines 6″ (0.152 m) wide at 12″ (0.305 m) centres. Width of each block 5′6″ (1.8 m). Gap between blocks 5′6″ (1.8 m) Length 100′ (30 m).

B *Centreline markings*   Blocks of lines consisting of eight lines 6″ (0.152 m) wide at 12″ (0.305 m) centres. Markings at 100′ (30 m) intervals. Width 7′6″ (2.3 m). Length 100′ (30 m).

C *Fixed distance markings*   Blocks of lines consisting of 31 lines on runways 150′-200′ (45-60 m) wide; 20 lines on runways 75-100′ (22.5-30 m) wide. Width 6″ (0.152 m) at 12″ (0.305 m) centres. Included on all runways 5,000′ (1500 m) or longer.

D *Touchdown zone markings*   Blocks of lines consisting of 12 lines 6″ (0.152 m) wide at 12″ (0.305 m) centres. Width 11′6″ (3.5 m). Length 75′ (22.5 m). Five sets at each end are included where the runway length is 7,000′ (2100 m) or over; three sets only at each end included on runways 7,000′ (2100 m) in length.

Figure 1-26   Runway Markings (instrument and precision approach)

the ground in the best possible position to be seen by the pilot of the oncoming aircraft, since he invariably has a full view of anything on his left side, whereas objects on his right side may be obscured, especially during his landing flare or take-off rotation.

Flight Plans (Arrival)

When a flight plan or flight notification is filed, a heavy responsibility rests upon the pilot-in-command to close the flight plan or notification promptly when the destination is reached, or if there has been any deviation from the original plan, to so notify the appropriate agency as soon as possible. The fact that the airport may be controlled and the control tower has given the aircraft a landing clearance does not automatically remove this responsibility.

Parking

When parking an aircraft remember that the responsibility for its welfare while so parked rests with its operator, even if the airport operator's equipment, such as tie-downs, is used to secure it.

PART TWO

Air Exercises

Familiarization

The first exercise will not normally involve any detailed training, but will consist of a flight during which your role as student will be mainly that of an observer, even though you will occupy the seat from which you will subsequently fly. This flight will begin to accustom you to the sensation of flying and to the appearance of the country from the air. However, it is the flight instructor's prerogative to take a more positive approach to instruction at this time, and he may also include Exercise 4, "Taxiing," and Exercise 5, "Attitudes and Movements."

The first flight will be an entirely new experience, but what may look complicated and difficult at this time will become less and less so as flight training progresses.

You may be asked to keep your hands lightly on the throttle and control column and your feet lightly on the rudder pedals. The instructor will emphasize that only small, smooth control movements are required to control the aircraft and will briefly discuss the procedures to be followed in future flight training exercises.

There will be a temptation for anyone who has never flown before to lean away from the bank as the aircraft turns. Resist this temptation as strongly as possible and become "one with the aircraft."

The flight instructor will point out readily identifiable local landmarks and explain their orientation to the airport. He will also explain the function of the airspeed indicator and the altimeter, and may from time to time ask you to tell him the altitude and the speed of the aircraft. The function of other instruments may also be explained. Do not hesitate to ask questions. The instructor's voice must be completely audible and understandable; if it is not, tell him so.

Aircraft Familiarization and Preparation for Flight

This exercise does not normally involve a flight. It begins by the flight instructor acquainting you with the type of aircraft to be used during the training period. The main components of the aircraft will be pointed out and the function of each carefully explained. For example:

(1) **Wings.** Another name for them is aerofoils. The wings provide the lift required to make the aircraft fly by obtaining a useful reaction from the air through which the wing moves.

(2) **Fuselage.** This is the main body of the aircraft. It is what is left if the wings, engine, landing-gear, and tail surfaces are removed.

(3) **Tail Surfaces.** These may be separated into horizontal stabilizer (tail plane) and vertical stabilizer (fin). As the names imply, they provide the aircraft with stability in certain planes of movement.

(4) **Ailerons, Elevators, and Rudder.** These are movable aerofoil surfaces, operated by the pilot, which enable him to manoeuvre and control the aircraft in flight. The ailerons are positioned on hinges towards the outer ends of the wings; one moves up as the other moves down when the control column is moved from side to side. They are used to control bank in flight. The elevators are hinged to the trailing edge of the horizontal stabilizer and are moved up or down when the control column is moved backward or forward. They are used to pitch the aircraft up or down in flight. The rudder is hinged to the trailing edge of the vertical stabilizer and is linked to the rudder pedals. The pilot controls yaw by means of the rudder.

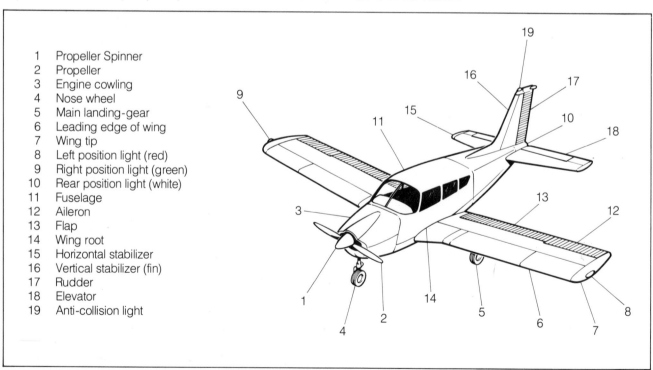

1	Propeller Spinner
2	Propeller
3	Engine cowling
4	Nose wheel
5	Main landing-gear
6	Leading edge of wing
7	Wing tip
8	Left position light (red)
9	Right position light (green)
10	Rear position light (white)
11	Fuselage
12	Aileron
13	Flap
14	Wing root
15	Horizontal stabilizer
16	Vertical stabilizer (fin)
17	Rudder
18	Elevator
19	Anti-collision light

Figure 2-1   Major Components of an Aircraft

(5) Landing-Gear. The function of this component requires little explanation, other than that it includes at least the supporting struts, wheels, tires, and any springs or other devices to absorb shocks due to uneven terrain or landing impact. Floats and skis are components of other types of landing-gear.

(6) Flaps. These are movable surfaces forming part of the wing and are mounted below the wing, at or near its trailing edge, between the wing root and the inner extremities of the ailerons. They extend and retract together and increase or decrease the effective lift of the wing by altering its camber. They are controlled by the pilot.

(7) Trim Tabs. These are small ancillary aerofoils hinged to the elevators and, in some aircraft, also to the ailerons and rudder. They help the pilot by reducing control pressures induced by changing flight attitudes.

(8) Flight Controls. These consist of the control column and the rudder pedals. The control column may consist of a straight "stick" or a wheel arrangement. Move the stick (or rotate the wheel) to the left and the left aileron moves up while the right aileron moves down; rotate the wheel (or move the stick) to the right and the right aileron moves up while the left aileron moves down. Push the left rudder pedal and the rudder moves to the left; push the right rudder pedal and the rudder moves to the right. The rudder pedals may also be used to "steer" the aircraft on the ground by means of a steerable nose wheel or tail wheel; pushing the left rudder pedal turns the aircraft to the left, and vice versa.

(9) Throttle. This is the power control. It takes various forms and, depending on the front seating arrangement, may be operated with the right hand or the left hand. To increase power move the throttle forward; to decrease power move the throttle back. Most throttle arrangements include a device for increasing or decreasing tension on the throttle; this is primarily to ensure that the power setting does not change should you remove your hand from the throttle.

(10) Ancillary Controls. These comprise the mixture control and carburettor heat control (see Exercise 3, "Ancillary Controls").

(11) Heating. The cabin heating arrangement of most aircraft in the training category consists of a controllable system of directing outside *ram* air (air entering an air inlet as a result of the forward motion of the aircraft), through an exhaust manifold heat exchanger and thence through flexible tubing into the cabin area. Many aircraft are also equipped with a controllable system for

bringing in outside air to cool the cabin during hot weather.

(12) Instrument Panel. The instrument layout directly in front of the pilot is called the instrument panel. The instruments may be divided into three categories: *flight instruments, engine instruments,* and *navigation instruments.*

Flight Instruments

(1) Airspeed Indicator. This instrument indicates the speed of the aircraft through the air in which it is flying; it relates only indirectly to the speed of the aircraft over the ground. It may indicate speed in miles per hour or knots.

(2) Altimeter. This is a pressure sensitive instrument which, if properly set, indicates the height at which the aircraft is flying. The customary procedure is to set the instrument so that it indicates height above mean sea level. When used this way the indication on the altimeter will be that of the elevation of the airport when the aircraft is on the ground.

(3) Turn-and-Bank Indicator. The needle portion of this instrument indicates whether the aircraft is turning, together with the direction and rate of turn. The ball portion of the instrument is fundamentally a reference for co-ordination of controls. In all co-ordinated flight the ball will be centred in its curved glass tube. Instead of a turn-and-bank indicator the aircraft may be equipped with a turn co-ordinator, which provides basically the same information as the former with a different display.

(4) Magnetic Compass. This is the basic reference for heading information. The compass correction card indicates the corrected heading to steer to allow for compass deviation.

(5) Heading Indicator. This gyroscopic instrument has no magnetic qualities of its own and therefore must be set periodically by reference to the magnetic compass. Its main asset is that it provides a stable directional reference, and unlike the magnetic compass is relatively free of error during turns, acceleration, and deceleration in normal flight manoeuvres.

(6) Attitude Indicator. This is a gyroscopic instrument. It provides the pilot with an artificial horizon, which together with a miniature aircraft superimposed on its face enables him to determine the aircraft's attitude relative to the real horizon.

Airspeed indicator

Attitude indicator

Altimeter

Turn-and-bank indicator

Heading indicator

Vertical speed indicator

Magnetic compass

Turn co-ordinator (*vice* turn-and-bank indicator)

Figure 2-2   Basic Flight Instruments

(7) **Vertical Speed Indicator.** This is a pressure sensitive instrument which indicates the rate at which the aircraft is climbing or descending, in feet per minute.

(8) **Outside Air Temperature Gauge.** This is not a flight instrument, but is a valuable aid to flight safety since its indications can help the pilot assess the possibility of icing conditions, including carburettor ice. The instrument usually registers outside air temperature in both degrees Fahrenheit and degrees Celsius.

Engine Instruments

(1) **Tachometer.** This instrument indicates to the pilot the number of revolutions per minute (RPM) that the engine crankshaft is making. In aircraft with a fixed pitch propeller, RPM is directly related to power. As the throttle is eased forward, the tachometer will indicate an increase in RPM and power. As the throttle is eased back the opposite effect is achieved.

(2) **Oil Pressure Gauge.** This vitally important instrument registers, usually in pounds per square inch, the pressure of the lubricating oil being supplied to the engine. Refer to the aircraft flight manual for limits and recommended pressures during particular phases of engine operation.

(3) **Oil Temperature Gauge.** This indicates the temperature of the engine lubricating oil. It reacts by

showing higher than normal temperatures if the oil pressure system malfunctions or if the engine is subject to the use of too much power for the amount of available engine cooling.

(4) Manifold Pressure Gauge. This instrument is calibrated in inches of mercury. It indicates the pressure in the intake manifold of the engine, which relates to the pressure developed for any given condition of throttle setting and RPM. It is mainly used on aircraft equipped with a constant speed propeller.

Fuel System

The fuel system of the average training aircraft is relatively simple, but the fact that the fuel supply to the engine is under the pilot's control requires that he understands it thoroughly. The fuel system must be managed as outlined in the aircraft flight manual.

Electrical System

The electrical system of a light aircraft is not a great deal different in principle from that of an automobile: there is a generator or alternator, a starter, a battery, a voltage regulator, and various switches for carrying out routine functions. However, some very important differences are:

Master Switch. This is used to provide a means for completely isolating the battery power supply from the electrical system. When the master switch is in the "off" position none of the normal components of the electrical system will operate. Note that the master switch exercises no control over the engine ignition system, nor, in most cases, over the emergency locator transmitter (ELT).

Ignition System. The engine ignition system uses magnetos for its electrical power source and is completely independent of the aircraft's normal electrical system. This is a safety feature: the engine will be provided with ignition power and continue to operate quite normally in spite of a complete failure of the aircraft's regular electrical system. As an added safety feature each engine has two magnetos and each cylinder has two spark plugs firing simultaneously.

Communications System

The air-to-ground communications system usually consists of a two-way radio operating on a choice of Very High Frequencies (VHF). Although two-way, it is not simultaneous like a telephone. The pilot presses a button on his microphone to talk, and during this period all other nearby transmitters and receivers on the same frequency are jammed. The pilot must release the microphone button after he has finished talking (transmitting) in order to receive a reply. Transmissions must be short and to the point.

Navigation Tracking Instruments (Radio)

(1) VOR (VHF Omnidirectional Range). **Receiver Display and Control Unit.** This instrument permits an aircraft to track to or from a VOR ground station on any track the pilot selects.

(2) ADF (Automatic Direction-Finder). The dial of this radio instrument includes a pointer (often referred to as the "needle") which points in the direction of any suitable ground radio station tuned into the ADF receiver by the pilot. To navigate accurately with an ADF the pilot must allow for wind drift effect. However, it is possible to "home" on a station without allowing for the wind.

Documentation

One of the most important operational documents is the *Aircraft Flight Manual* or, as it is also called, the *Pilot's Operating Handbook*. You will refer to it continually, and it should be readily available aboard the aircraft. The flight manual contains information, recommended procedures, and limitations concerning inspection, handling, and operation of the specific aircraft. Many of the items, particularly the recommended airspeeds for various manoeuvres, should be committed to memory.

The instructor will familiarize you with the various certificates, forms, permits, and other documents associated with the operation of the aircraft. See Chapter 5, "Aircraft Documents," for details.

A *weight and balance report* is an integral part of the aircraft's Certificate of Airworthiness, and the aircraft must be operated within the weight and centre of gravity limitations it prescribes. Most light aircraft flight manuals contain sample problems in weight and balance to help determine the correct loading formula for a particular aircraft. For additional information on this subject refer to Chapter 2, "Weight and Balance."

Flight Preparation

Before any flight, the pilot-in-command of an aircraft must ask himself the following questions concerning aircraft documents and weight and balance:

(1) Are the documents required by the Air Regulations on board the aircraft? Are they valid and/or properly certified?
(2) What is the maximum permissible gross take-off weight of the aircraft?
(3) With the proposed fuel, occupants, and baggage, is the aircraft's weight within the allowable limits?

Your first impression of an aircraft cockpit may be that it is cramped and complex. This impression will quickly disappear as you are instructed in the proper method of entering the cockpit and adjusting the seat and controls. Once seated and comfortable, the next action is to fasten the seat belt and learn how to adjust and release it. Fastening the seat belt as soon as possible after you are seated in the cockpit is a habit to acquire immediately.

In a seaplane operation, the practice concerning seat belts is slightly different. It is considered good seaplane practice to delay fastening seat belts until ready for take-off, and to release them when the aircraft reaches the taxiing mode following a landing.

After releasing the aircraft tie-downs, ensure that the following actions are carried out:

(1) Remove exterior flight control locks.
(2) Remove pitot tube cover.
(3) Remove wheel chocks.
(4) Free flight controls of any locking or securing system in the cockpit.

The flight instructor will explain the opening and proper securing of doors and windows. The unexpected opening of a poorly secured door during any phase of flight can be very disconcerting due to noise, and in many aircraft control may be affected.

The pre-flight external line check, often referred to as the "walk-around," determines from the pilot's point of view that the aircraft is serviceable and that it has sufficient fuel and oil for the intended flight. A recommended line check is included in most aircraft flight manuals.

The aircraft should be positioned so that the propeller slipstream does not present a hazard or nuisance to others, when the engine is started or during the subsequent engine run-up. It is discourteous and thoughtless to start an engine with the tail of the aircraft pointed towards a hangar door, parked aircraft or automobiles, or a crowd of spectators. The ground or surface under the propeller should be firm smooth turf or concrete, if possible, so that the propeller does not pick up pebbles, dirt, mud, or other loose particles and hurl them backward, damaging not only the rear portions of the aircraft but often the propeller itself. Avoid blocking a taxiway.

Before starting the engine, a geographic check of all items in the cockpit, and then a pre-start check, are performed. These checks are very important. For example, if the brakes are not on and secure as the engine starts, the aircraft may leap forward unexpectedly. The engine may be started with carburettor heat on, which can damage the carburettor heat system should the engine backfire. The battery may become discharged should you vainly attempt to start the engine with the mixture control in the "idle cut-off" position, or with the fuel selector valve in the "off" position.

The engine starting, warm-up, carburettor heat checks, and run-up procedures have already been covered in the section on engine handling and will not be repeated here. Your flight instructor will show you the procedures which apply to your own aircraft. The pre-take-off checks are carried out as specified in the aircraft flight manual. However, it is important to remember that if there is to be a change in fuel tanks before take-off, make it before the engine run-up so that, if a fuel malfunction exists, it will show up before take-off.

Be very selective in the choice of a surface upon which to park or stop an aircraft. Avoid icy surfaces, since the wind exerts considerable force upon an aircraft and may move it even though the brakes are securely applied. During engine start or run-up, the wheels must not be on a slippery surface, otherwise the aircraft may move forward against its brakes. When parking the aircraft make sure it is left on firm ground, otherwise it may settle and subsequently prove very difficult to move under its own power.

If for any reason there has been excessive use of brakes, the braking system may have been overheated. Should the parking brake be applied immediately under these circumstances, the brakes will self-release when the system cools down, leaving the aircraft parked in an unbraked condition. When overheated brakes are suspected, allow a suitable time interval for cooling to take place before you apply the parking brake, or chock the two main wheels, both ahead and behind each wheel, before leaving the aircraft.

When an aircraft is parked for any length of time, or if high winds exist or are forecast, it should be *tied down*. Tie-downs consist of appropriate lengths of rope or nylon line attached to weights, pickets, or other devices on or in the ground, with which the aircraft may be securely tied. The correct way to tie down a specific aircraft is usually outlined in the aircraft's flight manual. A tail wheel aircraft is secured by tie-downs located adjacent to each wing tip and to the tail wheel; a nose wheel aircraft is secured by means of a special fitting near the tail section.

The pilot-in-command is entirely responsible for the

security of the tie-down of his aircraft.

In addition to the tie-down, the aircraft being parked should also be secured as follows:

(1) Set the parking brake. For additional security place wheel chocks ahead and behind each main wheel.
(2) Secure flight controls in cockpit.
(3) Install the pitot tube cover.
(4) Install the exterior control locks, where applicable.

Survival Equipment and Clothing

Because the average light aircraft is as comfortable and warm as an automobile, there may be a temptation to treat the need for proper clothing and survival equipment too lightly. Should you be forced to make an unscheduled landing, there is every possibility that the landing site will be in a remote or isolated area where warmth and shelter are not immediately at hand. Proper clothing and equipment at such a time are essential to your welfare, perhaps even to your survival. Due to the varying climate and terrain of a country as vast as Canada it is difficult to specify all requirements; however, you can use as a guide the equipment and clothing listed under the following subject headings in Transport Canada's *Aeronautical Information Publication*:

"Sparsely Settled Areas"
"Emergency Locator Transmitter"
"Life-Saving Equipment"
"Single-Engine Aircraft Operations in
 Northern Canada"

Ancillary Controls

Although the usual definition of *ancillary* is "subordinate to" or "auxiliary," ancillary controls are vital to the safe and comfortable operation of an aircraft. The ancillary controls to be discussed here are the carburettor heat control and the carburettor mixture control.

Carburettor Heat Control

Icing

Under certain moist (and "moist" is a key word) atmospheric conditions, with air temperatures ranging anywhere from − 6 degrees Celsius to +32 degrees Celsius, it is possible for ice to form in the induction system (Fig 2-3). The rapid cooling in the induction system using a float type carburettor is caused by the absorption of heat from the air during vaporization of the fuel, and is also due in part to the high expansion of air through the carburettor venturi. As a result of the latter two influences, the temperature in the venturi may drop as much as 21 degrees Celsius below the temperature of the incoming air. If this air contains a large amount of moisture, the cooling process can cause precipitation in the form of ice, which may build up to such an extent that a drop in power output results, and if not corrected may cause complete engine stoppage. Indications of icing to the pilot are a loss of RPM with a fixed pitch propeller, and a loss of manifold pressure with a constant speed propeller, together with the accompanying airspeed loss and engine roughness with both types.

To counteract the formation of carburettor ice, an aircraft is equipped with a controllable system for pre-heating the air before it enters the carburettor.

Carburettor Heat

Always anticipate possible icing and use carburettor heat before the ice forms. However, should ice begin to

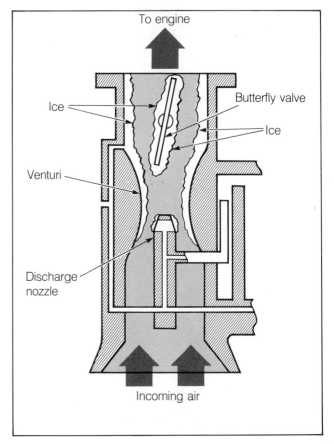

Figure 2-3   Carburettor Icing

form, use the "full heat" position long enough to be sure of eliminating the ice. Using full heat will initially cause a loss of power and possible engine roughness. Heated air directed into the induction system will melt the ice, which goes through the engine as water, causing some of the roughness and more power loss. Despite this temporary roughness and attendant moderate power loss, a pilot is not damaging the engine at a cruise power of 75 per cent or less with any amount of heat.

When using carburettor heat, there are related factors to remember. The engine loses an average of 9 per cent

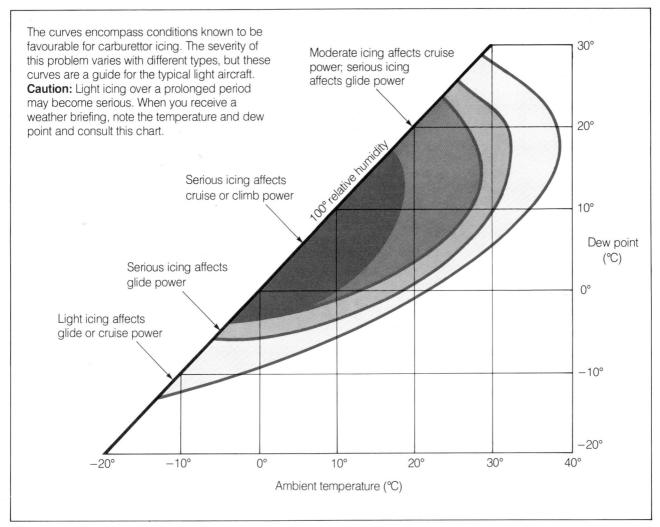

The curves encompass conditions known to be favourable for carburettor icing. The severity of this problem varies with different types, but these curves are a guide for the typical light aircraft. **Caution:** Light icing over a prolonged period may become serious. When you receive a weather briefing, note the temperature and dew point and consult this chart.

Moderate icing affects cruise power; serious icing affects glide power

100° relative humidity

Serious icing affects cruise or climb power

Serious icing affects glide power

Light icing affects glide or cruise power

Dew point (°C)

30°
20°
10°
0°
−10°
−20°

Ambient temperature (°C)

−20°   −10°   0°   10°   20°   30°   40°

Figure 2-4   Carburettor Icing Graph

of its power when heat is applied, due to the reduced volumetric efficiency of heated air and loss of the ram air feature. Carburettor heat also creates a richer mixture, which may cause the engine to run rough, particularly at full heat. If there is any throttle available, bring the power up to the former RPM setting, then lean out and readjust the mixture until the engine runs smoothly again. Readjust the mixture as subsequent throttle and carburettor heat changes are made.

At lower power conditions, such as are required during flight in the traffic pattern, it may be impractical to lean the mixture.

Carburettor icing may be controlled or avoided by adopting the following practices:

(1) Start the engine with the carburettor heat control in the "cold" position, to avoid damage to the carburettor heat system.

(2) When relative humidity is high and the summer ambient temperature is below 27 degrees Celsius, use carburettor heat immediately before take-off. In general, carburettor heat should not be used while taxiing because in the carburettor heat "on" position, intake air usually bypasses the carburettor air filter.

(3) Avoid using carburettor heat during take-off since it may cause detonation and possible engine damage. An exception to this might be in very low temperature areas, which call for special knowledge and procedures.

(4) Remain alert after take-off for indications of carburettor icing, especially when visible moisture is present.

(5) With instrumentation, such as a carburettor air temperature gauge, partial carburettor heat should be used as necessary to maintain safe temperatures to forestall icing. Without such instrumentation use full heat, if you consider it necessary.

(6) When carburettor ice is suspected, immediately apply full heat. Watch for a power loss to indicate the presence of carburettor heat, then an increase in power as ice melts.

(7) If carburettor ice persists after a period of full heat, gradually increase power to obtain the greatest amount of carburettor heat.

(8) Carburettor ice may be more prevalent in clouds and other visible moisture.

(9) In severely iced conditions and when equipped with mixture control, backfiring the engine can sometimes be effective in dislodging induction system ice. With the carburettor heat control "off" lean the mixture while at full throttle until backfiring occurs. This is never to be considered a routine procedure.

(10) Carburettor icing can occur with the ambient temperature as high as +38 degrees Celsius and humidity as low as 50 per cent. Remain especially alert with a combination of ambient temperature below +27 degrees Celsius and high relative humidity. The possibility of carburettor ice decreases (a) in the range below 0 degrees Celsius, because of lessened humidity as the temperature decreases, and (b) at around -10 degrees Celsius because of ice crystals which pass through the induction system harmlessly. It should be remembered that if the intake air does contain ice crystals, carburettor heat might actually cause carburettor icing by melting the crystals and raising the moisture laden air to the icing temperature range.

(11) During descents when carburettor icing is present or suspected, apply full carburettor heat and periodically apply sufficient power so that enough engine heat is produced to prevent or disperse ice. This is a general rule for many aircraft. Consult the aircraft flight manual for the procedures in a specific aircraft.

The diagram of a carburettor heat system shows that when the system is in the "heat on" mode, air entering the carburettor is no longer filtered. This is the main reason for ensuring that the system is in the "heat off" mode when taxiing. At ground level the air may be laden with airborne particles harmful to the engine if ingested; at 100 feet above ground level this possibility is almost negligible.

There is a misconception that it does not matter to the efficiency of the engine whether the carburettor heat is on or off. If this were true, engine manufacturers would design their engines so that heated air was constantly directed through the carburettor air intake system, to completely eradicate the problem of carburettor icing. But they don't, because the application of carburettor heat in standard atmospheric conditions will:

(1) Reduce the maximum power output of the engine, and

(2) Increase fuel consumption.

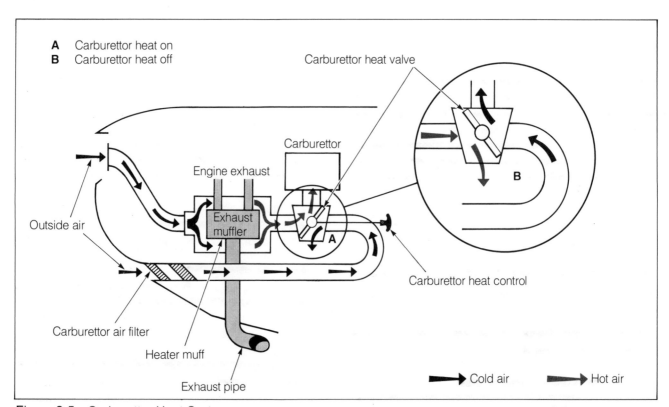

Figure 2-5   Carburettor Heat System

As the ambient temperature decreases, the effect of carburettor heat on the efficiency of the engine also decreases. Light aircraft engines operated at extremely low (winter) ambient temperatures may require the warming influence of carburettor heat to ensure adequate response to throttle application.

Mixture Control (normally aspirated engines)

As an aircraft gains altitude, the surrounding air becomes less and less dense. Atmospheric pressure of approximately 14.7 pounds per square inch at sea level is only, say, 10.2 pounds per square inch at 10,000 feet above sea level. At altitude, the engine draws a lesser weight of air into its cylinders than it does on the ground, but the weight of the fuel drawn into the cylinders is relatively unaffected. This means that if the carburettor had the correct fuel/air ratio mixture on the ground, the mixture would become too rich in fuel at altitude.

Since the carburettor of an aircraft engine is adjusted to give maximum power for take-off, as the aircraft gains height the fuel/air mixture gradually becomes too rich in fuel. At the proper time, this imbalance may be corrected by use of the mixture control, which is a lever or push-pull knob within easy reach of the pilot.

To obtain the best performance from an engine a proper fuel/air mixture is highly important, but unless otherwise specified, the customary procedure for aircraft equipped with a mixture control is to take off and climb with the control in the "full rich" position and leave it there while operating within the airport traffic pattern or below a certain altitude. Within certain bounds an aircraft engine runs cooler with a rich mixture, and since a power setting greater than that of normal cruising power generates much more undesirable heat, the enriched mixture contributes to the welfare of the engine. Some aircraft flight manuals suggest leaving the mixture control lever in the "full rich" position for flights conducted at 4000 feet ASL and below. Only on rare occasions would mixture control have to be considered for take-off and climb, for example at airports with a very high elevation. Some aerodromes on the North American continent have field elevations of over 5000 feet.

Correct procedures for mixture control are outlined in the aircraft flight manual. However, the generally accepted procedure for leaning the mixture is to move the mixture control slowly toward the "lean" position until maximum RPM is obtained with a fixed power setting. Then, and this is important, move the mixture control toward "rich" until a decrease in RPM is just perceptible. This produces optimum power for the throttle setting, with a slightly rich mixture to prevent overheating, since sustained operation with the mixture too lean can damage the engine. It is important to note that aircraft performance chart fuel flow and range figures are based on the recommended lean mixture setting detailed in the aircraft flight manual.

There may be reasons for not doing so in a specific aircraft, but many light aircraft pilots place the mixture control in the "full rich" position prior to a routine descent from altitude. The prime reason for doing this is so that the mixture will not be inadvertently too lean should there be a sudden need for power, and to guarantee that the control is in the proper position for the approach to landing. Ideally, the mixture should be adjusted gradually toward "full rich" as the descent progresses. An overrich mixture tends to cool an engine which is probably already being overcooled due to the lower power-to-speed ratio of the descent itself. Prolonged descents with the mixture in the "rich" position have been cited by some engine manufacturers as one of the causes of premature spark plug failure.

When carburettor heat is used it is important that the mixture control be adjusted to compensate for the fuel/air enrichment induced by the carburettor heat system. The mixture should be leaned out in the manner prescribed, and adjustments made to the mixture control to maintain the proper fuel/air ratio. This use of the mixture control may be necessary in spite of the customary operating procedure of leaving the mixture control in the "full rich" position at or below a certain altitude.

The correct adjustment of the mixture control and a technical knowledge of how it affects the engine, plus its overall effect on the total aircraft operation, are most important, especially during cross-country flights in a varying environment. For example, when the fuel/air mixture is too rich:

(1) It will not develop the engine power indicated by the throttle setting.
(2) The engine will run unevenly.
(3) The engine may operate cooler than is desirable.
(4) Fuel is wasted.
(5) There is increased possibility of spark plug fouling.
(6) Range is reduced.

On the other hand, when the fuel/air ratio is too lean:

(1) Power will be lost.
(2) The engine may run roughly and be subject to unnecessary vibration.
(3) The engine may operate hotter than is desirable.
(4) The engine may be damaged due to detonation.

Under normal flight conditions, if an aircraft is not equipped with fuel/air ratio instruments it is best to adjust the mixture so that it is on the rich side.

Windshield Defogger

Although the windshield defogging system is not classed as an ancillary control, a phase of its operation is included in this exercise.

The windshield of an aircraft should at all times be kept clear and free of anything that will interfere with forward visibility, not only for control purposes but also to see outside fixed obstructions and other air traffic clearly. Under no circumstances attempt a take-off with a fogged or partially fogged windshield. For those aircraft so equipped, the windshield defogging system will generally keep the windshield clear of interior fogging when the aircraft is in flight; however, while taxiing or waiting at the take-off position, or during run-ups, windshield fogging may occur. Upon these occasions, fogging may be controlled by opening the aircraft door slightly to improve interior air circulation. This procedure has also been found effective for aircraft without windshield defoggers.

Take care to ensure that the door is closed and properly latched again before take-off.

Taxiing

Taxi is the generally accepted word for manoeuvring an aircraft on the surface, and applies to either water or land surfaces. The prime purpose of taxiing is to manoeuvre the aircraft to the take-off position and return it to the apron after landing. Study the aerodrome chart and commit the runway and taxiway layout of your home base to memory so that taxiing can be carried out as expeditiously as possible.

At controlled airports (and some uncontrolled airports) the taxiways are identified by names taken from the phonetic alphabet, such as Alpha, Bravo, Delta, Echo, etc. On the sample aerodrome chart (Fig 2-6) these are depicted as A, B, D, E, etc.

Part of the taxi clearance that an aircraft could receive from a control tower might sound like this: ". . . the runway in use is two six — cleared to taxi via taxiways Bravo and Echo." This means that the first taxiway to use is Bravo and then, in this case, you make a right turn onto taxiway Echo. You must know the taxiway and runway layout in order to determine the direction of turn from one taxiway to another. In the above taxi clearance the control tower has cleared your aircraft *to* but not *onto* the runway in use; you will not have to ask permission to cross other runways. When the tower wants you to report crossing other runways they will say so in your taxi clearance, but this does not relieve you of the responsibility of ensuring that other aircraft are not using these runways before you cross them.

At large unfamiliar airports, especially those which use more than one runway simultaneously for take-offs and landings, taxiing an aircraft in the correct direction can be complicated and puzzling. Do not hesitate to ask the control tower or ground control for guidance if there is any doubt in your mind concerning correct procedure. Mention the fact that you are a student pilot or unfamiliar with the airport; you will find air traffic control personnel very co-operative and helpful.

At less complex airports, taxiways may be identified by numbers. At airports with only one taxiway, no special identifier may be necessary at all.

Taxiing a single-engine aircraft with a tail wheel landing-gear arrangement in moderate to high winds can require effort and skill, due to its tendency to *weathercock* (continually wanting to head into wind). However, in the case of the aircraft with a nose wheel arrangement the weathercocking tendency is far less; as a result such aircraft are easier to control and manoeuvre on the ground, except under adverse wind conditions.

To start an aircraft moving, more engine power is required than is needed to keep it moving. The amount of power required depends on several things, but the principal governing factor is the degree of firmness of the surface upon which the aircraft is resting. In any case the throttle may have to be used more or less liberally, but once the aircraft starts to move power must be reduced promptly. As soon as the aircraft starts moving, test the brakes by bringing it to a smooth full stop. The brakes may not operate to perfection but it is important to know just how efficiently they are working.

Most light aircraft have steerable nose wheels or tail wheels interconnected to the rudder system, and under most circumstances they may be manoeuvred on the ground by this feature alone, without using brakes to assist turning. To turn the aircraft to the left move the left rudder pedal forward; to maintain a straight heading neutralize the rudder pedals.

The amount of rudder pedal action required to establish a desired heading varies according to the radius of turn, the condition of the manoeuvring surface, and the strength and direction of the wind. Of these three the wind has the most influence. In aircraft with differential braking systems — i.e., a separate brake system for each mainwheel — a turn may be assisted by applying a sufficient amount of brake pressure on the same side as the rudder pedal being used to initiate the turn. Use brakes sparingly and never harshly.

It is considered poor practice to taxi an aircraft with excessive power settings and then control speed with continuing use of brake. The lower the speed the easier it will be to stop: taxi slowly and remember that there is a

GND 121.9			TWR 119.4 297.0						
DECLARED DISTANCES	08	26							
TORA	6000	6000							
TODA	7000	7000							
ASDA	6000	6000							
LDA	6000	6000							

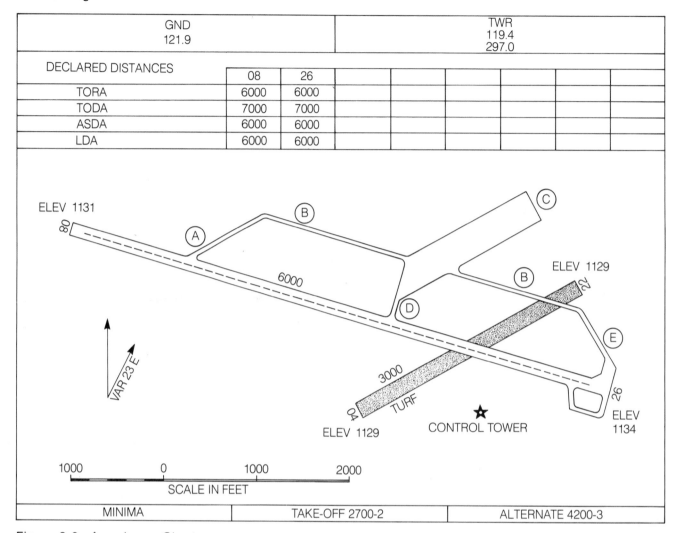

MINIMA	TAKE-OFF 2700-2	ALTERNATE 4200-3

Figure 2-6   Aerodrome Chart

slight interval between the time the pilot initiates a change in speed or direction and the time the change actually occurs.

It is essential that the view ahead be unobstructed by the nose of the aircraft; in the case of many tail wheel aircraft it may therefore be necessary to zigzag, first looking out one side of the aircraft and then the other to ascertain that the taxiway is clear.

When taxiing directly cross-wind, if the control column is held over to the side from which the wind is coming, the deflection of the ailerons will help maintain directional control. Various amounts of rudder will be required to prevent the aircraft from turning into the wind and to maintain a constant direction along the taxiway. When taxiing into wind and a turn is desired to the right, holding the control column to the left will assist the turn (and vice versa).

Take extra care when taxiing nose wheel aircraft, particularly those with a high wing, in strong *quartering tail winds*. To understand this term, picture an aircraft taxiing on a heading of, say due north. Any wind blowing

from a southeasterly or a southwesterly direction would be a quartering tail wind. When taxiing in strong quartering tailwinds, the elevators should be down (control column forward) and the aileron on the side from which the wind is blowing, down (Fig 2-7). As an added precaution, avoid sharp braking and sudden bursts of power.

You should realize that some manufacturers of nose wheel aircraft recommend the use of ailerons at variance to this method. In all cases the recommendations of the manufacturer should be followed.

When turning from downwind to upwind (into wind), slow down. The inherent tendency for an aircraft to turn into wind, further aggravated by too much forward speed, can introduce an excessive amount of centrifugal force. Coupled with the top-heaviness of most aircraft, the additional centrifugal force may cause the aircraft to capsize or heel over on one wing; at the very least an undesirable side force will be placed on various components.

When the manoeuvring area is soft or very rough, and

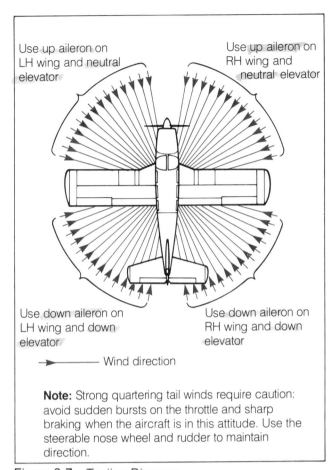

Use up aileron on LH wing and neutral elevator

Use up aileron on RH wing and neutral elevator

Use down aileron on LH wing and down elevator

Use down aileron on RH wing and down elevator

→ ———— Wind direction

Note: Strong quartering tail winds require caution: avoid sudden bursts on the throttle and sharp braking when the aircraft is in this attitude. Use the steerable nose wheel and rudder to maintain direction.

Figure 2-7 Taxiing Diagram

more power is being used than would be normal for a firm level surface, it is best to taxi with the control column held firmly back, unless the wind strength and direction dictate otherwise.

Except when the air is still, the amount of foot pressure which must be applied to a rudder pedal to execute a manoeuvre or maintain a heading on the ground depends basically on the wind velocity, the speed at which the aircraft is taxiing, and whether the aircraft has a tail wheel or a nose wheel landing-gear arrangement. Of these three the wind velocity is the most important.

Because of the many influencing factors, turning an aircraft on the ground varies in "positivity." In reasonably still air steering can be almost as positive as that of an automobile, but positivity decreases as wind velocity increases. Relatively little pressure on the rudder pedal is required to turn an aircraft into wind, but considerable pressure and coarse movement may be necessary to turn the aircraft out of wind. In addition, this pressure, once the aircraft is started into the turn, may have to be varied to maintain the desired radius of turn. It may be necessary under some circumstances, especially in the case of a tail wheel aircraft, to anticipate the need for a control action before the

requirement for such action becomes evident. For example, when turning into wind you may have to anticipate a need for opposite rudder pressure to arrest the turn, so that it does not become too sharp.

It is impossible to rule on a specific taxiing speed which will assure safety at all times. The primary requirement for safe taxiing is complete control of the aircraft, and the ability to stop or turn where and when necessary. The speed should be limited to where the aircraft's movement is dependent on the power settings — i.e., slow enough that when the throttle is closed, the aircraft may be stopped promptly. However, it is again emphasized that safe taxiing is directly related to wind velocity: the stronger the wind, the more slowly the aircraft should be manoeuvred on the ground.

When taxiing on a soft surface such as a muddy field or in slush or snow, maintain speed at a slow, steady pace, otherwise the aircraft may come to a halt before power can be reapplied. This may necessitate the use of near full power to begin moving again, which besides being bad for the engine carries the risk of the propeller picking up lumps of mud, ice, snow, etc., damaging itself or other parts of the aircraft.

It is poor practice to turn or try to turn an aircraft by pivoting it about a stationary mainwheel through the use of differential brake. If differential braking is used to assist a turn, allow the braked wheel to rotate forward sufficiently to avoid putting a twisting strain on the wheel and strut assembly.

When starting to taxi a nose wheel aircraft, first let it roll forward slowly and centre the nose wheel. This will prevent the possibility of a swerve into another aircraft or a nearby obstruction. While taxiing in a clear area, check the turn-and-bank indicator (T&B), attitude indicator (AI), and heading indicator (HI) for deflection, displacement, and indications as follows:

Instrument	Taxiing Straight	Turning Left	Turning Right
T&B Needle	Centre	Left	Right
T&B Ball	Centre	Right	Left
AI Bar	Steady	Steady	Steady
HI Degrees	Steady	Decreasing	Increasing

The slightest collision or upset on the ground can cause expensive damage to an aircraft. It is always wise to have competent outside help when taxiing on an icy surface, in high winds, or in congested areas.

When an aircraft is receiving outside guidance it is being *marshalled* by a *signalman*. If you recognize the signalman as a person qualified to marshall aircraft, you should keep your eyes on him at all times and obey his signals. The standard system of marshalling signals may be found in Transport Canada's *Aeronautical Information Publication*.

Never block a taxiway unnecessarily. If for some reason the engine warm-up or run-up will cause delays to aircraft behind you, choose some other convenient place on the airport to carry out these functions.

Attitudes and Movements

In this exercise you will learn the range of attitudes through which the aircraft will normally be operated and how the movements necessary to achieve and maintain the desired attitudes of flight are produced and controlled. You will be shown that yawing is not a desirable manoeuvre in co-ordinated flight and will learn how to control it. Some of these matters may appear complicated on paper, but you will gain understanding very quickly when they are actually demonstrated in the air.

Now that flight training has begun in earnest, start observing this rule: *look around*. For safety in flight, *keep alert for other aircraft*. Look continually. Realize that there is a blind spot beneath your aircraft and never assume that others see you. Be especially alert during periods of nose-up attitudes of your aircraft, when the blind spot enlarges due to a decrease in forward visibility.

A pilot must be constantly on the look-out for other aircraft and must keep up a continuing search of the sky. It is commonly believed that the eye sees everything in its field with equal clarity. This is not so. Fix your gaze about 5 degrees to one side of this page, and you will no longer be able to read the printed material. Studies have revealed that the eye perceives very poorly when it is in motion. Wide sweeping eye excursions are almost futile and may be a hazard, since they give the impression that large areas of sky have been examined. A series of short, regularly spaced eye movements is recommended for maximum efficiency in searching the sky.

During flight training there must be a clear understanding, between the student and the flight instructor, of who has control of the aircraft at a given moment. Whoever is handing over control should say in clear tones, "You have control." This should be immediately acknowledged by the words, "I have control." When the flight instructor wishes to take over control of the aircraft, he does so and at the same time says, "I have control." The student acknowledges immediately by saying, "You have control."

During the air exercises the position of the feet, when applying pressure to the rudder pedals, should be comfortable, with most of their weight supported by the heels in contact with the floor, thus allowing a fine sensitivity of touch in the toes. The control column should be held firmly but lightly with the fingers, not grabbed and squeezed. The tendency to choke the control column must not be allowed to develop since such a habit destroys "feel" and may be an underlying cause of apprehension and tension.

The basic attitude of an aircraft is termed a *cruise attitude*. Cruise attitude is the *datum* (reference point) to which all other attitudes of flight are related. It can be defined as the aircraft attitude for level flight at a constant altitude and airspeed, using a power setting recommended for the cruise range, with the wings parallel to the horizon. All attitudes are considered as being relative to the horizon.

The amount of control movement required to achieve a desired flight response depends to a great extent on the speed of the air flowing over or past the ailerons, elevators, and rudder. The cruise attitude airspeed may be considered the design datum for control effectiveness; at speeds above cruise speed the controls become firmer and there is a greater reaction to equivalent control movement. At lower cruising airspeeds, the controls become more yielding and less effort is needed to move them, but relatively more control movement may be needed to achieve an attitude change. The ailerons, being outside of the propeller slipstream, react consistently with airspeed changes, but the elevators and rudder do not (except in a power-off descent). Since the elevators and rudder are in the propeller slipstream they will remain sensitive to control movement. This sensitivity increases with increase of power more or less independently of airspeed in the low ranges, until the cruise attitude airspeed is reached. In a power assisted descent at a low airspeed, the aileron control will require relatively coarse movement, whereas elevator and rudder control movements will remain relatively fine, to achieve the desired control response.

The attitudes of flight may be broken down into two groups:

(1) Pitch Attitudes. Any attitude of the nose of the aircraft above or below the reference datum. Figure 2-8 illustrates a range of pitch attitudes above and below the reference datum and indicates the approximate attitude limits for this stage of training. The attitudes above the datum are termed "nose-up attitudes," and those below, "nose-down attitudes."

(2) Bank Attitudes. Any attitude of the wings of the aircraft when inclined relative to the datum. Figure 2-9 illustrates a range of bank attitudes relative to the reference datum. The illustration indicates the approximate bank attitude limits for this stage of training.

The airspeed for flight in the cruise attitude selected should be noted, as it will be referred to when nose-up and nose-down attitudes are demonstrated. The other flight instruments will be referred to frequently. If you have an appreciation of the performance of your aircraft by reference to flight instruments, as well as by outside reference, you will develop from the start the habit of monitoring your own and the aircraft's performance continuously.

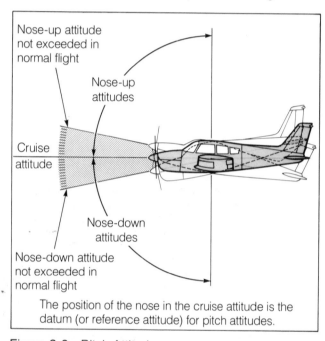

Figure 2-8   Pitch Attitudes

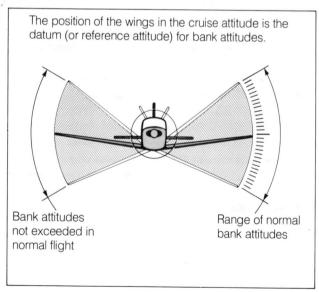

Figure 2-9   Bank Attitudes

Movements, Controls, and Axes

The fundamental consideration is the method of control of the three movements of the aircraft. In any aircraft all three movements are around one central fulcrum, normally the centre of gravity, and they can be defined relative to the pilot and/or the aircraft as follows (Fig 2-10):

(1) **Pitching**: any movement around the lateral axis
(2) **Rolling**: any movement around the longitudinal axis
(3) **Yawing**: any movement around the normal (vertical) axis.

These movements are always relative to the aircraft and the pilot, regardless of the aircraft's position relative to the horizon. This may be difficult to visualize here but will become apparent in the air exercises.

The three movements of an aircraft (Fig 2-10), pitching, rolling, and yawing, are governed by the three controlling surfaces — elevators, ailerons, and rudder. The elevators are used to produce and control the pitching movement required to achieve and maintain the desired pitch attitudes. The ailerons are used to produce and control the rolling movement required to achieve and maintain lateral level and bank attitudes. The rudder is used to control yawing movement.

Yaw may occur adversely for many reasons: turbulence, power changes, or misuse of rudder. Failure to control yaw may cause the aircraft to slip or skid and ultimately roll; control of yaw is therefore very necessary to maintain balanced flight.

The flight controls never change the results produced relative to the pilot; the pilot should always be considered the centre of movement of the aircraft and the reference point from which the movements of the

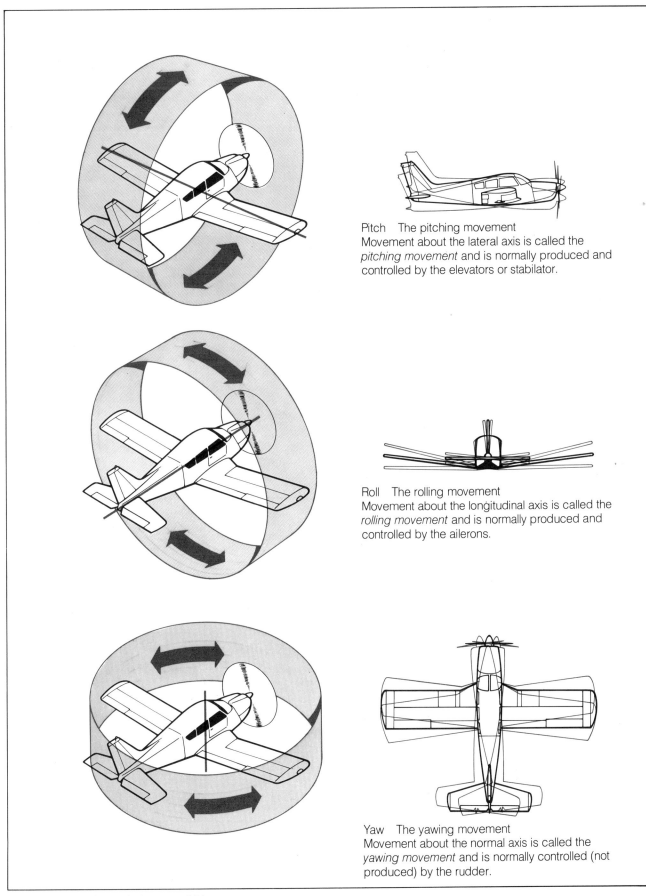

Pitch   The pitching movement
Movement about the lateral axis is called the *pitching movement* and is normally produced and controlled by the elevators or stabilator.

Roll   The rolling movement
Movement about the longitudinal axis is called the *rolling movement* and is normally produced and controlled by the ailerons.

Yaw   The yawing movement
Movement about the normal axis is called the *yawing movement* and is normally controlled (not produced) by the rudder.

Figure 2-10   Aircraft Axes and Movements

aircraft are judged and described. During this exercise the following statements concerning the flight controls will be true regardless of the position of the aircraft relative to the earth.

(1) When the elevators are raised, by backward pressure applied to the control column, the nose pitches up.
(2) When the elevators are lowered, by forward pressure on the control column, the nose pitches down.
(3) When the aileron control (control column) is turned to the right, the aircraft rolls to the right.
(4) When the aileron control is turned to the left, the aircraft rolls to the left.

In co-ordinated flight, the rudder is never used to induce yaw but only to control it. However, for demonstration purposes the flight instructor will show you the effect of rudder application as follows:

(5) When the left rudder pedal is pushed, the aircraft yaws to the left.
(6) When the right rudder pedal is pushed, the aircraft yaws to the right.

An aircraft possesses inertia: It tries to continue on its original path even when forces are introduced to change that path. Thus when the controls are moved there may be a slight lapse of time before the flight path changes, even after the attitude has been altered. The attitude of the aircraft is always referred to as relative to the horizon. The horizon referred to is the earth's natural horizon, but the inference also includes the horizon bar of the attitude indicator.

Flight Instrument Indications

During the pitch and bank demonstrations, the instructor will ask you to observe the indications of certain flight instruments.

When the aircraft is pitched into a nose-up attitude the

(1) Airspeed decreases, and
(2) The miniature aircraft will be above the horizon bar of the attitude indicator.

When the aircraft is pitched into a nose-down attitude the

(1) Airspeed increases, and
(2) The miniature aircraft will be below the horizon bar of the attitude indicator.

When the aircraft is rolled into a banked attitude for a turn the

(1) Miniature aircraft will indicate a bank in relation to the horizon bar on the attitude indicator,
(2) The heading indicator shows a change in direction, and
(3) The turn-and-bank indicator needle will be deflected in the direction of the turn; if the turn is a co-ordinated one, the ball will be centred.

When the aircraft is pitched up or down while banking left or right, the instrument indications will be a related combination of those indicated during the individual attitude demonstrations. For example, should the aircraft be pitched into a nose-down attitude while in a co-ordinated bank to the left:

(1) The airspeed will increase.
(2) The miniature aircraft will be below and banked to the left in relation to the horizon bar of the attitude indicator.
(3) The needle of the turn-and-bank indicator will be deflected to the left and the ball will be centred.
(4) The direction indicator will show decreasing degrees of heading.
(5) The altimeter will show a constant decrease in altitude.

This is your first real training exercise. Many new and relatively strange events seem to be occurring rapidly. Even after the exercise has been demonstrated in the air there are bound to be things you do not fully understand. This is perfectly natural, so do not hesitate to question your flight instructor concerning areas that still appear vague to you.

At a certain stage you may feel that you cannot do anything right, that you lack co-ordination and comprehension, that you aren't learning anything. All students go through this stage. Stay determined and you will discover that the learning and other processes tend to sharpen as you become more familiar with the aircraft and the environment in which it operates.

Straight and Level Flight

Straight and level flight may be described as holding a steady direction with the wings laterally level while maintaining a constant altitude. Straight and level flight is achieved by the restrained use of all three flight controls.

The necessity of forming correct habits in flying straight and level is impossible to overemphasize. The aim in straight and level flight is to prevent an error by prompt and small control movements, rather than to correct it after it has occurred. In smooth air the actual movements are so small that it is more a question of applying slight pressure than of making any appreciable displacement of the control column or rudder pedals.

In this exercise, straight and level flight will be demonstrated and practised, using the cruise attitude discussed in Exercise 5 as the focal point around which variations of attitudes and airspeeds in straight and level flight will be achieved. Cruise attitude is established by visually fixing the relationship of some portion of the aircraft, usually the nose and the wing tips, with the horizon. As experience is gained, you will develop a sense of being level, but the visual aids will be used as checks throughout your training.

Under standard conditions of flight and loading, an individual aircraft will achieve its cruise attitude when a specific power setting (RPM) is applied and a specific airspeed is maintained. It is emphasized that the cruise attitude assumes the wings are absolutely level with the horizon.

Straight flight may be maintained by keeping the wings level and applying the necessary pressures on the rudder pedals to prevent yaw. If, instead of keeping the wings level, you allow the aircraft to bank, it will begin to turn in the direction of the lower wing.

The air pushed backward by a propeller revolves with considerable force around an aircraft in flight, in the same direction as the rotation of the propeller, causing an increased pressure on one side of the fin. This pushes the tail sideways and causes the aircraft to yaw. To compensate for this action, the fin is aerodynamically or mechanically offset (slightly) to provide optimum directional balance in the cruise attitude. It follows, therefore, that an increase or decrease in power, which increases or decreases the rotational force of the propeller slipstream, will cause the aircraft to yaw to the left or to the right. This action can be readily observed if power is increased or decreased. An increase in power yaws the aircraft to the left and a decrease yaws it to the right. Any tendency for the aircraft to yaw with power changes should be anticipated and immediately corrected by appropriate use of rudder.

To maintain a constant heading by instrument reference, the best instrument to use is the heading indicator. This instrument must be first set by readings taken from the magnetic compass, and to remain accurate should be reset every 15 minutes thereafter. When taking readings from the magnetic compass, it is extremely important that the aircraft be held in straight flight at a constant airspeed. The reasons for this precaution are outlined in Exercise 23, "Pilot Navigation" (Vagaries of the Magnetic Compass). To change airspeed while maintaining straight and level flight (Fig 2-11) the principal reference instruments are the tachometer (RPM), the airspeed indicator, and the altimeter.

An aircraft in well trimmed straight and level flight undergoes a transition when engine power settings are changed. When engine power is increased, the nose will pitch up; if no compensating control movement is made, the aircraft will begin to climb. Decrease the power and the nose will pitch down; if no control adjustment is made the aircraft will start to descend. Power adjustments are made to increase or decrease airspeed in straight and level flight, but immediate flight control adjustments must be made to keep the nose of the aircraft from pitching up or down. As power is increased, keep the nose from pitching up with appropriate elevator control pressure. When the aircraft is at the desired increased airspeed, trim out the control pressure required to maintain straight and level flight.

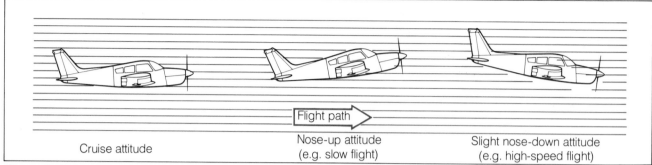

Cruise attitude   Nose-up attitude   Slight nose-down attitude
                         (e.g. slow flight)   (e.g. high-speed flight)

Figure 2-11   Level Flight

A question often arises concerning which cockpit controls have primary control over airspeed and altitude. The truth is that neither elevator nor throttle controls airspeed or altitude independently. About the only completely accurate statement that can be made about the use of cockpit controls is simply that the elevators control the attitude of the aircraft, and that the throttle controls the power. A term you will hear many times in your flight career which explains this fact is the formula: "Attitude (elevator control) plus power (throttle control) equals performance."

When an aircraft is in the cruise attitude, pressure on the control column will affect both speed and height. Likewise, changes in power settings can affect both speed and height. This may prompt the question of which control takes precedence in a manoeuvre which requires adjustment of both power and flight controls. The fact is that the controls must be considered interdependent, since changes in speed in the cruise attitude require simultaneous adjustment of the throttle and elevator controls. Any concept to the contrary will only delay progress in acquiring the control co-ordination needed to maneouvre an aircraft from one airspeed to another.

To reduce the airspeed while in straight and level flight, throttle back smoothly to the power setting estimated for the speed desired. At the same time apply sufficient back pressure to the control column to maintain the desired altitude. Keep the wings level. At first the back pressure needed will be barely perceptible, but as the aircraft's forward momentum decreases, the pressure needed will increase. When the desired reduced airspeed is reached, readjust the power setting if necessary, then trim the aircraft.

To increase the airspeed while in straight and level flight, advance the throttle smoothly to the power setting estimated for the speed desired, and at the same time apply sufficient forward pressure to the control column to keep the altitude from increasing. Keep the wings level. When the desired airspeed is reached, readjust the power setting if necessary, then trim the aircraft.

Besides a training exercise, increasing and decreasing airspeed in level flight has many practical applications. One of the more readily appreciable of these is the need for flexibility in airspeed to maintain correct spacing with other aircraft in the airport traffic circuit. At a busy airport, aircraft have varying circuit and approach speeds. It may be necessary at one point in the circuit to maintain a high cruise speed and then reduce speed at another point to fit safely into the traffic pattern, while maintaining a specific altitude.

Straight and level flight requires minimum use of the controls if the aircraft is properly trimmed and the air is smooth. However, in rough air, more physical effort and co-ordination are needed to keep the aircraft laterally level while maintaining heading and altitude.

Climbing

Entering a climb involves changes in attitude, airspeed, altitude, rate of climb indications, forward visibility, and under most circumstances, power settings (Fig 2-12). Climbs may be executed at various speeds, such as:

(1) Recommended *normal* climb speed
(2) Recommended best *rate of climb* speed
(3) Recommended best *angle of climb* speed
(4) En route climb airspeeds (cruise/climb speeds.)

The aircraft flight manual will specify the normal climb speed, best rate of climb speed, and best angle of climb speed.

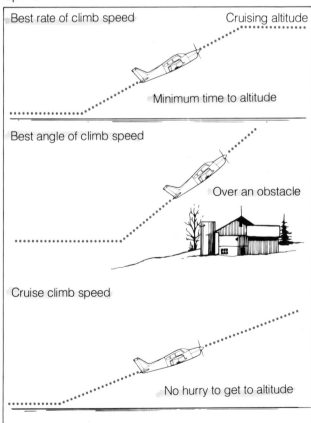

Best rate of climb speed   Cruising altitude

Minimum time to altitude

Best angle of climb speed

Over an obstacle

Cruise climb speed

No hurry to get to altitude

Figure 2-12   Climb Speed

The recommended best rate of climb speed is the airspeed which will afford the greatest gain in height in a given time. If it is important to reach a given altitude in the shortest possible time, this is the airspeed to use. The best angle of climb is used to achieve the greatest gain in height in a given distance. If there are obstacles in the take-off path, for example, the aircraft should be climbed at the best angle of climb speed so that within the shortest possible ground distance the aircraft will be well above the height of the obstacles.

It is possible for the engine to become overheated if the aircraft is flown for too long a period at the best angle of climb or best rate of climb speed. The normal climb speed should therefore be resumed as soon as it is appropriate to do so.

As the term implies, normal climb speed is the speed at which the aircraft is climbed under normal circumstances. Normal climb speed is higher than best rate of climb and best angle of climb speeds, and is recommended for routine climbing situations because:

(1) Forward visibility is better.
(2) Most light aircraft take off and climb at full throttle. At this power setting the engine is dependent upon a high volume of airflow for cooling. Therefore the higher the airspeed the more effective the cooling. The normal climb speed specified for an aircraft takes into account and allows for (among other things) the need for adequate cooling.

En route climbs are carried out at various airspeeds between normal climb and normal cruise speed, appropriate to all the factors involved at the time. The purpose could simply be to gain altitude slowly under a gradually upsloping cloud cover, using an airspeed slightly under normal cruise speed and a power setting slightly above cruise power. During this type of climb, convenience and comfort are the prime factors, since no climb time or climb distance limitations are assumed to apply.

As mentioned in Exercise 6, the propeller slipstream

is always attempting to yaw the aircraft to the left. This effect becomes especially apparent at low airspeeds with high power settings, such as during a climb. Keep the wings level and control any tendency for the aircraft to yaw to the left with rudder.

Before you begin a climb, look around carefully for other aircraft, more particularly in the area ahead. As the nose of the aircraft rises, your forward scan becomes limited, to the point where other aircraft at the same altitude or below become obscured.

To enter a normal climb, establish the aircraft in a nose-up attitude, one that you estimate will maintain normal climbing airspeed, and increase power to the recommended setting for a normal climb. At first the operation of flight and power controls will be separately timed movements, but as you gain experience they should occur almost simultaneously. When the airspeed has settled, adjust the aircraft attitude to attain the desired airspeed. Recheck the power setting, then trim the aircraft until no pressure is required on the control column to maintain the correct attitude. The altimeter will show a steady increase in height and the vertical speed indicator will show a steady rate of climb.

If the air is turbulent, even experienced pilots can have difficulty achieving steady indications on these instruments, especially the vertical speed indicator.

To return to straight and level flight from the climb, establish the aircraft in the normal cruise attitude, allow it to accelerate to cruising airspeed (care must be taken not to exceed maximum RPM at this time) and reduce engine power to that of normal cruise flight. Readjust attitude to maintain altitude, recheck power setting, then trim the aircraft for straight and level flight.

The density of the air plays an important part in the climb performance of an aircraft (Fig 2-13). The more dense the air the better the performance. Two generally true factors to remember about air density are:

(1) Density decreases as height increases.
(2) Density decreases as temperature increases.

Relatively good climb performance can be expected on a cold day from an aircraft at an airport with a field elevation of, say, 150 feet above mean sea level, whereas a much poorer performance can be expected on a hot day at an airport with a field elevation of, say, 2000 feet above mean sea level.

The air density, or lack of it, which affects the engine performance is also affecting the function of the airspeed indicator as the aircraft gains height. As the density of the air decreases with gain in height, the airspeed indicator indicates a progressively lower speed, although the actual speed of the aircraft may be relatively unaffected. Unless airspeed adjustments are made as the aircraft climbs, the rate of climb will become lower and lower until finally the aircraft will be flying level instead of climbing.

To maintain a reasonably accurate rate of climb, a rule of thumb is to decrease the recommended indicated sea level climb speed by 1.75 per cent (about 2 mph) for every 1000 feet increase in height above mean sea level, excluding the first 1000 feet. Suppose for example the recommended normal indicated climb speed of the aircraft is 90 mph. At an indicated altitude of 2000 feet, the indicated climb speed would be adjusted to 88 mph; at 3000 feet indicated, 85 mph; and so on.

Density altitude is the altitude corresponding to a given density in a standard atmosphere. It is a "condition," not a level of flight. Unless density altitude is known it is difficult to determine the performance of an aircraft accurately, and this can be a very important factor under some conditions of take-off and climb. For example, the flight manual for a certain aircraft states that at an airport with an elevation (altitude) of 3000 feet the initial rate of climb will be 400 feet per minute. The elevation (altitude) of the airstrip should be converted to density altitude to give a true picture of expected aircraft performance. Should the outside air temperature be +28 degrees Celsius at the time, the density altitude could be as high as 5000 feet. Looking at the flight manual again for an elevation of 5000 feet, the initial rate of climb is reduced to 260 feet per minute. Some climb data tables give mean temperatures with field altitudes, but they must be interpolated carefully under extremes of temperature. Density/altitude calculations can be

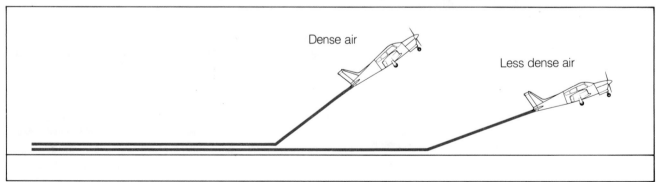

Figure 2-13   The Effect of Air Density on Take-off Run and Rate of Climb

resolved quickly on most circular slide-rule computers. As moist air (water vapour) weighs less than dry air, it is less dense. Therefore on a moist or rainy day the resulting climb performance is less than on a normal dry day. Thus, under some conditions, the rate of climb after take-off could be critical. An aircraft with retractable landing-gear climbs at a higher rate, and gains height in a shorter distance when the landing-gear is retracted. As soon as possible after the aircraft is established in its initial climb attitude, the landing-gear should be retracted to obtain optimum climb performance. Be prepared to make attitude corrections as the landing-gear retracts, since many aircraft are inclined to pitch upwards when the wheels are no longer offering resistance to the propeller slipstream.

On some types of aircraft a certain degree of flap is extended as a routine take-off procedure, but customarily flaps are used only when it is necessary to shorten the take-off run and steepen the initial angle of climb. In any case, consult the aircraft flight manual for correct usage, since even the flap setting offering optimum lift for minimum drag will lower the aircraft's rate of climb. Therefore, if flaps have been extended for take-off, retract them as soon as there is no longer any operational requirement for them, but not before the aircraft is established in the desired nose-up attitude for a climb, well above any obstacles.

Should there be a risk of carburettor ice, you may have to apply carburettor heat during the climb. In the case of full throttle climbs this has the effect of reducing available engine power. Do not allow the airspeed to decrease from the normal climb speed under normal flight conditions. Instead, maintain airspeed and accept a slight reduction in rate of climb. In an aircraft designed to climb at power settings less than full throttle, when carburettor heat is applied maintain the desired RPM (or manifold pressure) by advancing the throttle, and as air

density allows, maintain airspeed and rate of climb.

The visible effect of weight on the performance of a light aircraft is probably more pronounced in a climb than any other normal manoeuvre. Because of ground effect an aircraft may leave the ground within a tolerable distance when loaded to its maximum permissible gross weight, but once out of ground effect its rate of climb may be seriously affected. Climb performance data are of great importance if there are obstacles in the proposed climb path of the aircraft, especially if the airport (field) elevation is high and the ambient temperature is high. Consult the aircraft flight manual for climb performance data.

Occasions arise when it is necessary to balk (pull up from) an approach to landing and enter a climb when the aircraft is in the landing configuration with flaps fully extended. Take-off power must be applied smoothly but promptly as the aircraft is placed in a nose-up attitude consistent with a safe climb airspeed. With flaps fully extended, this attitude must be estimated by outside visual references based on a prior knowledge of the attitude. Since the trim was adjusted for a landing, the application of power will most likely pitch the nose upwards; therefore it is important that you be prepared to apply forward pressure on the control column and that trim be readjusted to provide the desired attitude. The flaps must be retracted as soon as possible to the missed approach setting, but gradually and in small increments. Each time the flap setting is changed, the trim must be readjusted. For those aircraft with mechanically defined flap settings, retract the flaps one setting at a time.

In prolonged climbs the heading should be changed at regular intervals to afford a better opportunity to search the sky ahead of the aircraft for other air traffic. The heading changes should be no less than 20 degrees, at frequent intervals as height is gained.

Descending

Descending an aircraft from a higher altitude to a lower can be carried out in several ways, to satisfy various operational requirements. Descents can be divided into two basic procedures:

(1) Power-on (power assisted) descents
(2) Power-off (glide) descents.

Power-on descents can be further divided into:

(a) Descents at cruise power setting
(b) Descents at cruising airspeed with power reduced to maintain a rate of descent
(c) Descents at reduced airspeed and reduced power settings to maintain a rate of descent and airspeed
(d) Descents at reduced airspeed and reduced power settings with flap extended to maintain an angle of descent.

Power-off descents can be divided into:

(a) Glides without flap
(b) Glides with flaps extended.

Either of the two basic methods of descending can be varied to meet the rate of descent and distance covered requirements of practically any situation. However, the power-on descent is the more flexible and easier to correct for errors in judgment.

Gliding, in its pure form, is a procedure used to keep an aircraft in the air for as long a period of time as possible without the use of power. In the practical application, however, distance covered over the ground (range) is generally of more importance than time in the air; therefore the objective in gliding is to establish an airspeed that will maintain the optimum lift/drag ratio attitude of the aircraft. Know this airspeed beforehand and commit it to memory, since the glide is the type of descent used for approaches to forced landings. Most aircraft flight manuals include the best glide speed in their maximum glide charts. One typical chart shows

that at its best glide speed of 70 mph (in still air) from a height of 6000 feet above ground level, the aircraft will glide a distance of 10 statute miles. The same aircraft flown at 60 mph may sustain a slightly lower rate of descent but it will not attain the 10 mile distance, because of the lower airspeed. If the same aircraft is flown at an airspeed of 55 mph, the lift/drag ratio deteriorates to the point where the rate of descent is much greater than it would be at 70 mph. This together with the lower airspeed would achieve a glide distance of less than 4 miles.

The recommended best gliding speed will provide an attitude that achieves the greatest range (distance) in still air. However, wind velocity plays a commanding role in determining the best attitude to cover the greatest distance per unit of height available, and the best attitude may have the effect of decreasing or increasing the recommended best gliding speed. Determining this attitude under the constantly varying conditions of wind direction and wind speed can be most difficult. So, in an emergency such as a forced landing, instead of complicating an already problematical situation, it might be better to use the familiar recommended still air gliding speed. Then estimate the range available to you under the circumstances. A visual method for estimating gliding range is outlined in the following paragraphs.

Estimating Range

You will recall from a previous chapter that if another aircraft appears to occupy a stationary position on your windshield and to be growing larger, you will eventually collide with it unless evasive action is taken. In relative terms, the other aircraft becomes a stationary object and since it appears to grow larger you are on a collision course with it. This same principle may be effectively applied when attempting to reach a specific point on the ground during power-on or power-off descents, such as when executing a normal approach, a precautionary landing, or a forced landing. The point on the ground may be the point of flare at an aerodrome or the touchdown point of a forced landing. If the selected spot on the ground remains stationary in relation to a fixed point on your windshield, the aircraft will subsequently touch down at the selected spot on the ground.

The "fixed point" on the windshield is any point on the windshield that you choose as a reference point. It could be so many inches up from the instrument panel, or adjacent to the magnetic compass, a mark you have made yourself with a china-marking pencil, or even a squashed bug. Everything is measured in relation to this imaginary, or actual, point on the windshield.

When stabilized in a constant power or power-off descent at a constant attitude and airspeed, visual observations of ground positions in relation to a fixed point on your windshield will provide information as follows:
(1) Positions on the ground which appear to move down from the fixed position on the windshield are ground positions which you can reach and fly over with height to spare (Fig 2-14, bottom).
(2) The position on the ground which remains stationary in relation to the fixed position on your windshield is the ground position which your aircraft should reach (Fig 2-14, top).
(3) Positions on the ground which appear to move from a fixed position on the windshield to the top of the windshield are ground positions which your aircraft cannot reach (Fig 2-14, middle). (In Fig 2-14, note that in most cases touchdown would actually be the point of flare rather than the touchdown point.)

To enter a power-off descent from straight and level flight:

(1) Complete any cockpit checks and note the altimeter reading.
(2) Search the sky, above and below, for other aircraft.
(3) Close the throttle smoothly but promptly.
(4) Keep straight (the aircraft will tend to yaw to the right) and allow airspeed to decrease.
(5) Assume approximate attitude for best glide airspeed.
(6) Trim.
(7) If necessary make minor adjustments to attain correct airspeed, and retrim.
(8) Note the steady decrease in altitude on the altimeter and the rate of descent on the vertical speed indicator.

To return to straight and level flight from a power-off descent:

(1) Search the sky ahead and above for other aircraft.
(2) Note the altimeter reading.
(3) (a) Advance the throttle to the power setting for cruise flight (carburettor heat "off").
    (b) Assume the cruise attitude and maintain it until the aircraft accelerates to cruise speed, and
    (c) Keep straight (the aircraft will tend to yaw to the left as the throttle is advanced).
(4) Trim.
(5) Adjust power and flight controls to maintain the desired airspeed and altitude.
(6) Retrim.

During power-off descents the engine must not be allowed to become too cool, otherwise it may fail to respond properly when the throttle is advanced to regain straight and level flight. Cruising power should be applied at appropriate intervals during the descent to keep engine temperatures near normal and to prevent fouling of the spark plugs. Many aircraft require carburettor heat during power-off descents; in others it is not recommended. Consult the aircraft flight manual for the correct procedure.

A power-on descent is used when precise control of the rate of descent and distance attained is desired. Most routine descents and approaches to landings are power-assisted to control the rate of descent for passenger comfort and meet the speed and spacing demands of airport circuit procedures. To enter a power-on descent carry out the cockpit checks, look around for other aircraft, then:

(1) Reduce engine power to an RPM setting judged (or predetermined) to give a desired airspeed and rate of descent.
(2) Allow the airspeed to decrease to that desired.
(3) Lower the nose to an attitude that will give the desired rate of descent.
(4) Trim to maintain this attitude.
(5) Check that the airspeed and the angle and rate of descent are those desired; if not, increase or decrease the amount of power until the flight condition required is obtained.
(6) Retrim.

To decrease the rate of descent while in a power-on descent, apply the amount of engine power that will give the desired rate of descent, and then adjust the attitude of the aircraft to maintain the best descent speed and retrim for the new attitude. In most aircraft the application of power will pitch the nose up, and as a result very little control adjustment is needed to establish the new attitude and maintain the original airspeed. If the need for a power-off descent ensues, as the throttle is closed the nose will pitch down and more or less assume the attitude for best gliding speed

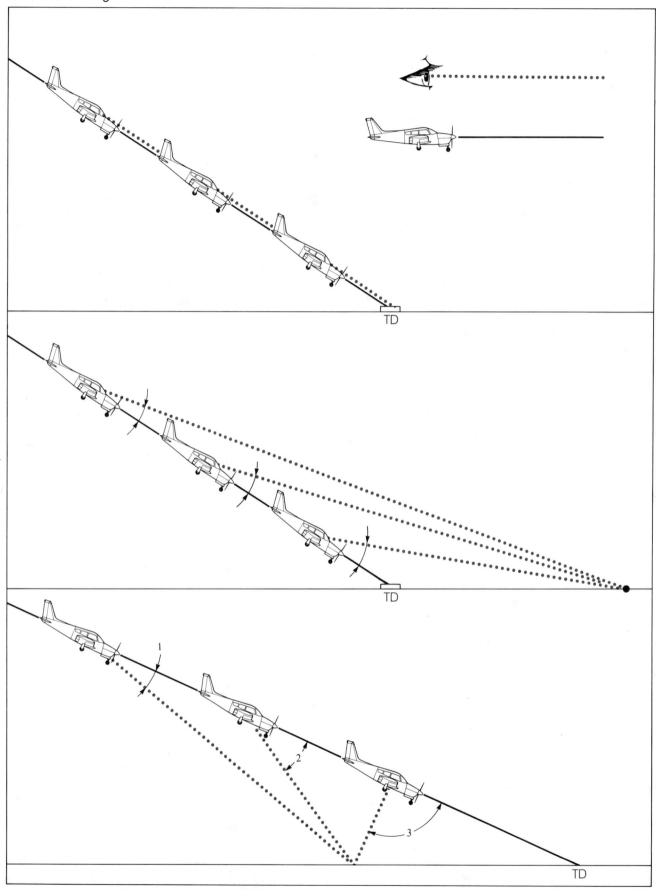

Figure 2-14   Fixed Reference Point for Landing

without a great deal of adjustment, if the aircraft is properly trimmed for each attitude. Proper trim is the key to smooth and accurate manoeuvring from one attitude or airspeed to another.

Any variation of airspeed and rate of descent may be combined to obtain the effect desired. An en route descent is usually a power reduction to provide a suitable rate of descent while still maintaining cruising airspeed. When approaching the destination airport it may be desirable to reduce power so that descent is made at a reduced airspeed. Finally, the power-on descent involves a power setting which will provide the desired rate of descent while maintaining the recommended approach to landing airspeed.

Power-on descents requiring high angles of descent, as in an obstacle clearing approach, usually involve full extension of the flaps and lower than normal approach airspeeds. Consult the aircraft flight manual or pilot operating handbook to determine the flap setting and airspeed. Should "calibrated airspeed" (CAS) be given, ensure that you use the airspeed correction table in the manual or handbook to calculate the "indicated airspeed" (IAS) to fly the obstacle clearance approach.

The angle of descent of aircraft with retractable landing-gear can be effectively steepened by extending the landing-gear. Most aircraft have too flat a glide angle for many purposes, such as clearing obstacles on the approach to landing. The angle of descent could be steepened by descending at a very high or a very low airspeed, but neither is satisfactory under normal circumstances. Therefore the aircraft is fitted with flaps. Flaps, when extended, steepen the angle of descent for any particular airspeed (Fig 2-15). The more the flaps are extended, the steeper the angle of descent for a given airspeed. Another advantage is that the steeper the descent attitude, the better the view ahead. In addition to the drag caused by extending the flaps, lift is increased for the same airspeed. It is therefore possible to descend at a lower airspeed than when the flaps are retracted.

If the intent is to remain in the air for the longest period of time (gliding for endurance) and not for the greatest distance, maintain an airspeed slightly less than that which gives the most range. The aircraft will not go as far but will remain in the air longer. For practical operation of light aircraft, the difference between gliding for range and for endurance, in still air, is considered small enough to be negligible.

The prevailing wind will affect the maximum gliding

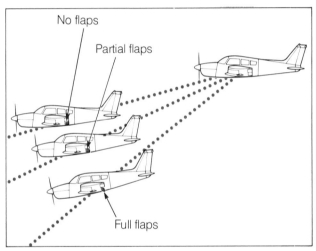

Figure 2-15   Wing Flaps Affect the Rate of Descent and Range

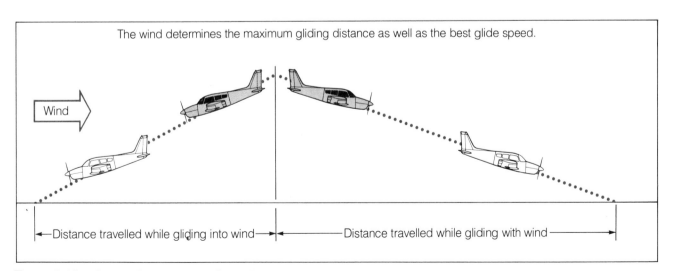

Figure 2-16   Gliding Distance and Glide Speed

distance greatly (Fig 2-16). When gliding into a head wind you can increase range by selecting an airspeed slightly higher than normal. When gliding downwind a greater distance can be covered by using an airspeed lower than normal. The same logic applies when cruise flying for range into, or with, a wind.

Turns

The *turn* is a basic manoeuvre used to change the heading of an aircraft. An accurate level turn may be described as a change of direction, maintaining a desired angle of bank, with no slip or skid, while maintaining a desired altitude. This is also the description of a balanced turn. Aerodynamically the turn is probably the most complex of fundamental manoeuvres and involves a close co-ordination of all controls, but in actual practice it is relatively simple to do.

To turn an aircraft, co-ordinated pressures are applied to the controls until a desired banked attitude is achieved. The object of bank during a turn is to incline the lift so that in addition to supporting the aircraft, it can provide the necessary force (centripetal force) towards the centre of the turn to oppose centrifugal force, which is endeavouring to pull the aircraft away from the centre of the turn.

In a level turn lift must be sufficient both to support the aircraft and to provide the inward force. Therefore, it must be greater than during straight and level flight. The additional lift can be acquired by increasing the angle of attack of the wings and accepting a varying degree of reduction in airspeed (Fig 2-17). Up to a certain degree of bank airspeed may be maintained by increasing power.

For training purposes turns are divided into three classes:

(1) **Gentle** turns, involving angles of bank up to 15 degrees.
(2) **Medium** turns, involving angles of bank from 15 to 30 degrees.
(3) **Steep** turns, involving angles of bank over 30 degrees.

In addition to level turns there are:

(1) **Climbing** turns. Normally, climbing turns are gentle turns.
(2) **Descending** turns. Descending turns may be gentle, medium, or steep.

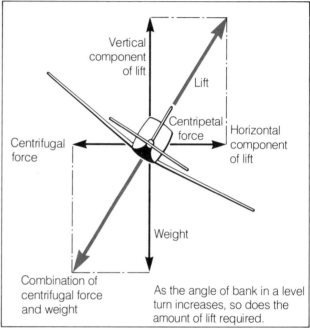

As the angle of bank in a level turn increases, so does the amount of lift required.

Figure 2-17   Forces in a Turn

Entering a turn, the rising wing creates more drag than the descending wing. This tends to yaw the aircraft towards the raised wing and causes the aircraft to attempt initially to turn in the wrong direction. This is *adverse yaw* (see "Aileron Drag," Chapter 1). To counteract adverse yaw, use appropriate rudder pressure, in the direction of the turn. The amount of rudder movement necessary varies according to the abruptness of the execution of the turn, and often the type of aircraft.

It is most important at this stage to understand fully that rudder is used in a turn only if there is any adverse yaw. Adverse yaw has almost been designed out of aircraft of recent manufacture, so that the rudder pressure required on turn entry to counteract adverse yaw has been very effectively reduced.

These are some basic facts you should understand:
(1) At a given airspeed, the greater the angle of bank:
    (a) the greater the rate of turn

(b) the smaller the radius of turn

(c) the higher the stalling speed

(d) the greater the load factor.

(2) The higher the airspeed at a given angle of bank:

(a) the lower the rate of turn

(b) the larger the radius of turn.

(3) To achieve a turn of the smallest radius and greatest rate for a given angle of bank, fly at the lowest possible airspeed for that angle of bank.

A fact applicable to all aircraft is that the stalling speed increases as bank angle increases and this increase in stalling speed accelerates very rapidly as the angle of bank continues to steepen. At 30 degrees of bank, the stalling speed increases to about 8 per cent over the stalling speed in level flight; at 45 degrees, 18 per cent; at 60 degrees, 40 per cent; at 75 degrees, 100 per cent; at 83 degrees, 200 per cent. Therefore, an aircraft with a level flight stalling speed of 50 mph has a stalling speed of 150 mph (50 + 100) when subjected to an 83 degree bank turn.

Similarly, the wing loading or load factor increases slowly at first as the angle of bank increases and very rapidly thereafter (see Chapter 4, "Load Factor"). As an example, the load factor on an aircraft executing a 60 degree bank turn at any flying speed while maintaining altitude is double that of straight and level flight while the load factor for an 80 degree bank turn is 5.76.

The importance of look-out, or searching the sky for other aircraft before and during a turn, cannot be overemphasized. Before entering a turn, look around carefully in both directions, above and below. A casual glance is just not good enough. During the turn continue to look out, especially in the direction of the turn. When recovering from the turn look around again, in both directions, above and below. To maintain a good look-out and manage the aircraft at the same time requires the pilot's constant attention.

Posture is important in all aircraft manoeuvres, but especially so in turns. Sit comfortably upright; do not lean away from the centre of the turn, but do not make a conscious effort to keep your body stiffly vertical. Relax and ride with the turn. Stiffening up or continually changing sitting position affects visual references and may cause handling of the controls to become tense and erratic (Fig 2-18).

An accurate turn requires a good entry, and the first requisite for a good level turn entry is that the aircraft be flying straight and level, as accurately as possible, prior to entering the turn. Any error made before entering the turn is likely to be grossly exaggerated as the turn develops; the same principle applies to turns while descending or climbing.

In making an accurate turn, the trained pilot co-ordinates the movement of all three controls so that the turn is entered, maintained, and recovered from in one

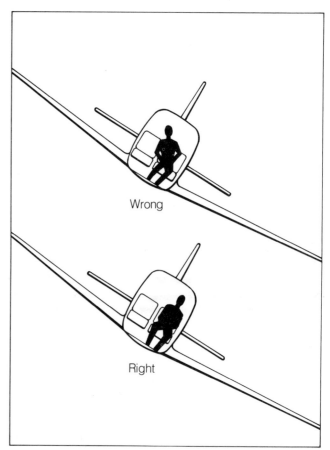

Figure 2-18   Posture during Turns

apparently simultaneous movement. Initially, however, it is best to think of each control as having one definite function, the ailerons controlling bank attitude, the elevators controlling pitch attitude, and the rudder controlling yaw. This will help eliminate some of the more common faults at the outset, such as overcontrol of the rudder.

To execute a turn from straight and level flight:

(1) Make sure that the aircraft is in accurate straight and level flight.

(2) Look around for other aircraft.

(3) Roll the aircraft gently to the desired bank attitude with aileron control. Maintain this attitude, and at the same time,

(4) Use appropriate rudder pressure to control any tendency for the aircraft to yaw adversely.

(5) Use elevators to maintain the aircraft in the correct pitch attitude in relation to the horizon.

(6) Maintain the look-out.

In a gentle turn, the position of the nose in relation to the horizon, which is the visual reference for pitch attitude, will remain relatively the same as in straight and level flight. However, as the angle of bank is increased, the pitch attitude must be altered (by backward pressure on the control column) to increase lift; this is to compensate for the added weight factor imposed by centrifugal force as the turn steepens. The loss in airspeed, or the need for an increase in power to maintain airspeed, becomes more apparent as the angle of bank increases.

As the aircraft settles into an accurate turn:

(1) The nose will move steadily around the horizon, neither rising nor falling.
(2) The airspeed will be constant.
(3) The turn indicator will show a constant rate of turn.
(4) The ball will be centred in its glass tube.
(5) The altimeter will be steady on the selected altitude.

One of the most common faults when entering turns is excessive use of rudder. This fault can be corrected quickly or completely prevented if you remember right from the outset not to apply rudder unless it is necessary to control adverse yaw.

To recover from a turn:

(1) Look around.
(2) Roll the aircraft to level flight with aileron control, and at the same time,
(3) Use appropriate rudder pressure to control adverse yaw.
(4) Keep wings level.
(5) Maintain correct pitch attitude with elevator control.
(6) Keep straight.
(7) Look around.
(8) Trim.

In gentle level turns the lateral stability designed into the aircraft will attempt to return it to straight and level flight, therefore slight aileron pressure may be required to maintain it in such a turn. However, as the banked attitude increases beyond a certain angle, lateral stability is overcome. Simply stated, this results from the outer wing travelling faster than the inner wing and therefore obtaining more lift, causing the aircraft to continue its roll unless the pilot takes some action to stop it. Therefore, aileron control must be used accordingly to maintain the desired angle of bank.

Climbing and descending turns are executed like level turns except that instead of maintaining a constant altitude, a constant climb or descent is maintained. While the control inputs to enter, maintain, and recover from the turn are the same as in level turns, there are additional considerations regarding power and attitude control.

In a climbing turn, power additional to cruise power is required in order to achieve the desired increase in altitude. The nose-up attitude selected and maintained during the climbing turn will depend upon the operational requirements at the moment and will be those attitudes described in Exercise 7, "Climbing." In a descending turn, power will be reduced in varying amounts from cruising to throttle fully closed. The nose-down attitude will again vary to achieve the desired results, but will correspond to those attitudes as discussed in Exercise 8, "Descending."

The lateral stability of an aircraft in a climbing or descending turn is affected by the angle at which the relative airflow meets each wing. As a result:

(1) In a descending turn, the aircraft moves a given distance downwards during a complete turn, but the inner wing, turning on a smaller radius, descends on a steeper spiral than the outer wing, like the handrails on a spiral staircase. Therefore, the relative airflow meets the inner wing at a greater angle of attack and so obtains more lift than the outer wing. The extra lift acquired this way compensates for the extra lift obtained by the outer wing due to its travelling faster. Therefore, in a power-off descent the angle of bank will tend to remain constant.
(2) In a climbing turn, the inner wing still describes a steeper spiral, but this time it is an upward spiral, so the relative airflow meets the inner wing at a smaller angle of attack than the outer wing. In this case the outer wing obtains extra lift, both from its extra speed and its greater angle of attack. Therefore, the angle of bank will tend to increase and the aileron control must be used accordingly to maintain the desired angle of bank.

Initially, climbing and descending turns will be entered from normal straight climbs and descents and the recovery made back to straight climbing or descending flight, to enable you to experience and readily observe the difference in pitch attitude necessary to maintain the desired airspeed. As you gain proficiency, these turns will be entered directly from straight and level flight and recovery made directly back to straight and level flight.

Power-off descending turns are particularly important, as they are directly related to forced landing procedures. It is necessary that you learn to execute this type of turn to reasonable proficiency almost subconsciously, since during a forced landing there are many other details to attend to. Because the controls may be less responsive than in power turns, power-off descending turns require the development of a different technique than that required for power manoeuvres.

When recovering from a power-off descending turn, the pressure exerted on the elevator control during the turn must be decreased, or the aircraft will pitch up too high and airspeed will be lost. Such an error will require a lot of attention and control adjustment before the correct attitude and airspeed can be resumed. It will be quite noticeable that more altitude must be sacrificed in a power-off descending turn than in a straight descent, since this is the only way to maintain the desired airspeed without power.

Steep Turns

Steep turns are a means of turning quickly in a relatively small area, but as an exercise in flying they have a value beyond purely practical application. They provide one of the best instances of sustained extra loading effect, together with excellent practice in co-ordinating all three flight controls and the power control. The practical applications of steep turns are almost all limited to emergency situations, and sooner or later in your career you will have to resort to the manoeuvre. Practise them diligently so you can execute them accurately and without hesitation.

Up to a limited angle of bank, a steep turn may be executed without increasing engine power. However, in order to maintain a constant altitude, airspeed must be sacrificed. When carrying out this procedure be mindful of the stalling speed increase with increase in angle of bank (Fig 2-19). (In a 60 degree bank, an aircraft with a level flight stalling speed of 50 mph would stall at 70 mph.)

The greater the angle of bank, the greater the amount of lift required to maintain a constant altitude. Increased lift produces increased drag, thus more engine power is required to maintain a constant airspeed. Therefore, the angle of bank that can be sustained in a level turn (disregarding structural limitations) depends on the engine power available (Fig 2-20).

A steep turn is entered like any other turn, but as the angle of bank is increased beyond the 30 degree angle of the medium turn, you will need extra engine power in order to maintain height and airspeed. A steep turn cannot be done by numbers; it requires complete simultaneous co-ordination of all controls. Because of the rapid rate of change of direction, the look-out for other aircraft before doing a steep turn is even more important than for other turns.

Enter as for a medium turn but allow the bank to continue beyond that of a medium turn. As the bank increases, move the control column back to maintain the correct pitch attitude. Start increasing power as necessary to maintain airspeed as the angle of bank increases beyond 30 degrees. When the required angle of bank is reached, keep it constant with aileron control. During the turn, control the aircraft as in a medium turn.

As the aircraft banks more and more steeply, the less a given movement of the elevator control affects the pitch attitude above or below the horizon, but the more it affects the turning of the nose around the horizon. This need not confuse you if you can still think of the elevators controlling pitch attitude and nothing else. In a steep turn, the rudder does not change its function: it is still used only to control yaw.

Maintain the look-out.

Recover from the turn exactly as from any other turn, except that engine power should be reduced simultaneously with return to straight and level flight. If the nose pitches too far down in a steep turn, do not attempt to correct by applying back pressure alone, since this may only serve to tighten the turn by increasing the angle of attack. Use co-ordinated aileron and rudder pressure to reduce the angle of bank, then correct the pitch attitude. Another frequent error is the use of too much back movement on the elevator control before it is needed when entering a steep turn.

Minimum Radius Turns

To turn an aircraft within a minimum radius requires a high angle of bank and a low airspeed. For minimum radius steep turns the suggested airspeed to use is that for endurance. You will recall that endurance airspeed is somewhere between the airspeed for slow flight and the airspeed for range. The radius of turn can be made even smaller by extending the flaps. Since this type of turn is for emergencies only it is seldom necessary to carry it beyond 180 degrees of change in direction.

After you have performed the look-out, and the aircraft is at the airspeed and attitude for endurance in straight and level flight, enter the turn promptly with co-ordinated use of all controls. As the aircraft approaches the 30 degree angle of bank apply maximum permissible power. Allow the angle of bank to increase to approximately 60 degrees, then maintain the bank and pitch attitudes and altitude. Airspeed will vary only insignificantly in a well co-ordinated, level, minimum radius turn of 180 degrees change in direction.

When recovering from a minimum radius turn, do not reduce engine power until the aircraft is again in straight and level flight.

Steep Power-off Turn

A steep power-off turn is a continuous steep bank while the aircraft is in a descent. It has practical applications and is excellent for improving power-off turns and learning orientation under difficult circumstances.

The aircraft must have adequate height before a steep power-off turn is begun, so that the manoeuvre may be continued through a series of turns. It will be found that there is relatively little difficulty in executing

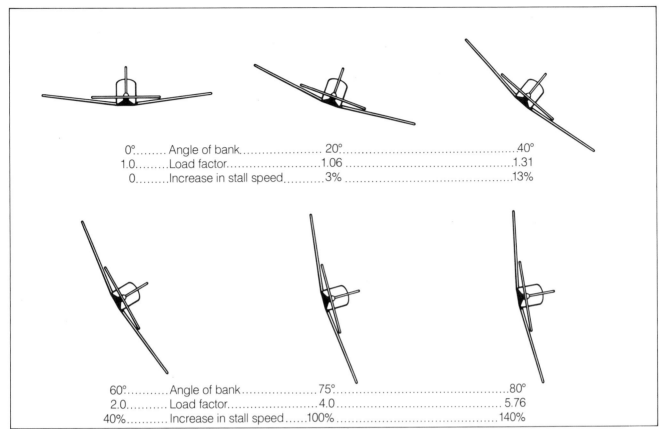

0°	Angle of bank	20°	40°
1.0	Load factor	1.06	1.31
0	Increase in stall speed	3%	13%

60°	Angle of bank	75°	80°
2.0	Load factor	4.0	5.76
40%	Increase in stall speed	100%	140%

Figure 2-19   The Relationship between Angle of Bank, Load Factor, and Basic Stall Speed

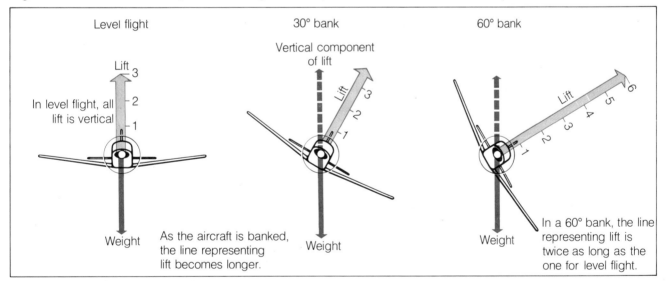

Figure 2-20   Lift and Angle of Bank

the first two or three turns. It is only when the turn is prolonged that it becomes difficult to hold the aircraft in the manoeuvre. A medium angle of bank is used at first, then, in successive practice, the bank is gradually increased for each turn until the desired bank is attained and held constantly throughout the manoeuvre without slipping or skidding. The objectives are a constant descent speed and a constant degree of bank.

Recovery from a steep power-off turn is particularly important. It must be smooth, with the controls so co-ordinated that no increase or decrease of airspeed occurs when the straight descent is resumed.

When first exposed to steep power-off turns, most students tend to allow the bank to increase beyond the desired angle. Should the bank become too steep, the aircraft will slip towards the centre of the turn and the nose will pitch down. If not corrected quickly, this situation can develop into a spiral and any attempt to raise the nose with elevators alone may cause a stall or only tend to worsen the spiral. Therefore, should the nose pitch down too far in a steep power-off turn, reduce the angle of bank and then ease back the control column to raise the nose.

Slipping Turn

The slipping turn is a turn in which the yaw induced by bank is partially prevented by application of opposite rudder. It is a useful manoeuvre if height must be lost during the turn onto final approach in a landing.

When flaps are extended or retracted there is always a change in aircraft attitude and performance in relation to a specific airspeed and/or power setting, together with a probable need for retrimming. In view of this, turns of all types and classes, except (in some aircraft) slipping turns, should be practised with varying degrees of flap extension.

Standard Rate Turn

The standard rate turn is a turn at the rate of 3 degrees per second. The rate at which an aircraft turns is determined by airspeed and angle of bank. At a given airspeed a specific angle of bank will provide a certain rate of turn. A simple way to estimate the angle of bank required for a standard rate turn at a given airspeed is to take 10 per cent of the airspeed (in miles per hour) and add 5 to the remainder. For example, at 120 mph, (12 + 5) = 17 degrees of bank. If the same aircraft has an airspeed indicator that registers in knots, the additive is 7 instead of 5 — i.e., at 100 kts., (10 + 7) = 17 degrees of bank.

The magnetic compass is unreliable when an aircraft is turning. The mechanical and other reasons for the eccentric behaviour of the magnetic compass will not be discussed here, but it is important to know that it can only be relied upon when the aircraft is flying straight, and at a constant airspeed (see "Vagaries of the Magnetic Compass," Exercise 23).

During a turn the reactions of certain instruments are as follows:

Turn-and-Bank Indicator. The needle will immediately deflect in the direction of the turn and will indicate the rate at which the aircraft is turning. In a co-ordinated turn the ball will be centred in its curved glass tube. If the ball is off-centre to the inside of the turn, the aircraft is slipping into the centre of the turn. If the ball is off-centre to the outside of the turn, the aircraft is skidding out from the turn.

Attitude Indicator. The horizon bar (of most instruments) will remain parallel to the real horizon, and the miniature aircraft, in relation to the horizon bar, will bank in the same direction as the real aircraft. This instrument indicates the angle of bank and the attitude of the aircraft in the pitching plane. The nose of the miniature aircraft, in relation to its artificial horizon, corresponds to the pitch attitude of the nose of the real aircraft in relation to the real horizon.

Heading Indicator. Immediately as a turn begins, this instrument begins rotating to indicate the successive new headings of the aircraft during the turn. When the turn stops, it stops. To decrease the numerical values on the face of the instrument turn left; to increase values turn right. A memory aid is "left for less."

Airspeed Indicator. The instrument that does not perceptibly react until well into a level co-ordinated turn is the airspeed indicator. Since the load factor increases as a result of the turn, additional lift must be obtained by increasing the angle of attack; this in turn creates more drag, resulting in a decreased airspeed. In a gentle turn the decrease is barely noticeable; even in a well executed medium turn the airspeed may be only slightly lower. In the case of a poorly co-ordinated turn the airspeed indicator will react more significantly. If the nose is allowed to pitch up too high there will be a decrease in airspeed; conversely, if the nose is allowed to pitch down too low, the airspeed indicator will rapidly indicate an increase in speed.

Altimeter. In a perfectly co-ordinated level turn the altimeter needle would remain stationary at the selected altitude. If the nose is held too high, there will be an increase in altitude. If the nose is allowed to drop too low, a decrease in altitude will be indicated.

Flight for Range and Endurance

When an aircraft is being flown for range, the objective is to fly the greatest distance possible per unit of fuel consumed. To do this the aircraft must be operated at an airspeed which provides optimum *lift/drag ratio* — i.e., at the airspeed which provides the greater amount of lift with the least amount of drag.

The flight manuals of most light aircraft provide readily interpreted cruise performance charts from which to select an airspeed for optimum range. For example, the cruise performance chart shown in Figure 2-21 shows that the range at 7500 feet of altitude in normal cruise at 110 mph is 515 miles, whereas at its optimum range airspeed for that altitude, 90 miles per hour, its range is 655 miles. Generally speaking, and from a review of many typical cruise performance charts, range flight performance is better when the flight is conducted at higher altitudes and if possible at full throttle height.

Remember that the range figures shown in cruise performance charts presume still air. Wind velocity may therefore be an important factor when selecting the best airspeed to fly the greatest ground distance. When flying into a head wind it may be advantageous to use a range power setting higher than recommended. As an exaggerated illustration, consider a typical light aircraft with fuel for 3 hours of flight at its recommended range cruising speed of 100 mph, planning to fly to a destination 160 miles away in a 50 mph head wind. (For illustration purposes, disregard the reserve fuel requirement.) At the ground speed of 50 mph and fuel for 3 hours, the aircraft would run out of fuel at 150 ground miles, leaving it 10 miles short of its destination. The same aircraft with power increased to give it a maximum cruising airspeed of 120 mph has also increased its fuel consumption so that only 2.5 hours fuel is available, but at a ground speed of 70 mph the aircraft will cover 175 ground miles on its available 2.5 hours fuel, 15 miles more than required to reach its destination.

A pilot contemplating a flight to an upwind destination and returning to the point of departure without refueling may feel that it is a simple case of "ground speed lost on the upwind flight will be exactly compensated for by ground speed gained on the return flight." This is not so. Because of the reduced ground speed on the upwind flight, the head wind will be affecting the aircraft for a longer period of time than the tail wind on the return flight. Working out sample trips with various wind velocities (and still air) will make this quite clear.

Since higher altitudes are generally involved when flying for range, a correct air/fuel mixture supply to the engine becomes increasingly significant (see "Mixture Control" in Exercise 3).

When flying for endurance the objective is to keep the aircraft in the air for the longest possible time per unit of fuel consumed. Distance is not of primary concern. For example, if a pilot had to wait an extended period aloft while the runway was being cleared of snow, or wait for a weather situation to improve at an airport, he might be wise to operate the aircraft in the maximum endurance mode while waiting. One light aircraft in common use has a fuel supply for 4 hours and 55 minutes flight at normal cruising speed, but in the endurance mode the same aircraft can remain aloft for 10 hours. The majority of light aircraft are capable of almost doubling their time in the air per unit of fuel when flown in the endurance mode.

The power setting for endurance is that which provides the lowest possible RPM (or lowest combined manifold pressure and RPM) which will sustain level flight. To establish the optimum endurance speed, reduce power in small amounts while maintaining the desired altitude. As airspeed decreases, the angle of attack must continually be increased to maintain altitude, resulting in increased drag.

Continued reductions in power will finally produce a point where drag becomes so great that power must be increased to maintain level flight. The power setting which you noted just before this point was reached is the setting for best endurance. Immediately increase power, then reduce it again in small increments until reaching the RPM noted to sustain the aircraft in level flight.

Figure 2-21   Cruise Performance

Gross Weight: 1600 lbs.   **Notes:** 1. Maximum cruise is normally limited to 75 per cent power.
Standard Conditions   2. Cruise speeds for the standard Model 150 (without speed fairings) are approximately
Zero Wind   2 mph lower than shown.
Lean Mixture   3. No allowance for take-off, climb, or reserve.

Altitude (ft.)	RPM	% Bhp	TAS mph	Gal/ Hour	22.5 gal (No Reserve)		35.0 gal (No Reserve)	
					Endr. Hours	Range Miles	Endr. Hours	Range Miles
2500	2750	87	124	6.6	3.4	425	5.3	665
	2700	82	121	6.1	3.7	445	5.7	690
	2600	72	116	5.4	4.2	480	6.5	745
	2500	64	110	4.8	4.7	515	7.3	800
	2400	56	105	4.3	5.2	550	8.2	855
	2300	50	99	3.8	5.9	585	9.2	910
	2200	44	94	3.4	6.5	615	10.2	955
	2100	38	88	3.1	7.3	640	11.3	990
5000	2750	80	123	6.0	3.8	460	5.8	720
	2700	75	120	5.6	4.0	480	6.2	745
	2600	67	115	5.0	4.5	515	7.0	800
	2500	59	109	4.5	5.0	550	7.8	855
	2400	52	104	4.0	5.6	585	8.7	905
	2300	46	98	3.6	6.2	615	9.7	955
	2200	41	92	3.2	6.9	640	10.8	995
7500	2750	73	122	5.5	4.1	500	6.4	775
	2700	69	119	5.2	4.3	515	6.7	800
	2600	62	114	4.7	4.8	550	7.5	855
	2500	55	108	4.2	5.4	585	8.4	905
	2400	49	103	3.8	6.0	615	9.3	955
	2300	43	97	3.4	6.6	640	10.3	995
	2200	39	90	3.1	7.2	655	11.3	1015
10000	2700	64	118	4.8	4.7	550	7.3	860
	2600	57	112	4.3	5.2	585	8.1	910
	2500	51	107	3.9	5.8	615	8.9	960
	2400	45	101	3.5	6.3	645	9.9	1000
	2300	41	95	3.2	6.9	660	10.8	1025
12500	2650	56	114	4.3	5.3	605	8.2	940
	2600	53	111	4.1	5.6	620	8.6	965
	2500	47	105	3.7	6.1	645	9.5	1005
	2400	43	99	3.4	6.7	660	10.4	1030
	2300	39	91	3.1	7.2	660	11.2	1025

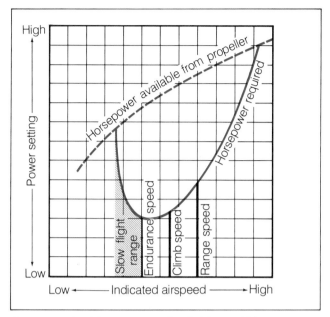

Figure 2-22 Horsepower Available and Horsepower
Required for Various Conditions of Flight

Slow Flight

Slow flight, for the purposes of this manual, may be defined as, "that range of airspeeds between the maximum endurance speed for a particular aircraft and the point just above its stalling speed for the existing flight conditions." Training in slow flight has three main purposes:

(1) To learn to recognize the symptoms when approaching the slow flight speed range to avoid inadvertent entry into this speed range,

(2) To maintain safe flight control, in all configurations, within the slow flight speed range, resulting in the development of co-ordination and instilling of confidence in the handling of the aircraft, and

(3) To acquaint the student with the possible consequences of failing to take prompt corrective action, particularly when flying at airspeeds close to minimum control speed.

There are several conditions where an aircraft may encounter the slow flight speed range. For example, some of these conditions are: take-offs, landings, recovering from a misjudged landing, an overshoot, and an approach to a stall. Of prime importance is your awareness of the effect of controls at the bottom of the slow flight speed range.

An aircraft would generally not be operated in the slow flight mode while waiting for weather to clear, while inspecting a potential landing area, or while searching for ground fixes when lost, since in this mode, control and management of the aircraft require the full attention of the pilot. Furthermore, operation in the slow flight range is not necessarily economical: fuel consumption is higher and engine damage can result from overheating during prolonged flight in this mode, particularily while attempting to climb.

When operating within the slow flight speed range, you must know and understand the characteristics associated with the performance and control of the aircraft while operating within this range, especially the control of altitude, airspeed, and yaw.

To enter the slow flight speed range, first establish the aircraft in the flight configuration for maximum endurance in straight and level flight. In this configuration, if the nose is raised beyond the normal nose-up limits for maximum endurance, the airspeed will decrease due to increased drag, and a loss of height will become apparent. To offset the loss of height and to maintain altitude, an increase in power will be required. The aircraft is now in the slow flight range.

With the aircraft established in the slow flight range, a controlled decrease in airspeed without a change in power setting will result in a loss of height. You must therefore increase power to maintain a constant altitude at the reduced airspeed. Conversely, a controlled increase in airspeed without a change in power setting will result in a decrease in the induced drag. You must then reduce power in order to maintain a constant altitude at the higher airspeed. There will be a slight loss of altitude during the transition period.

Slow flight at minimum controllable airspeed should be practised in straight and level flight, descending, level turns, and descending turns. Exercise caution when manoeuvring close to the ground in slow flight in gusty wind conditions. The airspeed must be adjusted upwards to allow for the gust factor.

Dual flight instruction should include exposure to slow flight in a climb for the purpose of simulating the conditions which may be experienced during an overshoot at a high density altitude, or when affected by obstacles, to demonstrate the need for prompt and proper transition from the slow flight mode. It should be remembered that slow flight climbs should be of short duration because of the insufficient airflow for engine cooling.

When you are established in a constant rate of descent in the slow flight range, a reduction in airspeed will result in an increase rate of descent, thereby necessitating an increase in power in order to maintain the former rate of descent.

During slow flight the aircraft's response to the use of its flight controls diminishes. As the airspeed decreas-

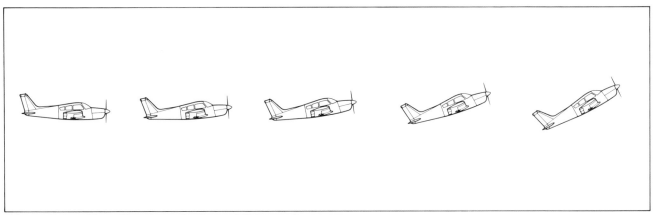

Figure 2-23   Transition from Cruise to Minimum Controllable Airspeed

es, the effectiveness of the controls decreases disproportionately. For example, there may be a certain loss of effectiveness when the airspeed is reduced from 30 to 20 mph above the stalling speed, but there will normally be a much greater loss as the airspeed is further reduced to 10 mph or less above stalling speed, particularly in the case of ailerons (Fig 2-23). Approaching stalling speed the aircraft's general stability is reduced, due to the decreased velocity of the airflow and the increased effect of aileron drag. Slipstream and asymmetric propeller thrust will contribute to an increase in the aircraft's tendency to yaw. This means you must have a proper understanding of the use of the rudder to maintain direction. Counteract yaw immediately with appropriate rudder pressure and increase power to maintain the height or rate of descent desired.

As speed is further reduced, more power is required to maintain the desired height (or rate of descent), but when the nose pitches down with full power applied the airspeed has gone below the minimum controllable. At this point the aircraft has entered a stalled flight condition. Near the stalling speed, factors such as air density, aircraft weight, and the drag from flaps and undercarriage (when applicable) may produce a condition in which it becomes impossible to maintain height. This may happen in attempting a turn after take-off with a high all-up weight and a critical density altitude.

The physical sensations of flight in the slow flight speed range, particularly in a strong wind, can result in a critical situation when flying at low altitude. This means you must monitor flight instruments closely in order to achieve balanced flight and maintain a safe airspeed.

The slow flight speed range does not automatically imply serious control difficulties or hazardous conditions. However, it does amplify any errors of basic flying technique. Hence, proper technique and precise control of the aircraft are essential in this speed range.

Stalls

The word *stall* has many meanings, but for our purposes it means that an aircraft has been allowed to reach a condition of flight in which the wings can no longer provide the lift necessary to sustain flight. Two important reasons for teaching stalls are so that you may: (1) recognize stall symptoms early enough to do something about them; and (2) develop the habit of taking prompt and effective corrective action.

Why Does a Wing Stall?

Simply stated, a stall occurs when the wing is no longer capable of providing the lift required to counteract the weight of the aircraft. The lift generated is dependent upon a smooth accelerated airflow over the wing. As the wing approaches its critical angle of attack, this airflow becomes mildly turbulent until the stalling angle is reached. At that point, the airflow becomes violently turbulent, the downwash and the pressure differential are greatly reduced, and loss of lift results. With so much lift suddenly disappearing, the wing stalls and the aircraft ceases to fly. The four parts of Figure 2-24 show the airflow over the aerofoil at various stages leading to the stall.

It is basic in recognizing stalls to remember that, unlike angle of incidence, angle of attack is a relative factor. Therefore you cannot rely upon aircraft attitude entirely to indicate the possibility of a stall. Angle of attack may be simply defined as the angle between the mean chord of an aerofoil and its direction of motion relative to the airflow (relative airflow). In this manual, the term "relative airflow," rather than the "relative wind" used in other texts, is used to describe the direction of the airflow with respect to an aerofoil in flight. An aircraft may be stalled in practically any attitude and at practically any airspeed.

The term "stalling speed" can be misleading, especially when it is referred to as the stalling speed of a specific aircraft. The flight manual for a specific aircraft may list its stalling speeds for various flight configurations but the following factors always affect stalling speeds:

(1) Aircraft Condition. A clean, well maintained, properly rigged aircraft will invariably have better stalling characteristics and lower stalling speeds than a similar aircraft in poor general condition.

(2) Balance. An improperly loaded aircraft may display poor stalling characteristics.

(3) Weight. Since weight opposes lift, a lightly loaded, properly balanced aircraft will have a lower stalling speed than a similar aircraft operating at its maximum permissible weight.

(4) Power. Because of the additional upward thrust and other lift contributing factors of a power-on stall, the stalling speed in such a flight configuration will be lower.

(5) Angle of Bank. The greater the bank angle, in co-ordinated flight, the higher the stalling speed.

(6) Flaps. When flaps are extended the camber of the wing is effectively increased. This deflects more of the airflow downwards for a given airspeed, thereby increasing lift. This factor allows the aircraft to be flown at a lower speed before the stall occurs.

(7) Pitch. When an aircraft is pitched upward, more or less abruptly, the load factor is increased correspondingly and a higher stalling speed is introduced for the duration of change in pitch attitude (see Chapter 4, "Loading Factor").

(8) Retractable Landing-Gear. Extending the landing-gear increases drag. The effect on stalling speed varies from aircraft to aircraft, but generally in the classic wings level nose-up attitude a slightly lower

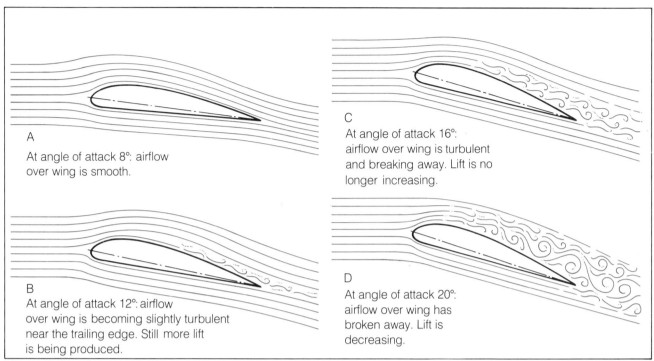

A
At angle of attack 8°: airflow over wing is smooth.

B
At angle of attack 12°: airflow over wing is becoming slightly turbulent near the trailing edge. Still more lift is being produced.

C
At angle of attack 16°: airflow over wing is turbulent and breaking away. Lift is no longer increasing.

D
At angle of attack 20°: airflow over wing has broken away. Lift is decreasing.

Figure 2-24   Angles of Attack

stalling speed will be noted, more especially in the power-on configuration.

Stalling speeds vary according to the type of aircraft: those with a high wing loading have a higher stalling speed. However, regardless of loading or airspeed, an aircraft always stalls when the wings reach the same angle of attack. Remember, angle of attack and aircraft attitude are not consistently related. Since there is no instrument available to the pilot of a light aircraft to determine the angle of attack, the airspeed must therefore be used as a guide to identifying the approach to stall. The other symptoms of an approaching stall are:

(1) A decrease in the effectiveness of the controls, especially elevator and aileron control: the "live" resistance to pressures on the controls becomes progressively less and less as speed decreases
(2) Loss of height, despite rearward movement of the elevator control
(3) Buffeting (the beating effect of disturbed airflow on the aircraft's structure, which can be heard and/or felt): this varies in intensity with different types of aircraft
(4) Audible or visual stall warning devices fitted in most aircraft are activated prior to the stall.

Always remember that should the approach to stall symptoms begin when a stall is not intended, no gross, abrupt, or panicky movement of the controls is needed to restabilize the typical light aircraft. Most aerofoils stall at about 17 degrees angle of attack; therefore, the stall

symptoms occur at 15 to 16 degrees. The alert pilot will be able to recognize the stall since it normally occurs gradually, because of the wash-out of the wings, with the stall beginning at the wing roots, and as the angle of attack is increased, moving progressively towards the wing tips. To remove the symptoms a relatively small (but prompt and decisive) forward movement of the elevator control, to reduce the angle of attack, will return the aircraft to stabilized flight. If additional power is available you may effectively reduce the angle of attack by applying appropriate power, without any change in the aircraft's pitch attitude. However, under normal conditions you can eliminate stall symptoms by adding available power and lowering the nose to reduce the angle of attack. Intentional stalls must be preceded by:

(1) The cockpit check. Check for such things as carburettor heat, seat belts, windows shut, loose articles secured, etc.
(2) The look-around. Do a very careful look-around in all directions, especially below.

Practise stalls only over an unpopulated area and at sufficient altitude, even though the amount of height normally lost during a stall and immediate recovery is not generally excessive. During training in this manoeuvre your instructor will emphasize repeatedly that the objective is not how to stall an aircraft but how to recognize the proximity of a stall condition and take prompt corrective action.

Power-off stalls are generally entered from straight and level flight. Close the throttle smoothly and hold the

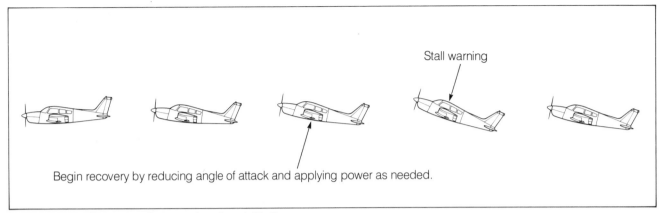

Stall warning

Begin recovery by reducing angle of attack and applying power as needed.

Figure 2-25   Recovery from an Imminent Stall

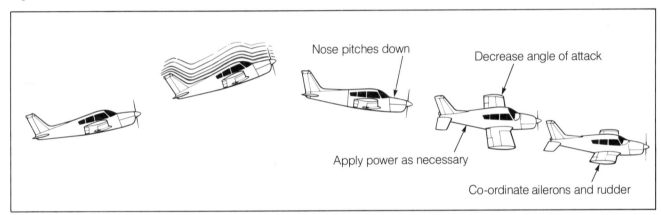

Nose pitches down

Decrease angle of attack

Apply power as necessary

Co-ordinate ailerons and rudder

Figure 2-26   Full Stall Recovery

aircraft in level flight by continued back pressure on the control column. The airspeed will gradually decrease back through endurance speed and enter the slow flight range. As the airspeed decreases, the response to the controls diminishes and coarser movements are required to produce a desired result. You will also notice distinctive sounds at the various airspeeds, especially in the slow flight range. Now raise the nose to about the attitude used in a normal climb, in order to stall the aircraft. When the stall occurs keep straight with rudder control.

Recovery

A simplified explanation of the procedure for recovering from a stall is: (1) reduce the angle of attack immediately; and (2) regain a correct flight attitude with co-ordinated use of flight and power controls. Not every situation demands the application of power but its use must become an integral part of the recovery procedure (Figs 2-25 and 2-26).

First, at the indication of a stall lower the nose positively and immediately. The amount of forward control movement required varies from aircraft to aircraft — in most cases only moderate pressure to

about the neutral position is needed. Too much forward travel on the control column for the particular aircraft may impose a reverse load on the wings and impede recovery rather than hasten it. The objective is to reduce the angle of attack sufficiently to smooth the airflow over the wing. Keep straight.

Second, apply adequate power promptly and smoothly. At altitude a cruise power setting is normally sufficient, but at low altitudes application of full power may be necessary to maintain or regain altitude. Open the throttle promptly but do not slam it open; improper throttle operation can make the engine sputter and lose its power at a most crucial moment, especially if it has cooled off during a glide. Due to the low airspeed there is very little risk of overspeeding the engine if you apply too much power, as long as you readjust it as soon as possible. Better too much power at this point than too little. Resume the normal power setting as soon as recovery is accomplished and you have regained cruise attitude.

Straight and level flight is regained by co-ordinated use of controls. Recovery from the stall should result in regaining normal flight with the least loss of height. With the use of power, in the average light aircraft, lowering the nose to the cruise attitude, or slightly below, will accomplish this end. Diving steeply will possibly hasten

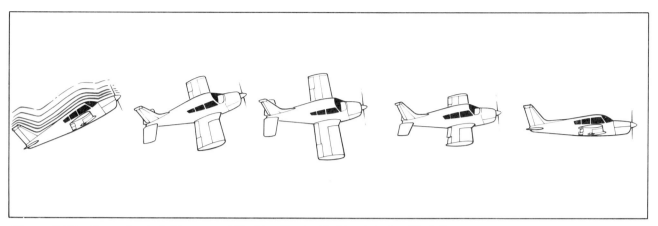

Figure 2-27   Co-ordinated Aileron and Rudder Control is Used during Stall Recovery

recovery but only at a greater and undesirable sacrifice of height.

In practising stalls from descending turns, take care that the turn continues at a uniform rate until the stall occurs. Then, using the standard procedure exactly, the recovery is made straight ahead with the least loss of altitude. If the descending turn is improperly co-ordinated during the approach to the stall, a wing may drop abruptly. Should this happen, carry out the same recovery procedure: unstall the aircraft, keep straight, and level the wings with co-ordinated use of flight controls (Fig 2-27).

Stalling Speeds

With altitude, the density of the air in which an aircraft is flying decreases. Although the stalling speed is higher at altitude, the airspeed indicator, which itself functions by the effect of the air density, will record the same speed when the aircraft stalls at altitude as it did at or near ground level. Indicated stalling speeds will remain the same at all altitudes.

When practising stalls, avoid raising the nose of the aircraft too far above the horizon to produce the stall (Fig 2-28). This will provide more realistic symptoms of what an accidental stall will feel and look like, and allow a clearer study of these symptoms.

The principles which apply to power-off stalls also apply to stalls entered with power, although there are some differences in the manoeuvres. The pitching of the aircraft from a full stall with power on is much more steep and rapid. The aircraft is also more difficult to control during recovery, since in many cases there is a tendency for one wing to drop at the same time as the nose pitches down.

When you enter a stall with power on, the elevators retain their effectiveness longer, due to the propeller slipstream. Because of the additional thrust the nose must be raised higher to accomplish a stall. The rudder also remains much more effective, due to the

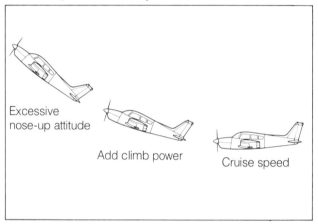

Excessive nose-up attitude

Add climb power

Cruise speed

Figure 2-28   Improper Stall Entry from Cruise

slipstream. However, the ailerons are less effective than in a power-off stall, thereby establishing a new relationship in relative control effectiveness. This is partially due to power causing the stalling speed to be slightly lower, which decreases aileron effectiveness, but at the same time the slipstream keeps the elevators and rudder very effective at the lower airspeed. There are other factors, such as torque, which contribute to making control of a power-on stall more difficult.

To enter a stall with power on, bring the nose smoothly up to a nose-up attitude which is obviously impossible for the aircraft to maintain, and hold it there until the stall occurs. (Ordinarily you will avoid extreme nose-up attitudes, since they serve no useful purpose). In most aircraft, after the stalling attitude is established, the elevator control will be brought progressively back as the speed decreases. At the stall the control will have reached its full extent of rearward travel.

Recovery from a power-on stall is made in the same manner as recovery from any other stall. Since the throttle is already set at cruising or climbing power, its advance will only be slight but of greater importance, because the stall will have been more violent and the loss of control more complete.

At the same gross weight, configuration, and power setting an aircraft will consistently stall at the same indicated airspeed, provided no additional load factor is incurred by reason of a manoeuvre or abrupt use of the controls. The aircraft will, however, stall at a higher airspeed when manoeuvring loads are imposed by sudden turns, pull-ups, or abrupt changes in its flight path. Stalls entered from such flight situations are called *acceleration* stalls. Regardless of airspeed trend, any movement of the controls which increases the "G" factor produces an acceleration. In a turn the aircraft is accelerated towards the centre of the turn; the steeper the turn, the greater the acceleration, hence the greater the load factor and the higher the stalling speed. Therefore, acceleration forces generated by turns or abrupt changes in upward pitch, regardless of whether the airspeed is high or low, will always increase the stalling speed. This holds true in climbing turns, level turns, gliding turns, steep turns — in fact any turn, regardless of power. The reason for applying power in a steep turn is to maintain airspeed; power does not have any effect on the significantly increased stalling speed in such a manoeuvre.

When we say that an aircraft may be stalled at any airspeed, we are not implying that it is permissible to do so. The lower the airspeed when a stall occurs the less the possibility of structural damage, since the load factors are minimal. However, the higher the airspeed the higher the load, and correspondingly the greater the chance of inflicting structural damage. This is why aircraft flight manuals and owner's manuals include "manoeuvring speed." Manoeuvring speed is the maximum speed at which the flight controls (of a specific aircraft) may be fully deflected without causing structural damage to the aircraft.

A *high-speed* stall, so-called, is an undesirable manoeuvre which may be induced by an abrupt rearward movement of the control column at any speed the aircraft is capable of attaining. Following an intentional stall, if the nose has been allowed to pitch down at a large angle the airspeed will increase rapidly. Should the elevator control be brought back too rapidly to recover from the dive the aircraft will enter a "secondary stall" at a much greater speed than that experienced in a normal stall. An abrupt pull-up and turn at cruising speed, to avoid another aircraft, can impose a heavy load factor and may possibly induce a high-speed stall.

The high-speed stall can also be demonstrated in the steep turn. Here the load factors imposed by both pitch and turn accelerations can reach severe proportions when bank and pitch control are increased beyond a certain point. An aircraft with a normal power-on stall speed of 50 mph may stall at a speed well in excess of 100 mph in a steep turn when the angle of bank exceeds 60 degrees. Any control movement which increases centrifugal force will result in a higher stalling speed. A

manoeuvre which requires special attention to airspeed and angle of bank is the power-off (gliding) turn, especially when conducted close to the ground.

Turbulence can cause a significant increase in stalling speed. An upward gust causes an abrupt change in the relative airflow, which results in an equally abrupt increase in angle of attack. All stalls are caused by exceeding the critical angle of attack, and the base from which this angle is measured is the direction of motion of the relative airflow. This is why an airspeed slightly higher than normal is usually recommended when approaching to land in turbulent conditions.

Stalls During Turns

When an aircraft is stalled during a level or descending turn, the inside wing normally continues to drop lower until it is brought under control. It is therefore not unusual for the novice to think that this holds true of all stalls entered into during a turn. In a level turn the inside wing is travelling more slowly than the outside wing and obtains less lift, causing it to sink and increase its angle of attack. This, under the proper conditions, will produce a stall. During a descending turn the path described by the aircraft is a downward spiral; therefore the inside wing is meeting the relative airflow at a steeper angle of attack and is the one to stall first and drop lower.

However, during a climbing turn the path described by the aircraft is an upward spiral. Therefore, the outside wing is meeting the relative airflow at a steeper angle of attack than the lower wing. As a result the higher wing will stall first and drop abruptly when the stalled condition occurs.

Departure Stalls

During take-off and the initial stage of its departure, an aircraft enters into and passes through a critical condition of flight. Every aircraft, as it is rotated for take-off, is for a brief period in a critical condition of flight, though should a mishap occur at this point and good airmanship has prevailed, the throttle can be closed and a landing safely made on the runway length remaining. However, should an aircraft attitude be too nose-high after rotation, a stall may occur from which a successful recovery cannot be made, or, if the aircraft is in a near stalled condition, it will not climb sufficiently to clear obstacles in the flight path (Fig 2-29). Therefore, establishing the correct nose-up attitude for a climb after lift-off is imperative. As part of the departure procedure, take great care to establish the correct nose-up attitude when executing a climbing turn, especially if the turn must be carried out before safety height is reached.

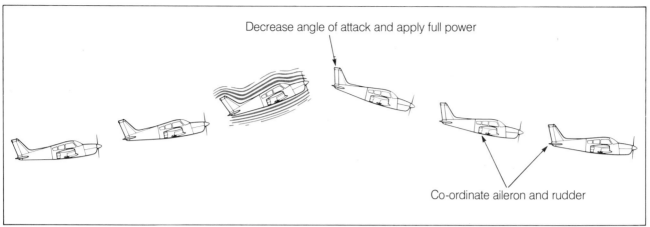

Figure 2-29   Take-off Stall

Another critical departure procedure is the "pull-up" resulting from a missed approach. More often than not when a decision is reached to abandon an approach the aircraft's attitude is level instead of nose-down, the airspeed is low, and the flaps are extended. In addition it may also be necessary to execute a turn very shortly after abandoning the approach (for traffic pattern purposes). Some of the errors which may lead to a stalled or near stalled condition following an over-shoot are:

(1) Insufficient application of power. Remember that this is a form of take-off under adverse conditions, so nothing less than climbing power is adequate.

(2) Permitting the aircraft to assume an attitude which is too nose-high. Application of power plus nose-up trim will tend to force the aircraft into a very nose-high attitude if these are not promptly compensated for.

(3) Forgetting to retract the flaps or retracting them too abruptly. Very few aircraft are able to sustain a climb with flaps fully extended. When flaps are totally retracted immediately, a sudden loss of height can occur. Attempts to arrest this descent by raising the nose suddenly may induce a stall.

(4) Nose too high if an immediate turn is necessary. It would be better to lower the nose to an attitude slightly lower than that for a normal climbing turn than risk a stall or near stall at this point.

Spinning

The *spin* has no practical application in normal flight. You are trained in spins in order to learn recognition, avoidance, and recovery.

It is imperative that only aircraft certified for intentional spinning be used for any form of spin training. The type certificate, pilot operating handbook, or cockpit placards must be consulted to determine under what conditions, if any, spin practice may be undertaken in a particular aircraft. The pilot of an aircraft placarded against intentional spins should assume that it might become uncontrollable in a spin. Entry and recovery techniques recommended in this text apply to the average light training aircraft. Should the pilot operating handbook dictate different techniques, they must be followed.

Autorotation

Spinning may be defined as autorotation which is allowed to develop after an aggravated stall.

If for some reason one wing of an aircraft produces more lift than the other, the aircraft will roll and the downgoing wing will meet the relative airflow at a greater angle of attack. At ordinary angles of attack, this increase in angle will cause an increase in lift, which tends to restore the aircraft to its previous attitude. When a downgoing wing experiences an increased angle of attack at or near the stalling angle, it loses lift, becomes more stalled, and automatically continues to drop. The upgoing wing, because of its relative upward

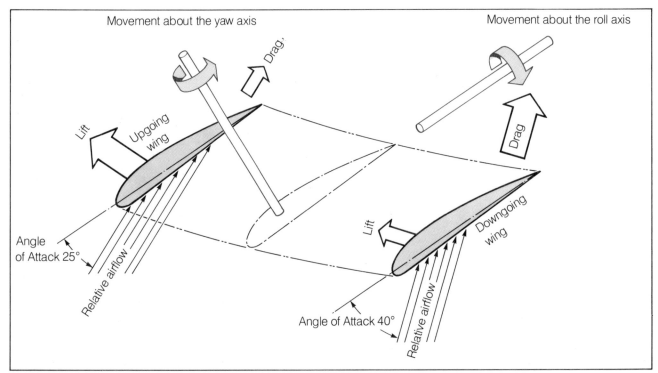

Figure 2-30   Angles of Attack of Wing Tips and Forces Acting in a Spin

movement, meets the airflow at a reduced angle of attack, becomes less stalled, and produces more lift, which accentuates the roll. Also, drag on the downgoing wing increases sharply, adding to the existing yaw force, which effectively increases the angle of attack of the downgoing wing, stalling it further (Fig 2-30). The nose drops owing to the loss of lift, and autorotation or spinning sets in.

The spinning motion is complicated and involves simultaneous rolling, yawing, and pitching. The aircraft follows a helical or corkscrew downward path, rotating about a vertical axis. Pitch attitudes may vary from flat to steep while forward and vertical speeds are both comparatively low. Load forces are somewhat above normal but are relatively steady.

The spin consists of three stages:

(1) the *incipient*-stage,
(2) the *fully developed* stage, and
(3) the *recovery*.

These are illustrated in Figure 2-31.

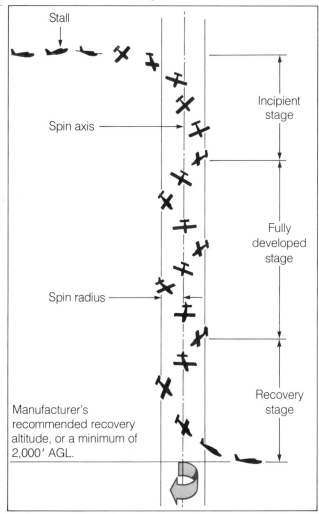

Figure 2-31   The Three Stages of a Spin

The Incipient Stage

The incipient stage occurs from the time the aircraft stalls and rotation starts until the spin axis becomes vertical or nearly vertical. During this time the flight path changes from horizontal to vertical and spin rotation increases from zero to the fully developed rate. The incipient stage usually occurs rapidly in light aircraft, some 4 to 6 seconds, and consists of approximately the first 2 turns. Model and actual tests show that the typical incipient stage motion starts during the stall with a wing drop. As the nose drops the yawing motion begins to increase. About the half-turn point, the aircraft is pointed almost straight down but the angle of attack is usually in excess of that of the stall, because of the inclined flight path (Fig 2-31). Near completion of the first turn, the nose may come back up and the angle of attack continues to increase. As the aircraft continues to rotate into the second turn, the flight path becomes more nearly vertical, and the three spinning motions become more repeatable and approach those of the fully developed stage.

The Fully Developed Stage

In the fully developed stage the attitude, angles, and motions of the aircraft are somewhat repetitious and stabilized from turn to turn with a nearly vertical descent. The spin is maintained by a balance between the aerodynamic and inertia forces and moments (Fig 2-32).

Entry

A spin, whether deliberate or inadvertent, may be entered in many ways. It is not necessary for an aircraft to have a relatively high pitch attitude for it to stall and spin. The angle of attack is the key factor, not the attitude. It is possible to enter a spin with the aircraft in a descending, level, or climbing attitude. A spin can also be entered from a high-speed stall. Many types of aircraft require special techniques to get the spin properly started. Strangely enough, these same aircraft have been known to spin accidentally, due to mishandling in routine turns or in slow flight.

One method of inducing a spin is outlined below. The primary requirement is that the aircraft be fully stalled, otherwise it might not spin and the result would likely be a skidding spiral of increasing airspeed. If this occurs, immediately recover from the spiral dive and start over again.

(1) Complete safety precautions — cockpit checks, minimum altitude, suitable area, look-out, etc.

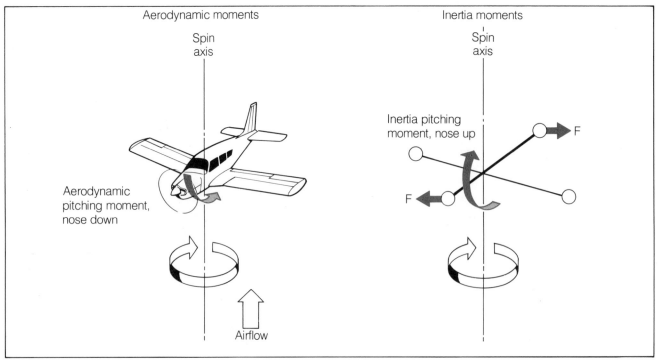

Figure 2-32   Balance of Aerodynamic and Inertia Pitching Moments in a Spin

(2) Reduce power to a minimum and stall the aircraft by gradually applying full aft control column while maintaining a near normal climb attitude. At or slightly before the stall, apply full rudder in the direction of the desired spin.

(3) Allow autorotation to occur by maintaining full rudder and holding the control column fully back, as at this point there may be an instinctive tendency to release pressure.

(4) Allow the spin to progress through the desired number of turns, but never through more than six. Approved aircraft are not tested beyond these limits. Normally, two complete turns of a developed spin should be sufficient.

Recovery

The aim in recovery is to upset the balance between the aerodynamic and inertia moments. Because aircraft spin characteristics differ, recovery techniques specified in the pilot operating handbook must be followed. The procedures outlined below are suitable for most small aircraft and may be used in the absence of manufacturer's data for recovery from either the incipient or fully developed stages.

(1) Power to idle, neutralize ailerons.

(2) Apply and hold full rudder opposite to the direction of rotation.

(3) Just after the rudder reaches the stop, move the control column positively forward far enough to break the stall. Full-down elevator might be required.

(4) Hold these control inputs until rotation stops.

(5) As the rotation stops, neutralize rudder, level the wings, and recover smoothly from the resulting dive.

Transition Recovery Action

The transition stage between a stall and the incipient stage can be defined as the period between the stall and the commencement of autorotation. Recovery action to pick up a wing drop at the stall must be as specified in the pilot operating handbook. If the manufacturer does not provide a recovery technique, the procedure used in the transition stage should be the same as that needed to lift a wing that has dropped in a stall (Exercise 12).

Factors Affecting Recovery

The most important difference between the fully developed stage and the incipient stage is an increase in recovery time, for some aircraft, and to a lesser extent the amount of control input needed. From the fully developed stage it is not unusual for a full turn or more to occur after the application of recovery controls before rotation stops. Therefore, it is very important to apply the recovery controls in the proper sequence and hold them until rotation stops. Premature relaxation may extend the recovery time.

Some of the factors likely to affect spin behaviour and recovery characteristics are: aircraft loading, including

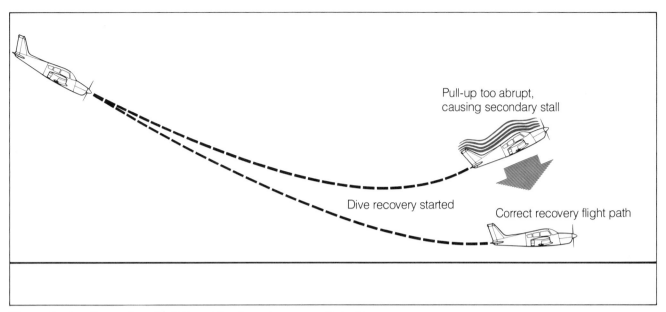

Figure 2-33 Secondary Stall Resulting from Improper Spin Recovery

distribution, centre of gravity and weight; altitude; aileron; flaps; and, power.

Distribution of the weight in the aircraft can have a significant effect on spin behaviour. The addition of weight at any distance from the centre of gravity of the aircraft will increase its moment of inertia about two axes. This increased inertia, independent of the centre of gravity location or weight, will tend to promote a less steep spin attitude and more sluggish recoveries. Forward location of the centre of gravity will usually make it more difficult to obtain a pure spin, due to the reduced elevator effectiveness. The farther back the centre of gravity, and the more masses distributed along the length of the fuselage, the flatter and faster the spin tends to become. Changes in gross weight as well as in its distribution can have an effect on spin behaviour, since increases in gross weight will increase inertia. Higher weights may extend recoveries slightly.

High altitudes will tend to lengthen recoveries since the less dense air provides less "bite" for the controls to oppose the spin. However, this does not suggest you should use low altitudes for spin practice.

The effect of the use of ailerons, either with or against the rotation, apparently follows no set rule for all aircraft. As application of ailerons might increase the rotation rate and delay recovery, there must be no tendency to use ailerons, particularly in a cross-control manner.

If a spin occurs with flaps extended, retract them, as extended flap might:

(1) Prolong the spin, because it induces a flatter spin attitude and lower spin rate

(2) Reduce the effectiveness of the rudder, due to deflected air flow

(3) Incur damage from high speed or high loading, or both, in recovery from the dive.

With power on, the attitude of the aircraft might be less nose-down and the propeller will tend to add some gyroscopic inputs, which will be reversed between left and right spins. The effect of leaving power on during a spin is to lengthen recoveries on some aircraft. Additionally, a power-on recovery will likely result in increased airspeed and height loss during the dive recovery.

If disorientation prevents determining the direction of rotation, refer to the turn needle or turn co-ordinator to establish the direction of rotation. For example, if the turn needle or turn co-ordinator indicates a turn to the left, the aircraft is spinning to the left. Do not refer to the ball indicator because the ball does not remain in a constant position, due to transient yaw.

Secondary Spin

A secondary spin may result from mishandling the controls following recovery from the initial spin. An abrupt or premature pull-up from the dive recovery could cause a secondary stall (Fig 2-33). If yaw is present — for example, from inadvertent retention of anti-spin rudder — the aircraft might enter a secondary spin.

Spiral Dives

A spiral dive may be informally described as: "a steep descending turn with the aircraft in an excessively nose-down attitude." The spiral is not usually considered a normal or useful manoeuvre and in its accidental form it can become very hazardous. A spiral may be recognized by the following:

(1) Excessive angle of bank
(2) Rapidly increasing airspeed
(3) Rapidly increasing rate of descent.

It can be readily seen why this manoeuvre is considered hazardous, especially if it occurs at a low altitude. A high-speed stall could result from incorrect use of elevator in an attempt to check the rapid rate of descent. If airspeed is permitted to increase beyond normal limits the aircraft can be structurally damaged, especially in the pull-up from the dive if loading becomes excessive.

In a way, a spiral resembles a spin. Therefore, when executing practice spins it is possible to become temporarily disoriented, so that what appears to be a spin is actually a spiral. Under these conditions always remember that the main difference between the two manoeuvres is airspeed. In a spin the airspeed is constant and low — at or about the stalling speed; in a spiral the airspeed will be well above stalling speed and increasing rapidly. A spiral may result from attempting to force an aircraft into a spin too soon before a stall occurs or from relaxing the elevator controls once a spin has started.

A spiral may also result from mismanagement of controls during manoeuvres in which additional engine power is used, such as steep turns. In these circumstances be sure that the throttle is closed, to bring the rapidly increasing airspeed under more effective control and to reduce the load factor build-up when recovering from the dive.

A spiral dive, once recognized, is not difficult to recover from. The following action must be taken promptly and in this order:

(1) Close the throttle.
(2) Level the wings. (The first and second actions should be almost simultaneous.)
(3) Keep straight.
(4) Ease out of the dive.
(5) Apply power as required to maintain height.

The spiral is not a manoeuvre to be practised, but for recognition and recovery action purposes the flight instructor will demonstrate it, either from an incorrectly entered spin or a poorly executed steep turn. During this demonstration the sudden increase in airspeed and wing loading will be very evident. You will also see how any attempt to pull out of the dive without first levelling the wings only further tightens and aggravates the manoeuvre.

In carrying out intentional spirals the following points are stressed so that you can take adequate precautions:

(1) Considerable height will be lost.
(2) Airspeed increases rapidly; take care not to exceed the speed limitations of the aircraft.
(3) An attempt to recover from the ensuing dive too abruptly could result in an excessive load factor, with the danger of a pilot black-out, structural damage, or a secondary high-speed stall.

Side-Slipping

When an aircraft is placed in a banked attitude, its normal tendency is to yaw (turn) towards the direction of the lower wing. *Side-slipping* is a manoeuvre in which the aircraft is placed in a banked attitude but its tendency to yaw is either reduced or prevented by appropriate rudder control.

The side-slip may be used to: (1) steepen and control the angle of power-off descent without increasing the forward speed; (2) increase rate of descent while turning; and (3) counteract drift resulting from a cross-wind while landing. The last is probably the most common use of the manoeuvre today.

Although it requires co-ordination by the pilot to establish the correct degree of side-slip, the manoeuvre itself is carried out by deliberate and calculated use of the controls to produce unbalanced flight. Some aircraft are capable of a greater degree of slip than others; to a large extent this is governed by the effectiveness of the rudder.

With the general installation of flaps on modern light aircraft, side-slips are no longer commonly used to steepen the angle of descent or lose height. However, situations occasionally occur when the side-slip can prove of great value, perhaps more particularly in the case of aircraft without flaps but also in the case of flap unserviceability. You should therefore become competent in the execution of the manoeuvre. Side-slips may be divided into three classes: (1) the *forward side-slip*; (2) the *regular side-slip*; and (3) the *slipping turn*. If there is a cross-wind component the effectiveness of a side-slip is always enhanced by slipping into the wind.

The forward side-slip is used to lose height or steepen the glide slope on approach to landing, while maintaining the centre-line of the flightway. It also affords an excellent view of the approach and landing area if the lowered wing is on the pilot's side of the aircraft.

To execute a forward side-slip, bank the aircraft in the desired direction and simultaneously use opposite rudder to control or induce the degree of yaw to maintain the desired flight path direction. Maintain the desired airspeed with the elevators. In the forward slip the longitudinal axis will be at an angle to the desired descent path. The amount of this angle depends on the amount of bank being counteracted by opposite rudder and must be continually adjusted to compensate for changes in wind velocity during the approach to landing (Fig 2-34).

You can recover from the forward side-slip by (a) releasing rudder pressure to allow the aircraft to return to its original heading, (b) levelling the wings, and (c) adjusting the pitch attitude to resume normal descent and airspeed. (When operating near the ground make allowances for the higher rate of descent in a side-slip.)

A regular side-slip, unlike the forward side-slip, is a side-slip during which the longitudinal axis of the aircraft remains approximately parallel to the original direction of flight (heading) but in which the flight path is moved to the left (or right) at a rate of change governed by the steepness of bank, which in turn may be dictated by wind velocity. To execute a regular side-slip (Fig 2-35) the aircraft is banked to give the desired rate of movement left (or right); simultaneously opposite rudder is used to hold it to its original direction of flight (heading). The nose must be raised above the normal gliding attitude to prevent the airspeed from increasing. The regular side-slip has limited use as a means of steepening normal approaches to landing, but is essential in the execution of cross-wind landings.

To recover from the regular side-slip, level the wings, maintain heading to establish normal co-ordinated flight, and simultaneously adjust the pitch attitude to resume the desired angle and airspeed to avoid stalling.

The slipping turn as a means for losing height is probably the easiest side-slip to understand and execute. It is a turn in which the yaw induced by bank is only partially prevented by application of opposite rudder. It differs from forward and side-slips in that during that manoeuvre the aircraft is changing its heading while losing altitude. It is a useful manoeuvre if you must lose height during the turn onto final approach.

If airspeed is allowed to get too slow during a slip, the

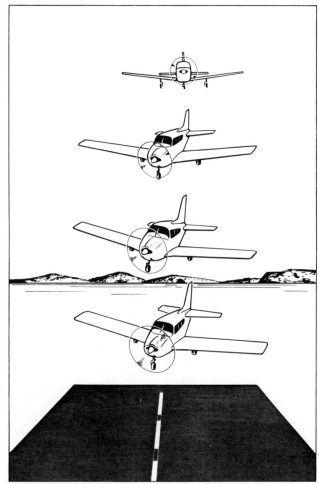

Figure 2-34   Forward Slip

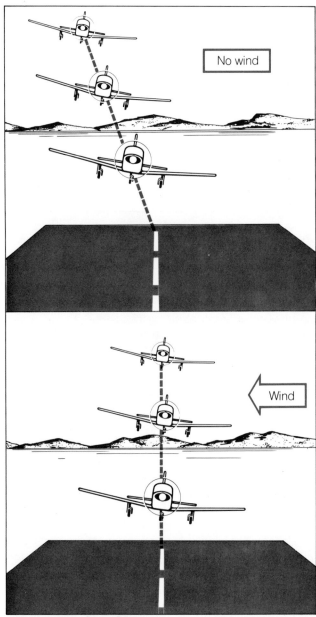

Figure 2-35   Side-Slip

reduced airflow over control surfaces, more particularly the rudder, will create the effect of the aircraft endeavouring to recover from the manoeuvre of its own accord. Should this symptom occur, you would be wise to recover from the side-slip and increase the airspeed before re-establishing the manoeuvre.

In a side-slip, the pitot tube and static air vents of an aircraft are no longer properly aligned with the relative airflow. As a result the airspeed indicators of most aircraft are subject to error during this manoeuvre. Given the possibility of this error, it is therefore incumbent upon you to recognize a correct slipping attitude by the attitude of the aircraft and the feel of the controls. An excessive nose-up attitude during the recovery could produce an angle of attack in excess of the stalling angle of the wing.

Side-slips should not be used to counteract a cross-wind during the climb following a take-off. With correct aileron and rudder control during a cross-wind take-off, the aircraft will lift off the ground in a slight side-slip, but this should be corrected promptly by executing a co-ordinated turn into wind sufficient to eliminate drift and maintain a straight path over the runway.

Take-off

Taking off, as defined in the Air Regulations in relation to an aircraft, means "the act of abandoning a supporting surface and includes the immediately preceding and following acts." In a normally executed take-off the aircraft becomes airborne smoothly and efficiently, with the minimum take-off run consistent with positive control and good climb performance. It is a requirement of the Air Regulations that take-offs of aircraft operated on aerodromes be executed into wind, insofar as practicable, unless otherwise authorized by an appropriate air traffic control unit. It makes good sense to take off into the wind since it:

(1) Permits the shortest run and the lowest ground speed at the moment of take-off
(2) Eliminates drift, so that there is no additional strain on the landing-gear
(3) Affords best directional control, especially at the beginning of the run
(4) Results in better obstacle clearance owing both to a shorter run and a steeper angle of climb (Fig 2-36)
(5) Establishes circuit pattern direction for all aircraft in the case of an uncontrolled airport.

The safety, and very frequently the quality, of a take-off can depend on the proper execution of the pre-take-off check. You must consider carrying out this check, in the sequential manner prescribed by the authority responsible for the operation of the aircraft or as laid down in the aircraft flight manual, as a compulsory action at all times.

A thorough knowledge of take-off principles, both in theory and practice, will prove extremely valuable throughout your flying career. Such knowledge, well learned, will prevent a take-off that could result in an accident, or in an emergency make a take-off possible under critical conditions. The manoeuvre is one of the easiest and most enjoyable to learn, provided you are fully conversant with all the factors involved. Many of the difficulties encountered are likely to stem from opening the throttle too suddenly and, in the case of the tail wheel aircraft, attempting to raise the tail at the same time. As you gain experience, you may combine these two operations more easily, but it is never good practice to do them simultaneously, since this leads to other faults, including overcontrol of the elevators.

The first few yards of any take-off are vastly important. If a good, straight, well controlled start is made, the success of the take-off is fairly well assured. Avoid the use of brakes if possible, since any use of brake will cause an undesirable increase in the take-off distance.

At first it is difficult to appreciate the varying control pressures required as the speed of an aircraft increases during the take-off run. There is therefore a tendency to move the controls through a wide range, seeking the pressures expected, and as a consequence to overcontrol badly. This will be aggravated by the initial sluggish reaction of the aircraft to the control movements. It is necessary that you develop a feel for control resistance, and accomplish the desired results by pressing against them. With increased practice and experience, you will be able to sense also when sufficient speed has been attained for rotation so that you do not have to direct your attention to the airspeed indicator too soon. Achieving the recommended airspeed before beginning rotation is important, but until that time you must give full attention to outside references.

During the take-off run the engine and propeller thrust-line should be approximately parallel to the ground, because in this attitude the thrust is effective in the direction of desired motion and the minimum amount of aerodynamic drag will be experienced up to the point of rotation. "Rotation," in this case, means the act of rotating the aircraft about its lateral axis to increase the angle of attack of the wing so as to lift the aircraft off the ground.

For normal take-offs in nose wheel aircraft, the aircraft should be carefully aligned with the runway centre-line (or mythical centre-line). Ensure that the nose wheel is centred. Power should be applied by

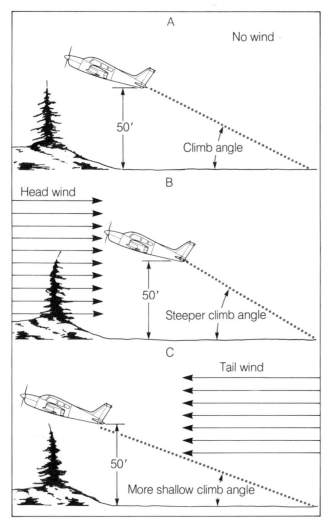

A

No wind

50'

Climb angle

B

Head wind

50'

Steeper climb angle

C

Tail wind

50'

More shallow climb angle

Figure 2-36   The Effect of Wind on an Obstacle Clearance Climb

opening the throttle smoothly but positively. No pressure on the elevator control is necessary at the outset, except as necessary to steady it. As the take-off roll commences, exert sufficient back pressure on the elevator control to lighten the weight on the nose wheel. As the speed of the aircraft approaches that required for take-off, gradually ease back further to raise the nose to the take-off attitude. Premature or excessive raising of the nose will delay take-off because of the increased drag. Keep straight by concentrating on something at the far end of the runway and maintain directional control with appropriate, smooth rudder pressures. Keep the wings level with appropriate aileron control.

Tail Wheel Aircraft. At the outset of the take-off run, keep the tail wheel on the ground so that directional control may be maintained by means of tail wheel steering. When speed has reached the point where both the elevators and rudder become effective, lower the nose to the take-off attitude.

As rotation speed is attained, ease the control column back to assist the aircraft into the air. It should not be forced into the air prematurely. When the aircraft lifts off the ground, it should be at approximately the attitude of its best rate of climb airspeed and allowed to accelerate to this airspeed before any attempt is made to reset the throttle for the climb, if the aircraft is subject to the latter procedure. Normally, if the aircraft has been correctly trimmed, some pressure will be required on the elevator control to hold this attitude until the proper climb speed is established. If back pressure on the control column is relaxed before a climb has been established, the aircraft may "settle," even to the point of dropping down onto the runway again.

The best rate of climb attitude and speed should be maintained until a safe height is reached, except when there are obstacles in the flight path, in which case the best angle of climb speed should be used. Unless the aircraft flight manual states otherwise, light aircraft should maintain full power until at least 500 feet above the ground. The combination of full power and best rate of climb speed gives an additional margin of safety in that altitude is gained, in a minimum of time, from which the aircraft can be safely manoeuvred should there be an engine failure. Also, in many light aircraft, full throttle automatically provides a richer mixture for additional engine cooling during the climb.

There may be a tendency for the aircraft to yaw to the left during the take-off run. The main reason for this is undoubtedly the propeller, but which of its effects is the chief cause is not so easy to determine. For example:

(1) The torque reaction of the clockwise rotating propeller being anti-clockwise, the left main wheel will be pressed on the ground and the extra friction at that point should tend to yaw the aircraft to the left. (This is similar to having a partially flat tire on the left front wheel of an automobile.)

(2) The slipstream will strike the fin and rudder on the left side, tending to yaw the aircraft to the left.

(3) Gyroscopic effect will enter the picture when the tail is being raised (in the case of tail wheel aircraft), and will tend to yaw the aircraft to the left.

(4) Asymmetric thrust. In the case of a tail wheel aircraft, since the right side of the propeller's plane of rotation is developing more thrust than the left side, it will cause the aircraft to yaw to the left, while the tail wheel is on the ground.

Nose wheel aircraft are not ordinarily subject to gyroscopic effect or asymmetric thrust during the take-off run since, until rotation for lift-off is executed, the thrust-line remains constantly parallel to the ground. The exception would be the nose-up attitude required in a soft field take-off.

Special Considerations

Most flight training occurs upon an airport with hard or firm surfaced runways, of adequate length and free of flightway obstacles. More often than not the landing area is kept reasonably clear of snow or slush of any significant depth. Up to this point we have been dealing with take-offs executed under these relatively ideal conditions. Very often, however, a take-off has to be made under less than ideal conditions, therefore there are special take-off procedures you must learn to contend with: (1) cross-winds, (2) short fields, (3) soft fields, (4) rough fields, obstacles in the flightway, or (5) any combination of these. (In this text, "upwind" will signify the direction from which the wind is blowing. An east wind blows from the east to the west.)

Cross-Wind Take-off

It is not always possible or practical to take off directly into the wind. Consequently, the principles involved in cross-wind take-offs must be learned and practised until they offer no difficulty or hazard.

An aircraft taking off directly into the wind tends to maintain a straight heading while it is rolling on the runway, with minimum control assistance from the pilot. However, during a take-off run with the wind blowing across the runway (Fig 2-37), the following factors must be taken into consideration:

(1) Since the aircraft has more keel surface exposed aft of the main wheels than ahead of them, a cross-wind tends to turn the aircraft into the wind.
(2) The pressure of the wind on the keel surface tends to make the aircraft drift, and so imposes a side-strain on the landing-gear.
(3) The upwind wing will develop more lift than the downwind wing and tend to lift the upwind wheel off the ground because
  (a) dihedral effect increases the angle of attack of the upwind wing;
  (b) wind striking the aircraft at an angle exposes more of the upwind wing to the relative airflow, depending upon whether the aircraft is of high wing or low wing design;
  (c) the downwind wing is "blanketed" by the fuselage.

When an aircraft is held firmly down on the runway and a straight heading maintained, the cross-wind puts some acceptable strain on the landing-gear. However, when the aircraft is lifted off the runway and permitted to drift (move sideways relative to the runway) and then

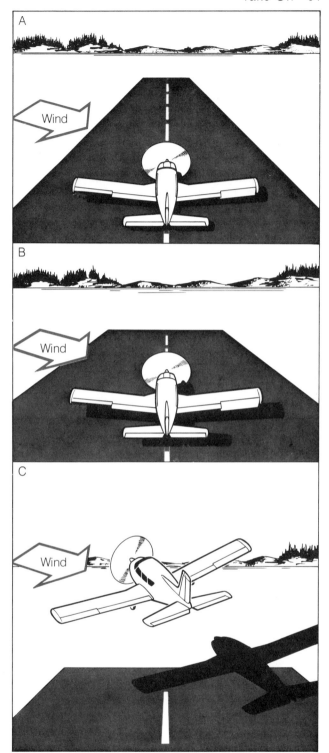

Figure 2-37   Effects of a Cross-Wind during Take-off

allowed to contact the runway again, the sideways movement is immediately arrested by the contact, which imposes a severe side-strain upon the landing-gear and its components. Therefore, the aim in taking off in a cross-wind is to ensure that the aircraft is transferred cleanly and positively from the ground to the air and not permitted to contact the runway again. For these reasons, and because the take-off run is likely to be longer, it is not advisable to take off at a greater angle to the wind than necessary.

During a cross-wind take-off in a single-engine aircraft, the aileron control is held to the upwind side of the aircraft and the take-off path held straight with the rudder. In tail wheel-type aircraft this may require significant pressure on the rudder pedal on the downwind side, to compensate for the stronger weathercocking component in this type of aircraft. Use full aileron deflection initially, then as speed increases progressively reduce the amount of deflection to keep the wings level.

As soon as the aircraft is airborne and there is no possibility of settling back on the runway, a co-ordinated turn is made into wind. The turn is stopped and the wings levelled when the new heading compensates adequately for drift. A steady climb is maintained on this heading, which should result in a ground track aligned with the centre-line of the runway. From time to time the term *crab* or *crabbing* may be used to describe an alteration to the heading of an aircraft to compensate for drift. Crabbing is a very descriptive and convenient term, but always bear in mind that the activity being described is relative to the ground only.

Except in the case of a direct head wind or a 90 degree cross-wind, a wind from any forward angle contains both a cross-wind component and a head wind component. A wind blowing at a 90 degree angle contains only a cross-wind component. One of the simpler methods for determining acceptability of cross-winds uses this principle as a basis for calculation.

It is a certification requirement that an aircraft be capable of safe operation in a 90 degree cross-wind provided the speed of the wind does not exceed 20 per cent of the stalling speed of the aircraft in question. This information, in conjunction with the known stalling speed of a particular aircraft, makes it possible to use the cross-wind component graph (Fig 2-38) to derive a general rule for most light aircraft. This method must be used as a guide only, since acceptability of winds of any angle or strength depends on all circumstances involved, including the pilot-in-command's level of competence. Examples of the method used in this interpolation are shown below:

Example 1
Aircraft with a CAS Stalling Speed of 60 mph

Wind (Degrees off Runway)	Permissible Wind Speeds
90 degrees	(0.2 x 60 mph stalling speed) = 12 mph
60 degrees	Using cross-wind component graph = 14 mph
30 degrees	Using cross-wind component graph = 24 mph
15 degrees	Using cross-wind component graph = 45 mph

Example 2
Aircraft with a CAS Stalling Speed of 50 mph

Wind (Degrees off Runway)	Permissible Wind Speeds
90 degrees	(0.2 x 50 mph stalling speed = 10 mph
60 degrees	Using cross-wind component graph = 12 mph
30 degrees	Using cross-wind component graph = 20 mph
15 degrees	Using cross-wind component graph = 38 mph

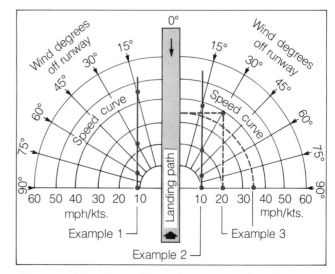

Figure 2-38   Cross-Wind Component Graph

When you have determined that a strong cross-wind is within acceptable limits, it is often important to know the value of the head wind and cross-wind components. Both of these values may be determined by using the graph in Figure 2-38. Say, as an exaggerated example, the wind is 30 degrees off the runway at 40 kts. (Example 3). The point where the 40 knot "speed curve" intersects the 30 degree "wind degrees off runway" line becomes the datum. Draw a vertical line down from the datum, and where it intersects the "mph/kts." line read off the cross-wind component (20 kts.). Draw a horizontal line from the datum to the "runway edge," then from this point parallel the "speed curves" to a point on the "mph/kts." line and read off the head wind component (34 kts.).

Minimum Run and Obstacle Clearance Take-offs

Occasions arise when you will have to carry out special procedures for the purpose of taking off in the shortest distance possible. Some of the reasons necessitating minimum run take-off procedures are:

(1) limited overall field length
(2) snowdrifts, puddles of water, or other similar

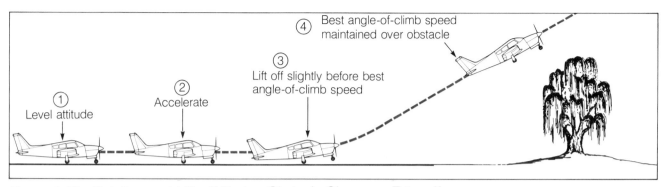

Figure 2-39   Rotation and Lift-off During Obstacle Clearance Take-off

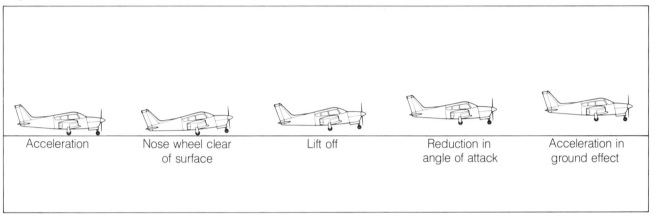

| Acceleration | Nose wheel clear of surface | Lift off | Reduction in angle of attack | Acceleration in ground effect |

Figure 2-40   Soft Field Take-off

hazards which may shorten the available length of an otherwise suitable runway

(3) obstacles at the windward end of the runway or in the take-off flightway (Fig 2-39)

(4) soft or rough-surfaced fields (Fig 2-40).

Whenever a minimum run take-off must be contemplated, consult the take-off-distance tables in the flight manual, taking care to interpolate them carefully against existing conditions of wind velocity, aircraft weight, and altitude. Since the tables assume a firm, level take-off surface, also make adequate allowance for a soft surface or an uphill gradient.

The aircraft flight manual will also state the procedure to follow concerning the use of flap for minimum run take-off performance. For example, in the case of a certain aircraft in general use at training establishments, flap is used provided there is no obstacle at the upwind end. The use of flap is not recommended for obstacle clearance, since the rate of climb of this aircraft deteriorates with flap extended and therefore the benefit of using flaps to shorten the take-off run is lost in the subsequent reduced rate of climb directly after take-off.

In addition to other conditions which can affect minimum run take-off performance, the strength and direction of the wind is a most vital factor. If a cross-wind exists, calculate the components very carefully since ideally the head wind component should have a higher value than the cross-wind component. Only under very unusual circumstances should an intentional minimum run take-off be attempted in a tail wind, or a cross-wind with a tail wind component.

All other factors such as cross-winds, obstacles, etc., taken into account, there are two separate procedures for minimum run take-offs. Which one is to be used depends on the nature of the take-off surface.

(1) Firm, Level Surface. Unless otherwise stated in the aircraft flight manual, this procedure requires that the aircraft's attitude be maintained at the angle which results in the minimum aerodynamic drag during the take-off run. This attitude is similar to the normal cruise attitude and can tempt you to try to lift the aircraft off the ground too soon, resulting in a stalled condition at a very critical point in the take-off. Allow the aircraft to reach the minimum recommended take-off speed before lifting it off the ground. Then, if necessary, accelerate to the best angle of climb speed before assuming a climbing attitude in order to ensure adequate clearance of the obstacle.

Where the need for optimum climb performance immediately after take-off is not an important factor, and following the manufacturer's recommendations, lift the aircraft off the surface at the lowest airspeed that will allow continued safe flight and acceleration to the desired climb speed.

(2) Soft, Loose, or Rough Surface. The procedure for take-off from a soft, rough, snow or slush-covered surface is quite different from that appropriate for a firm, level surface. The weight of the aircraft should be transferred as rapidly as possible from the wheels to the wings as the take-off run proceeds, by maintaining a nose-high attitude with the elevator control. The nose wheel or tail wheel should be lifted off the surface as soon as the elevators become effective. When held at a nose-high attitude throughout the take-off run, the wings will progressively relieve the wheels of more of the aircraft's weight, reducing the rolling resistance caused by surface irregularities or adhesion. If this attitude is maintained, the aircraft will lift clear of the surface at an airspeed slower than a safe climb speed, because of the action of ground effect. The lift-off airspeed must therefore be high enough to allow continued safe flight and acceleration to the desired climb speed. After lift-off, the angle of attack should be reduced gradually, keeping the wheels just clear of the surface until the desired climb speed is reached.

Tail Wind After Take-off

Due to surface friction and other causes, it is possible to have a condition of "no wind" at ground level, but at several feet above the ground sufficient wind to affect climb performance. Should this phenomenon develop into a tail wind aloft, there is a risk of the aircraft not being able to clear obstacles adequately in the climb-out flightway. When the wind is calm or light and very variable at the surface, be suspicious of the wind above ground level and carry out a take-off procedure which makes adequate allowance for the possibility of a tail wind shortly after the aircraft has left the ground.

Hydroplaning

The wheels of an aircraft rolling on a wet paved runway press a "bow wave" ahead of them and a film of water can form, between the tires and the runway, of sufficient strength to "float" an aircraft during the take-off run. Under these conditions the aircraft may drift sideways and brakes can become ineffective, making control of the aircraft difficult at critical points during the take-off. When raindrops appear to bounce on the runway, the possibility of hydroplaning should be suspected. Depressions in the runway which cause extensive "ponding" to occur during heavy rain, or ponding which occurs during spring thaws, may also cause an aircraft to hydroplane during the take-off run. If a take-off must be made under suspected hydroplaning conditions, be prepared to control the aircraft without the

aid of brakes after an estimated ground speed of 30 mph has been achieved.

Ground Effect

Anything that will impede the acceleration of the aircraft during its take-off run, such as mud, snow, surface irregularities, grass (or other vegetation), grade, etc., must be fully considered in respect to the additional take-off distance penalty that these factors may impose. Under these circumstances it would be wise to use the soft field take-off technique, which makes use of phenomenon called *ground effect*. This effect is due to the interference of the surface with airflow patterns about a wing in flight. As a general rule the results of ground effect can be detected up to a height equal to one wing span (of the aircraft being used) above the surface (Fig 2-41). The phenomenon of ground effect has one important aspect which if not recognized can be extremely hazardous. It is possible to lift an aircraft off the ground into ground effect with insufficient power or too great a load to permit it to climb out of ground effect.

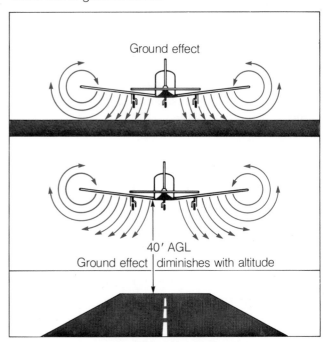

Ground effect

40' AGL
Ground effect | diminishes with altitude

Figure 2-41   Ground Effect

Many of the finer points associated with other than normal take-offs vary as to aircraft type and existing conditions. Aspects of these procedures are continually open to discussion and the apparent solutions will vary with the background and experience of the individual pilot. Such points include whether to apply take-off power before releasing brakes or as the aircraft moves forward, when commencing a take-off; whether to use flaps or not to use flaps; whether to extend flaps before the take-off run commences or as the take-off roll progresses. The answers to these questions are generally outlined in the procedures recommended in the manufacturer's manual, and should be carefully followed. Other points of judgment arise as to the advisability of commencing to build up speed for take-off while moving from the run-up position to the runway centre-line on a short field or obstacle take-off. The decision to follow this technique must be governed by the manufacturer's recommendations, since some types of aircraft suffer an engine failure on the take-off roll following the so-called "rolling take-off." In some aircraft, the fuel will flow to one side of the tank, due to centrifugal force, leaving the outlet momentarily dry and exposing the engine to the possibility of failure at a critical point of the take-off. The amount of fuel in the tanks is another governing factor. During soft field take-offs brakes must be used with caution, since mud can build up in front of the wheel due to incorrect braking action and prevent the aircraft from moving forward again. Also, during a soft field take-off the taxiways and proposed take-off surface must be carefully inspected for extra soft spots. Provided the surfaces are deemed usable, the inertia of the aircraft and perhaps extra power must be used to carry it through these areas. When lining up for a soft field take-off you generally do not require brakes, due to the restraining effect of the ground surface. The advisability of stopping once lined up will be governed by the condition of the take-off surface, the manufacturer's recommended procedures, or a combination of the two.

The base measurement for development of the performance data for a particular aircraft is customarily the performance rendered by the aircraft in a standard atmosphere, or, as it is sometimes called, standard air density. Standard atmosphere is the air density when the barometric pressure is 29.92 inches of mercury and the temperature is 15 degrees Celsius (59 degrees Fahrenheit).

The density of the air plays an important part in the take-off performance of an aircraft. Cold, dry air is denser than hot, moist air and the denser the air, the better the performance. Factors to remember about air density at airports are:

(1) Airport elevation high, air less dense = reduced performance
(2) Ambient air temperature high, air less dense = reduced performance
(3) Relative humidity high, air less dense = reduced performance
(4) Combination of 1, 2, and 3 = poor performance (Fig 2-42).

Good take-off performance can be expected from an aircraft at an airport with a field elevation, say, of 150 feet above mean sea level on a cold day, whereas a poorer performance can be expected from the same aircraft at the same airport on a hot day.

The worst possible take-off (and climb) performance can be expected when the following four conditions are combined:

(1) Air temperature—High (above 15 degrees Celsius)
(2) Airport elevation—High
(3) Atmospheric pressure—Low (below 29.92)
(4) Relative humidity—High

(The above combination represents a high density altitude).

Density altitude is the altitude corresponding to a given density in a standard atmosphere. It is a "condition," not a level of flight. Unless density altitude is known it is difficult to determine the performance of an aircraft accurately, and this can be a very important factor under some conditions of take-off. Density altitude calculations can be resolved very quickly on the pilot's circular slide-rule computer.

Full use should be made of the take-off distance tables in the aircraft flight manual, which show the changes in performance resulting from various airport elevations and air temperatures. The aircraft manufacturer's recommendations are always the best source for this information but should these recommendations not be available, useful take-off performance data may be calculated by using the Koch chart (Fig 2-43).

The straight line (No. 1) used as an example in the Koch chart illustrated shows that an aircraft at an airport with a pressure altitude of 6,000 feet with an outside (ambient) air temperature of 38 degrees Celsius (100 degrees Fahrenheit) requires 220 per cent more take-off distance than the same aircraft would require at sea level in standard atmosphere. Even at a common airport pressure altitude of 1,000 feet, 30 per cent more take-off distance is required if the ambient air temperature is 27 degrees Celsius (80 degrees Fahrenheit) (Line No. 2).

When using the Koch chart remember that the airport altitude factor is pressure altitude. To determine the pressure altitude of an airport upon which the aircraft is standing, set the altimeter barometric pressure scale to 29.92, then read off the altitude in the normal manner. After determining the pressure altitude of the airport, do not forget to reset the altimeter to the actual field elevation or barometric pressure.

The Koch chart indicates typical representative values only. Therefore, if it is available the take-off distance chart in the aircraft flight manual is a preferred reference guide. In addition, the Koch chart may

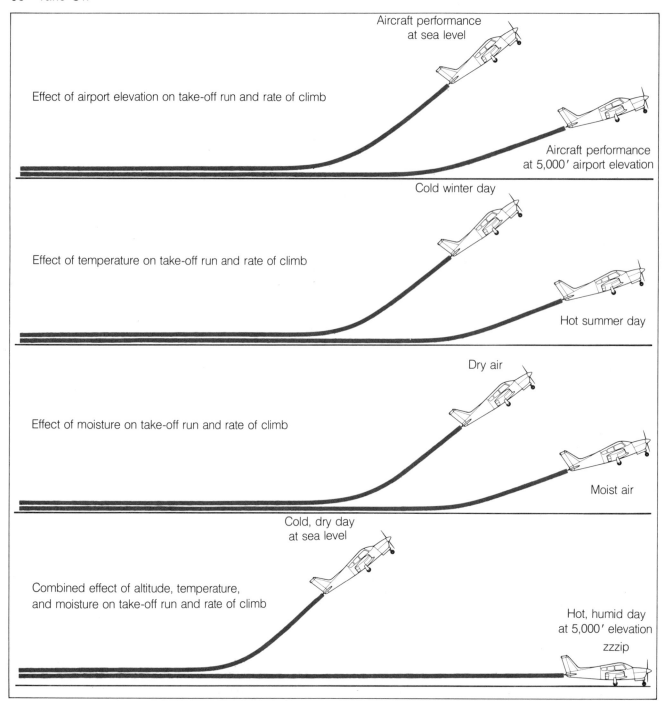

Figure 2-42   Effects of Elevation, Temperature, and Moisture on Take-off Run and Rate of Climb

be conservative when used to calculate the take-off and climb performance of aircraft with supercharged engines.

Wheelbarrowing

Wheelbarrowing may be described as a condition in nose wheel landing-gear equipped aircraft that is encountered when the main wheels are lightly loaded or clear of the runway during take-off or landing. This causes the nose gear to support a percentage of weight greater than normal while providing the only means of steering.

During take-off, wheelbarrowing may occur at relatively low speeds due to the slipstream increasing the lifting effect of the horizontal stabilizer, and excessive forward elevator control pressure being applied during take-off to hold the aircraft on the ground to speeds above those normal for take-off. When taking off in a

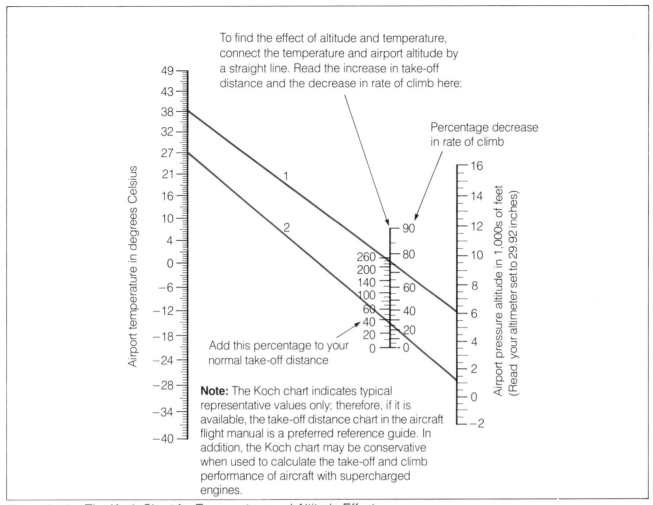

Figure 2-43   The Koch Chart for Temperature and Altitude Effects

cross-wind, or if any other yaw force is introduced at this time, an aircraft in this flight condition tends to pivot about the nose wheel, and if not brought under control quickly may execute a manoeuvre similar to a ground loop in a tail wheel-type aircraft.

Corrective action must be based on a number of factors—i.e., degree of development of the wheelbarrowing, the pilot's proficiency, remaining runway length, and aircraft performance versus aircraft configuration. Only after considering at least these factors should you initiate one of the following corrective measures:

(1) If the aircraft is not pivoting, ease back on the control column to take weight off the nose wheel and continue with the take-off and climb procedure.
(2) If pivoting has begun, relax forward elevator control to lighten the load on the nose wheel and return steering to normal. If pivoting stops, resume the take-off; if pivoting continues, abort the take-off.

Wake Turbulence

Wake turbulence (Fig 2-44) caused by wing tip vortices of departing or arriving aircraft, especially large, heavy aircraft, must be avoided by aircraft about to take off. An aircraft flying into the core of a wing tip vortex will tend to roll with that vortex. It is entirely possible that this induced roll will be at a greater rate than a light aircraft's capability to counteract it.

Wake turbulence from any preceding aircraft will be maximum:

(1) just before the point of touchdown for a landing aircraft; and (2) just after the point of take-off for a departing aircraft.

On take-off, wake turbulence can best be avoided:

(1) if following an aircraft that has just departed, by planning the take-off so as to become airborne prior to the point of take-off of the preceding aircraft. Avoid passing through the flight path of the preceding aircraft.

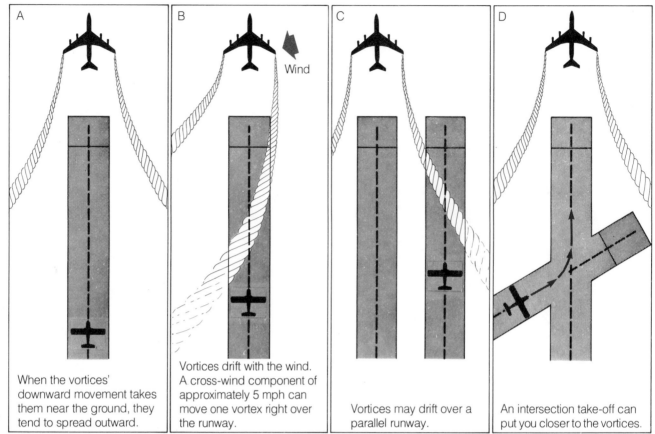

Figure 2-44 Wake Turbulence

A — When the vortices' downward movement takes them near the ground, they tend to spread outward.

B — Wind — Vortices drift with the wind. A cross-wind component of approximately 5 mph can move one vortex right over the runway.

C — Vortices may drift over a parallel runway.

D — An intersection take-off can put you closer to the vortices.

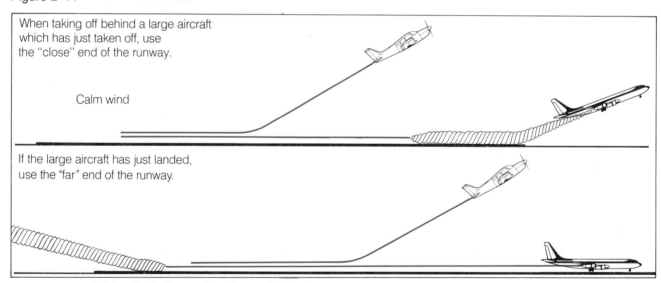

When taking off behind a large aircraft which has just taken off, use the "close" end of the runway.

Calm wind

If the large aircraft has just landed, use the "far" end of the runway.

Figure 2-45 Wake Turbulence Avoidance Procedures

(2) If following an aircraft that has just landed, by planning the take-off so as to become airborne beyond the point of touchdown of the preceding aircraft (Fig 2-45).

Should you have the remotest doubt or indecision concerning wake turbulence on take-off, delay the take-off for up to two minutes to allow the vortices of a landing aircraft to dissipate and up to four minutes in the case of a preceding take-off. The larger the preceding aircraft, the longer the delay. Remember that although the strength of the wind is a vortex dissipation factor, a cross-wind may move or hold a vortex directly in the proposed take-off path.

It is unlikely that a control tower will clear a light aircraft for an immediate take-off in the wake of a large heavy aircraft, but in any case there should be no hesitation whatsoever on the part of the light aircraft pilot in requesting a take-off delay, should such a clearance be given.

Even though a clearance for take-off has been issued, if you consider it safer to wait, or alter your intended operation in any way in the interest of safety or good airmanship, ask the control tower for a revised clearance. The air traffic controller's chief interest is safety of aviation, but he may not be aware of all circumstances, especially a pilot's level of competency when unusual conditions prevail.

At an uncontrolled airport (an airport without a control tower), each pilot-in-command is responsible for control decisions concerning his own aircraft and such decisions must be consistent with safety, good airmanship, and the Air Regulations. In this regard, two of the most important Air Regulations are:

(1) 529. Where an aircraft is in flight or manoeuvring on the ground or water, the pilot-in-command shall give way to other aircraft landing or about to land.

A landing aircraft has priority in the use of the landing area and an aircraft proposing take-off must not usurp this priority in any way. Whether a take-off may be made, in view of the distance a landing aircraft is from the landing area, is a matter of good judgment and courtesy. Never presume that a landing aircraft can always abort its landing in favour of a pilot who has exercised poor judgment in timing his take-off.

(2) 531. No aircraft shall take off or attempt to take off until such time as there is no apparent risk of collision with any other aircraft.

Search the entire sky for other aircraft with which a take-off may conflict. Another aircraft may be landing downwind on the runway; this may be in conflict with the Air Regulations but such an aircraft still has priority over aircraft proposing take-off. The aircraft landing downwind may have reasons compelling it to do so. Do not take off, or position your aircraft for take-off, until a landing aircraft has cleared the runway. When positioned for take-off, the pilot no longer has a view of the runway approach and possible landing traffic.

It is an indication of poor airmanship and lack of courtesy on your part to proceed onto the active runway when you are not fully prepared to take off as soon as the runway is clear. Remain clear of the active runway until you have carefully completed all pre-take-off checks. Do not delay aircraft taxiing behind you by carrying out cockpit procedures which you should have completed at the apron or ramp. If there is some difficulty which may delay your take-off, position your aircraft so that others may pass. Before doing an engine run-up look carefully behind in all directions to ensure that other aircraft will not be affected by your propeller slipstream.

The Circuit

The international (ICAO) terminology for the circuit is "Aerodrome Traffic Circuit." It is defined as: "The specified paths to be flown by aircraft operating in the vicinity of an aerodrome." The circuit is often erroneously referred to as the "traffic pattern." Although the latter does involve the circuit, the correct definition of traffic pattern is: "The geographical path flown by an aircraft after it enters a control zone and until it enters the downwind leg of the Aerodrome Traffic Circuit." (Remember that "aerodrome" is just another word for

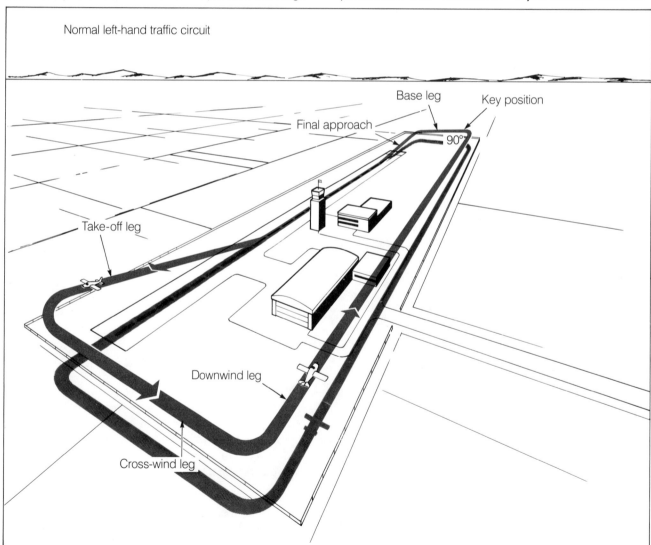

Normal left-hand traffic circuit

Base leg

Key position

Final approach

90°

Take-off leg

Downwind leg

Cross-wind leg

Figure 2-46   Aerodrome Traffic Circuit

"airport" — an "airport" is an aerodrome which has been issued a licence under the authority of the Air Regulations.)

The prime purpose of an orderly and well defined circuit is safety. However, circuit procedures are also fundamental to the execution of good approaches and landings.

The basic pattern of the circuit remains fixed, but its orientation is determined by the heading of the runway in use at the time. A plan view of the circuit (Fig 2-46) shows that it is rectangular in shape and has the following components:

(1) The climb after take-off
(2) The cross-wind leg; (not to be confused with circuit joining cross-wind)
(3) The downwind leg
(4) The base leg
(5) The final approach leg.

In actual practice, at controlled airports it is customary for pilots and controllers to omit the word "leg" when referring to the circuit components, i.e.: "Burton tower / CFABC / downwind;" "CFABC / Burton tower / report turning base." It is recommended that the downwind call be when the aircraft is abeam the control tower.

Unless special conditions exist and there is authorized advice to the contrary, all circuits are left-hand, therefore all turns within the circuit are left turns.

In addition, unless there is authorized advice to the contrary, all normal circuit heights are 1000 feet above ground level.

After take-off there will be a straight climb into wind, normally to a height of 500 feet, and then a 90 degree turn cross-wind. The cross-wind leg is a continuous climb up to circuit height where the aircraft is levelled off. Then a 90 degree turn brings the aircraft onto the downwind leg. The downwind leg is flown so as to track exactly parallel with the intended landing path. On the downwind leg any necessary pre-landing check is made. When past the downwind boundary an appropriate distance, another 90 degree turn is made onto the base leg. When within gliding distance of the landing area, and it is desired to make a gliding approach, the throttle is closed and the aircraft is put into a glide. Just before reaching the intended line of the final leg, another 90 degree turn is made onto the final leg and the aircraft is kept straight until the landing is completed (see Fig 2-46).

The strength of the wind will affect the heading to be steered on the cross-wind and base legs of the circuit. Maintain a track over the ground which is at right angles to the landing path. Thus, during the base leg an aircraft in a very strong wind will be heading well in towards the aerodrome and the landing path, although its path over the ground will be at right angles to the landing path.

On all legs of the circuit it is essential to maintain a good look-out on both sides, and above and below.

The latter part of the circuit is usually called the approach. Technically, the approach to landing commences on the downwind leg, at the turning point from downwind to base leg. Exactly where or when the turn onto the base leg is made will depend largely on the strength of the wind. The stronger the wind, the steeper the angle of descent will be during the final straight approach, and therefore the sooner the turn onto the base leg should be made.

When on the base leg, adjust the heading to allow for drift and judge when to start the glide (or descent) by the angle at which the runway is observed — the stronger the wind the greater this angle should be. Once the descent has begun, you can judge whether the aircraft is going to be too high or too low on the final approach, and correct the approach by appropriate use of flaps or power.

Judge the whole circuit in relation to the runway, and not in relation to other points on the ground. This way your judgment of approaches will improve rapidly and not be upset by changes of runway, landing direction, or aerodrome. It will also help you considerably in judging other types of approaches.

Spacing

It is extremely important that you be constantly aware of the position of other aircraft in the circuit, more particularly those that are ahead of you in the pattern. One of the unforgivable sins is to "cut off" a preceding aircraft by carelessly turning onto the base or final leg out of proper sequence. Maintain a suitable spacing between your aircraft and the one ahead of you, so as to allow time for that aircraft to land and taxi clear of the runway. If you crowd the preceding aircraft it may be necessary for you to execute a missed approach and "go around," which in these circumstances can be an unnecessary waste of flight time. At the same time, overspacing in a busy circuit can also be inconsiderate of others and may invite being cut off yourself by someone endeavouring to fly a more acceptable circuit. Correct spacing is a judgment you must develop as quickly as possible. It takes into account such matters as wind direction and strength, and the circuit speeds of other aircraft. Correct spacing may be accomplished by widening or narrowing your circuit and/or increasing or decreasing airspeed.

Control Zones

A control zone is a controlled airspace about an airport of defined dimensions extending upwards from the surface to a specified height above ground level. Many control zones are designated as "positive control zones," within which special regulations apply. For all practical purposes, civil airports with control towers may be considered as being within positive control zones.

Leaving the Circuit (Controlled Airport)

When an aircraft leaves the circuit after take-off, it does one of two things. It either operates outside the circuit while remaining within the positive control zone, or it leaves the positive control zone. When an aircraft remains within the positive control zone, the control tower will most likely ask that it: (1) remain on the control tower frequency; (2) advise the type of exercise; (3) advise the altitude at which the aircraft will be flown; and (4) advise where the flying will be carried out. When an aircraft intends to leave the positive control zone, permission to cease monitoring the control tower frequency must be granted by the control tower so long as the aircraft is in that tower's positive control zone. The control tower exercises jurisdiction over all VFR traffic within its positive control zone. A VFR aircraft may not operate within a positive control zone without permission from the appropriate control tower, even though the aircraft may be using another airport within the positive control zone.

When leaving the circuit, if the airport has a left-hand traffic pattern you may execute a right-hand turn after take-off only with permission from the control tower. If this permission cannot be granted, continue on runway heading until well clear of the traffic pattern and above circuit height, before turning right.

After leaving the circuit it may be necessary to fly through the positive control zone of another airport at which you do not intend to land. It is compulsory that you make radio contact with the control tower in this zone and remain under its control until out of the zone again. Unless some special prior arrangement is made with the appropriate control tower, aircraft without two-way radio communication should remain clear of positive control zones.

Automatic Terminal Information Service (ATIS) is provided at many larger airports. The recorded broadcast includes weather, runway, and NOTAM information affecting the airport. Where it is provided, you should monitor the ATIS broadcast prior to calling the ATC facility, and inform ATC on first contact that you have received the pertinent information.

Joining the Circuit (Controlled Airport)

When returning to an airport for landing, advise the control tower of your identification, geographical location, or estimated distance in miles and direction from the airport, and altitude. Then request landing instructions. If you are outside the positive control zone you must do this prior to entering the zone. When the control tower gives you clearance "to the circuit" you are expected to join the circuit on the downwind leg at circuit height. The descent to circuit height must be made outside of the area occupied by the circuit.

"Cleared to the circuit" authorizes you to make a right turn, if required, to join cross-wind, or to join the downwind leg provided the right turn is only a partial turn that can be carried out safely (Fig 2-47). When cleared by the control tower for a "straight in" approach, you are authorized to join the circuit on the final approach leg without having executed any other part of the circuit.

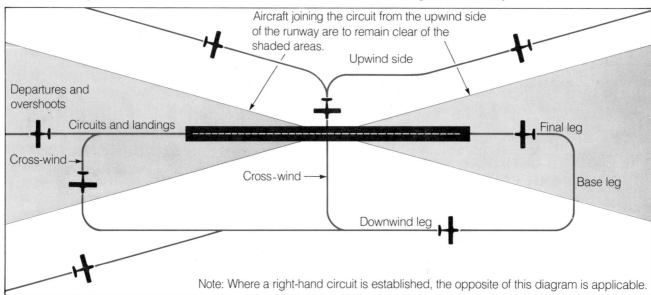

Figure 2-47   Standard Left-Hand Traffic Circuit at Controlled Airports

The same ruling applies to being authorized to join on base leg.

Uncontrolled Airports

An uncontrolled airport is an airport (or aerodrome) which does not have a control tower operating. There may be no air-to-ground radio communication at an uncontrolled airport. However, at many sites there is a mandatory or advisory radio frequency on which communication can be established with a Transport Canada Flight Service Station or a locally based aircraft operator. These facilities exercise no control over aircraft but can be very helpful in advising of surface winds, favouring runway or runway being used by others, known air and ground traffic, runway conditions, weather, etc. Pilots are encouraged to monitor and make use of any radio or unicom communications that may be available at uncontrolled airports, and to transmit position reports and broadcast their intentions while in the circuit.

Aircraft executing a series of take-offs, circuits, and landings should, after each take-off, reach circuit height before joining the downwind leg.

Leaving the Circuit (Uncontrolled Airports)

After take-off, climb straight ahead on the runway heading until well clear of the circuit. All turns should be to the left in the vicinity of the airport, unless a right-hand circuit has been designated. Be especially alert for other aircraft since you do not have the benefit of the extra eyes of a control tower.

Joining the Circuit (Uncontrolled Airports)

When returning to the airport for landing take full advantage of air-to-ground communications for advice. Many conditions can change at an airport after even a short absence. If you cross the airport to make observations, the crossover must be done well above circuit height, and subsequent descent to circuit height should be made on the upwind side. Under normal circumstances, circuit height is 1,000 feet AGL (above ground level).

Normally the runway to use for landing is the one most nearly aligned into wind. However at an uncontrolled airport, the pilot has final authority; therefore, for the safe operation of his aircraft another runway may be used if he deems it necessary.

Aircraft should join the circuit at uncontrolled airports (Fig 2-48) as follows:

(1) From the upwind side: enter cross-wind at circuit height in level flight, then taking account of other traffic, join the downwind leg, or
(2) Straight into downwind leg, at circuit level, in level flight; join the circuit where the downwind leg and cross-wind intersect, taking account of other traffic.

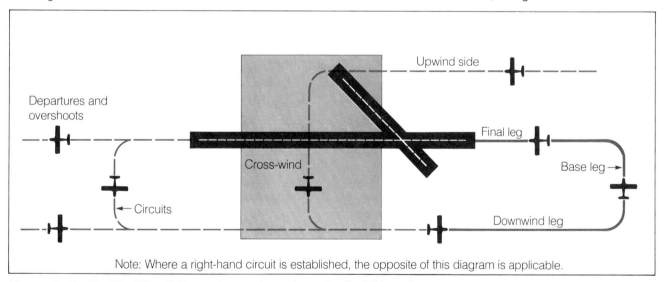

Figure 2-48   Traffic Circuit Procedures at an Uncontrolled Airport

Approach and Landing

It is common for the student to believe that the landing of an aircraft is the sum total of flying; if he can learn this he has learned about all there is to know. This belief, if allowed to persist, produces two unfortunate results: (1) mental hazards, based on attaching undue importance to the landing procedure, which may hinder progress in learning the procedure; and (2) slacking off once reasonable proficiency in executing landings has been attained.

Actually the landing is just another manoeuvre, representing the logical result of all the preparation up to this point, and only one of a series of extensions of principles by which learning has progressed and will continue to progress toward the goal of pilot competency. A landing is the last of a sequence of major manoeuvres, during which the altitude must be controlled, air traffic observed, and the whole process performed safely with an acceptable degree of proficiency.

Landing an aircraft consists of permitting it to contact the ground at the lowest possible vertical speed, and under normal circumstances, at the lowest possible horizontal speed consistent with adequate control. The first step towards reducing the horizontal velocity relative to the ground is to land against the wind; the second step is to obtain the desired airspeed and attitude at the appropriate moment.

Although the approach to landing and the landing itself may be considered as two separate manoeuvres, one is usually an integral part of the other. The success of a landing depends on the type of approach technique used to meet the operational requirements of a specific landing procedure.

Landings may be classed as follows:

(1) *Normal* landing
(2) *Cross-wind* landing
(3) *Short, soft,* and *unprepared field* landing.

Except under the most ideal conditions, even a normal landing involves some degree of cross-wind, and other landings may involve a combination of all three classes. For example, a short field landing will very likely also involve the techniques required for cross-wind landings and those for landing over an obstacle. The techniques for each class of landing will be treated separately in the sequence shown, beginning with the normal landing.

A normal landing is a slow transition from the normal glide attitude to the landing attitude. This transition is referred to as the flare, or the round-out. It is started approximately 15 to 30 feet above the ground, and

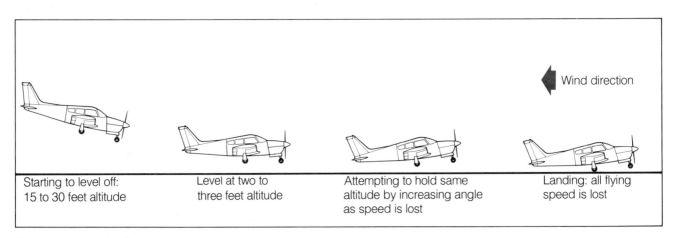

| Starting to level off: 15 to 30 feet altitude | Level at two to three feet altitude | Attempting to hold same altitude by increasing angle as speed is lost | Landing: all flying speed is lost |

Figure 2-49   Landing

progressively increased and continued as altitude is lost until, in tail wheel aircraft, the main landing-gear and the tail wheel touch the ground simultaneously. Aircraft with tricycle landing-gear should contact the runway on the main landing-gear, with no weight on the nose wheel (Fig 2-49).

Your body's sense of motion has been built up a little in glides and stalls, but will not have developed enough at this stage to be of primary assistance in landings, although it will be a factor. Vision is therefore the most important sense you use and you will operate the controls in accordance with it. Reactions on the controls to prevent the aircraft from flying into the ground will be instinctive, but untrained reactions are likely to be wrong, particularly as to degree and often as to type as well.

Accurate estimation of distance and depth, besides being a matter of practice, depends how clearly objects are seen. It requires that your vision be focused properly so that important objects stand out as clearly as possible. Speed blurs objects at close range; nearby objects seem to run together while objects farther away stand out clearly. At the time of landing you should focus ahead of the aircraft, at about the same distance as you would in a car travelling at the same speed. The distance at which the vision is focused should be proportionate to the speed of the aircraft. Thus, as speed decreases, the distance ahead of the aircraft at which it is possible to focus sharply becomes closer; therefore the focus should be brought closer according-ly. However, if your vision is focused too closely, or straight down, objects become blurred and reactions will be either too abrupt or delayed too long.

At the very outset, form the habit of keeping one hand on the throttle control throughout the landing. If a situation suddenly arises that requires an immediate application of power, the time necessary for recognizing the problem, moving the hand to the throttle, opening it, and having the engine respond, is too great. Bounces are common at the initial stages of training and proper use of the throttle at the exact instant is imperative.

In addition to landings at the prescribed approach speed, and power settings to control the descent, at every opportunity you should practise landings from full glides, with the engine throttled back to idling. This type of approach is very necessary to develop the judgment and planning required for forced approach procedures.

When the aircraft is within 15 to 30 feet from the ground, the flare (round-out) should begin. Once started, it should progress continuously until the aircraft is on the ground. If your speed is correct, as back pressure is applied to the control column the aircraft will begin to lose speed and start to settle. As the ground "comes up," ease the control column farther and farther back. This movement of the elevator control is timed so that the slow, smooth, continuous, backward movement

holds the aircraft just above the surface until the desired landing attitude is attained. Nose wheel aircraft should contact the ground on the main wheels first, with no weight on the nose wheel. In tail wheel aircraft all wheels should touch the ground simultaneously, with the elevator control all the way back and the throttle closed. This requires the development of fine timing, technique, and judgment of height and distance.

Once the actual process of landing is started, the elevators should not be pushed forward to offset any ordinary error in backward movement of the controls. If too much back pressure has been exerted, this pressure may be either slightly relaxed or held constant, depending on the degree of error. In some cases it may be necessary to advance the throttle slightly to compensate for a loss of speed.

When the aircraft has come to within 2 or 3 feet of the ground, check its descent by further back pressure on the elevator control. At this point the aircraft will be very close to its stalling speed; therefore backward pressure does not increase or maintain height as might be expected. Instead, it slows up the settling phase, so that the aircraft will touch the ground gently in the desired landing attitude. The point at which the descent is checked makes all the difference to the subsequent landing. Much research has been done with a view to finding out how an experienced pilot judges this point. Here are some suggestions which may be helpful:

(1) Try to judge the distance of the ground ahead—i.e., along the path of glide.
(2) Try to judge that point at which the ground seems to be coming up so rapidly that something must be done about it.
(3) Watch the ground where touchdown is expected. When it appears to start to approach rapidly, check the rate of descent by easing the control column back.
(4) Note the point at which the whole area of the ground seems to expand.
(5) Note the point at which movement of ground suddenly becomes apparent.

The completion of the touchdown should be judged by the change in attitude of the aircraft rather than by movements of the control column. The attitude should be changed by reference to the landing horizon (edge of the aerodrome) and the front of the aircraft.

Once a tail wheel aircraft is on the ground, the control column should be held as far back as firmly as possible until the aircraft comes to a stop. This will shorten the landing roll and tend to prevent bouncing and skipping of the tail, together with improving directional control.

In the case of a nose wheel aircraft, allow the nose wheel to lower gently to the runway of its own accord as the forward speed decreases and the elevators lose their effectiveness. Do not relax your attention at this point. Keep straight. This type of aircraft should not normally be "flown on" and held on the runway with excessive speed, since this may impose excessive stress on the nose wheel and possibly cause the undesirable condition known as wheelbarrowing, discussed in Exercise 16.

When the initial stage of landing instruction has been completed, you will be required to plan the approach and landing while the aircraft is on the downwind leg of the traffic circuit. This may be done by visualizing the flight path, or by referring to the aircraft ahead in the circuit, and estimating where you will reduce power and where you will make the turn onto final approach to land on the landing area in use. As practice progresses, the descent should be initiated by reducing the power and airspeed to produce the desired flight path on the base leg, and then making a 90 degree descending turn onto final approach. When the descent has been started, make drift corrections on the base leg to follow a ground track which will approximate a right angle to the runway. The base leg should be flown to the point where a turn of medium bank will bring the aircraft to the final approach directly in line with the landing runway. This turn must be completed at a safe altitude, which will depend on the elevation of the terrain at this point, and the height of any obstructions. Make the turn to final approach long enough to estimate the point of touchdown and allow for any necessary reductions of power and airspeed in preparation for the landing. This will require some planning for the starting point and radius of the turn.

Flaps and Trim

To avoid undershooting a runway, there is often a natural tendency to be too high on the normal approach,

with the result that height must be lost when this becomes apparent. Older techniques got rid of the excess of height by side-slipping, s-turns, or slipping turns. Today it is considered that the last 500 feet of a normal approach should be straight, without any slipping or turning, and that height should be controlled by the use of flap. Extending the flaps changes the airflow pattern over the top of the wing, under the bottom of the wing, and around the tail plane, all of which affects the trim requirements of an aircraft on the approach to landing. Thus corrective control and/or trim action is required to maintain the desired rate of descent and airspeed.

A good landing is invariably the result of a well executed approach, which in its turn depends upon the visual maintenance of the desired approach slope at a constant angle. One method of achieving this is by using the perspective phenomenon. A runway appears to change its shape as the pilot's observation point changes. For example, seen from directly overhead a runway will appear wider at the approach end than at the opposite end. When a constant approach angle is maintained, the apparent configuration of a runway will also remain constant. The pilot sees the runway as a 4-sided figure with the approach width much greater than that of the far end, and the runway sides of equal length but converging towards the horizon. If the approach angle is made steeper, the runway will appear to grow longer and narrower. If the approach angle is made more shallow the runway appears to grow shorter and wider.

Although the runway area steadily grows larger as the approach progresses, so long as the relationship of the sides of the runway configuration remains the same the approach angle is remaining constant and touchdown will be near the threshold (Fig 2-50).

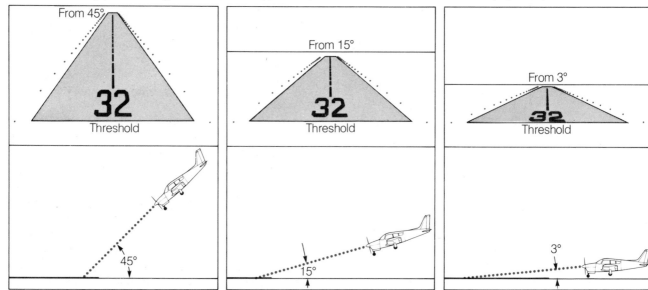

Figure 2-50   A Runway as It Appears from Different Angles

Cross-Wind Landings

It is not always possible or practical to land directly into the wind. Consequently, the principles involved in cross-wind landings must be learned and practised until they offer no difficulty or hazard. A significant change in wind direction is possible between the time an aircraft takes off and the time it lands, even during one circuit, so that it is important that you be able to cope with cross-winds before your first solo.

An aircraft landing directly into the wind tends to maintain a straight heading while it is rolling on (or about to touch down on) the runway, with minimum control assistance from the pilot. However, in a cross-wind, which is any wind affecting the aircraft at an angle to its longitudinal axis, a more complex situation exists, which if not properly attended to can cause a loss of control. The landing heading of an aircraft is normally determined by the direction in which the runway is oriented, rather than by the actual wind direction. Therefore, an aircraft landing in a cross-wind has the wind striking it from one side or the other while it is in contact with the ground, and due to the aircraft's inherent tendency to weathercock it is being forced off its intended heading. Prior to landing, the aircraft will tend to drift across the runway instead of running true to the centre-line. If no corrective action is taken an undesirable side force is exerted on the landing-gear when it touches the surface. The same condition will occur if the path of the aircraft is held true to the centre-line, with drift compensated for by crabbing, and the wheels allowed to touch the surface while not aligned with the direction of the runway.

Cross-wind landings are normally a little harder to manage than cross-wind take-offs. This is mainly due to the difference in the difficulties presented in maintaining control over the aircraft while speed is decreasing instead of increasing, as in the take-off. During take-off, as the speed of the aircraft increases, aerodynamic control of the aircraft becomes progressively more positive; as the aircraft's speed decreases, following touchdown, the effect of this control decreases. Unless you have absolutely no doubt as to the safety of the proposed manoeuvre, before attempting a landing in a cross-wind, other than a very slight one, consult the Cross-Wind Component Chart (Fig 2-38) in Exercise 16. It is applied as in a cross-wind take-off.

There are two basic methods for counteracting drift while executing a cross-wind landing; a third procedure evolves through combined use of the two basic methods and is employed by experienced pilots when unusual or special circumstances prevail (Fig 2-51).

The side-slip, or wing down method, of counteracting drift is probably the most popular of the two basic

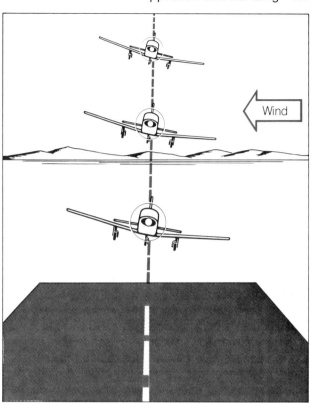

Figure 2-51 Landing in a Cross-Wind

methods. It affords the important advantage of continuity of general flight control positioning, from before touchdown to the end of the landing roll, and will compensate adequately for acceptable cross-winds under most conditions. When using this method, avoid initiating the slip too far back on the final approach unless there are other reasons for slipping. As you approach the landing area, and drift becomes apparent, side-slip into wind sufficiently to counteract this drift. Keep the longitudinal axis of the aircraft aligned with the centre-line of the runway by use of the rudder. On touchdown devote all possible attention to keeping the aircraft rolling in a straight line to forestall any tendency for the aircraft to ground loop. The aileron control should be held toward the upwind wing after contact with the ground to prevent it from rising out of control.

When the side-slip method is used, the upwind main wheel will make contact with the surface first. However, when this occurs the downwind side of the aircraft is still airborne and under normal circumstance the upwind wheel is not subjected to undue weight or impact stress.

The second basic method for eliminating drift when landing in a cross-wind requires much skill, excellent timing, and a great deal of practice and experience. For these reasons it is seldom used in elementary training. With this method the aircraft is maintained on a heading (crabbed) into wind so that the flight path of the aircraft is aligned with the runway centre-line. This means that the longitudinal axis of the aircraft is not aligned with the intended landing path and if contact with the surface is allowed in this condition, there is a risk of damaging the landing-gear or subsequent difficulty in controlling the aircraft. Therefore, at the precise moment prior to touchdown the longitudinal axis of the aircraft must be swung into line with the runway, primarily by coarse use of rudder. This method requires prompt and accurate rudder action to line up the aircraft exactly with its direction of travel over the ground at the instant of contact. If contact is made too soon the aircraft will land with crab; if contact is too late, it will land with drift. Either will impose sideloads on the landing-gear and impart ground looping tendencies. Since the safety factor of the upwind wing being low is absent, a gust at the wrong moment can easily cause trouble.

Short, Soft, and Unprepared Field Landings

Approach

The objective when landing in short, soft, or unprepared landing fields is to touch down on the desired spot at the lowest possible airspeed commensurate with maximum safety and control. The aircraft is normally manoeuvred so as to cross the threshold, with flaps extended, at the airspeed recommended by the aircraft manufacturer. This airspeed is normally shown in the aircraft flight manual or pilot operating handbook, together with tables for converting calibrated airspeed to indicated airspeed. When approaching for a landing under strong wind conditions, the necessity for a reduced approach speed diminishes as the wind speed increases. In gusty wind conditions it is advisable to add an amount equal to half the gust factor to the calculated approach speed. For example, if the wind is gusting from 20 to 40, the gust factor is 20; therefore, an approach which would normally be flown at 65 should be increased to 75 to allow for gusts. The altitude above the threshold for any given

circumstance is largely determined by the height of the obstructions in the aircraft's approach path.

Power

The use of power for this type of approach is desirable because it allows a more accurate control of descent. When this is done, very little change in the aircraft's pitch attitude is necessary to make necessary corrections in the approach slope. When making a final approach at the recommended airspeed, the initiation of the flare must be judged accurately to avoid stalling, or flying into the ground. Leave power on until the landing flare is completed.

Touchdown

The aircraft should touch down at its minimum controllable airspeed, in approximately the pitch attitude which results in a power-off stall. Nose wheel-type aircraft should be held in this attitude as long as the elevators remain effective, and tail wheel types should be held in the three-point attitude during braking action.

The retraction of the flaps after touchdown must be determined by the procedure recommended in the flight manual for the aircraft, or by the instructor. The aerodynamic type braking produced by the flaps may be more effective than the use of wheel brakes, but conversely, the effect of wheel brakes may be reduced so long as the flaps are left extended. In an aircraft with retractable landing-gear, exercise care in raising the flaps during the landing roll to avoid unintentional gear retraction.

Soft or Unprepared Fields. Hold the nose wheel clear of the surface as long as possible and use brakes with care to prevent excessive loads on the nose gear (Fig

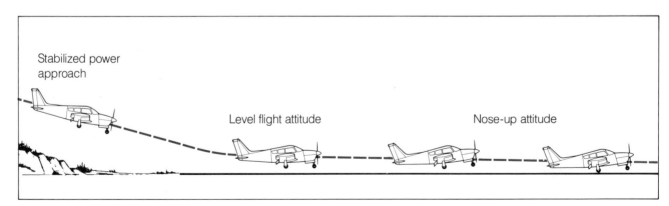

Stabilized power approach

Level flight attitude

Nose-up attitude

Figure 2-52 Soft Field Landing with Full Flaps

2-52). In tail wheel-type aircraft, the tail wheel should touch down with or just before the main wheels, and should be held down with the elevators throughout the landing roll.

The use of flaps for soft or unprepared field landings must be governed by the conditions and circumstances. In low wing aircraft particularly, the flaps may suffer damage from mud, rocks, or slush thrown up by the wheels. On soft surfaces heavy braking is usually not required and may be undesirable, imposing destructive loads on the nose wheel, or tend to initiate a nose-over in the tail wheel-type aircraft.

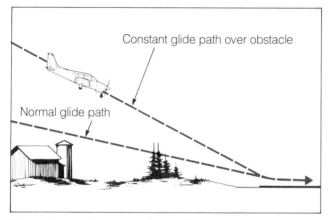

Figure 2-53   Approach Angle Comparison

therefore, for any wind change that may affect the safety of an operation into (or out of) short, soft, or unprepared fields.

Landing Run

It can be said that the objective of any landing is to use as short a landing run as is consistent with safety and good judgment. Several factors which can lengthen the landing run must therefore be taken into account. Identifying them requires knowledgeable observation, and good judgment and skill are then needed to compensate for them adequately. Some of these factors are:

(1) Cross-Winds. The skills required for this factor have been adequately covered in this exercise; however, when contemplating a landing in a cross-wind, give due consideration to the diminished head wind component. In fact, in cross-winds of 70 to 90 degrees other control factors make it necessary to make allowances in the length of the landing run as though a no-wind condition existed.

(2) Light, Shifting Winds. Under these conditions you may be wise to allow for a landing run length that the aircraft would experience under no-wind conditions.

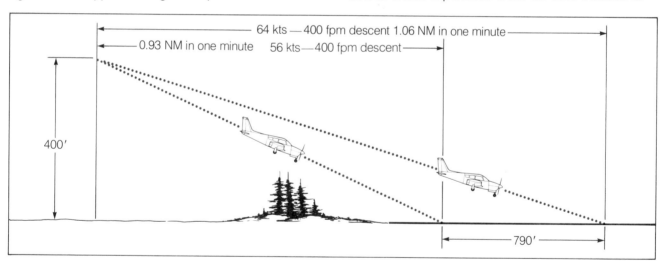

Figure 2-54   Descent Path Comparison at the Same Rate of Descent

Landing over an Obstacle. Landing over an obstacle (Figs 2-53 and 2-54) is an approach procedure rather than a landing procedure and invariably requires the same techniques as a short field. Very often it must also encompass landing procedures required for soft and/or unprepared fields.

Wind Shear. Wind shear is usually associated with weather phenomena only, but a serious change in wind strength or even a wind reversal can be caused by lines of trees, buildings, bodies of water, etc. Keep alert,

(3) Tail Winds. Occasions may occur when you have no alternative to accepting a tail wind. Provided weather and other conditions permit, use the short field landing technique, not only to bring the landing run more into keeping with a normal into wind landing, but also to reduce the ground speed at which the wheels make contact with the ground. To understand the effect of a tail wind on a typical light aircraft performing a normal landing on a hard surfaced runway with a pilot of medium skill, consider the following.

With flaps extended until it comes to rest, and only

moderate use of brake towards the end of the landing run, a certain aircraft touching down at 60 mph in a 20 mph head wind requires a landing run of 800 feet. The same aircraft in a 20 mph tail wind requires a landing run of 1600 feet, with moderate to heavy braking starting at the 800 foot point. When an aircraft must be landed in a tail wind, retract the flaps and place all controls in the neutral position as quickly as possible after the aircraft is positively on the ground to stay.

(4) Runway Gradient. When constructing an airport, the construction engineer does all he can to provide a landing area without any gradient. However, this is almost impossible to do and in many cases there may be a considerable downgrade or upgrade to a runway. This situation may be amplified considerably at remote airstrips or fields not primarily constructed as aircraft manoeuvring areas. Even a relatively imperceptible downgrade can increase the landing run considerably. When a downgrade is readily perceptible, and this often is the case in a precautionary landing, all the factors must be carefully assessed and perhaps a decision to land uphill with a slight tail wind may have to be made. Some of the factors to consider here are: degree of gradient, strength of wind, length of landing area, type and condition of surface, obstacles on approach, condition of aircraft braking system, and the skill and experience of the pilot.

(5) Gross Weight. Operating conditions being equal, the heavier an aircraft is, the longer a landing run it will require. The reasons for this fact are basic, but it is surprising how often it is ignored when a marginal landing area is being assessed. An unbraked light aircraft in still air (empty weight 1000 lbs, gross weight 1500 lbs) will roll an additional 5.3 inches for every pound of load between its empty weight and its gross weight. With pilot only and half its fuel load (total fuel 70 gals.) it will roll, say, 500 feet after touching down. With a full fuel load and a passenger (260 more pounds), it will roll an additional 138 feet. Under normal conditions this may not be too important, but with a short field, obstacles on the approach, a slippery surface, and a light and variable wind, it becomes increasingly significant.

(6) Grass Surfaces. A suitably sized, well maintained grass area, free of soft spots, depressions or protrusions, probably offers one of the best landing surfaces for light aircraft. A grass surface helps absorb the shock of a hard landing and is much more tolerant of a landing made without sufficient compensation for cross-wind drift or imprudent sudden application of brake. In addition, even short clipped grass will offer significant resistance to the roll potential of the wheels, this resistance becoming greater as the aircraft slows

down. The end result is that a grassy surface which is suitable in other respects will afford a much shorter landing roll than you could expect from a paved surface. However, if you are making a landing into a short grassy field and you know that braking action will be required, it is also important to know that if the grass is wet, or even damp with dew, the wheels will skid very easily and provide up to 30 per cent less braking capability than a wet paved surface. One rule of thumb is: the greener the wet grass the more slippery the surface. To illustrate this point, float planes have landed and successfully taken off again on wet, lush grass.

(7) Wet Runways — Hydroplaning. When hydroplaning occurs, the tires of the aircraft are completely separated from the actual runway surface by a thin film of water. They will continue to hydroplane until a reduction in speed permits the tire to regain contact with the runway. This speed will be considerably below the speed at which hydroplaning commences. Under these conditions, tire traction drops to almost negligible values and in some cases the wheel will stop rotating entirely. The tires will provide no braking capability and will not contribute to the directional control of the aircraft. The resultant increase in stopping distance is impossible to predict accurately, but it has been estimated to increase as much as 700 per cent. Further, it is known that a 10 knot cross-wind will drift an aircraft off the side of a 200 foot wide runway in approximately 7 seconds under hydroplaning conditions. When hydroplaning is suspected, release the brakes immediately, then reapply a very slight pressure. This pressure may be gradually increased as the aircraft slows down, but be prepared to release the brakes and reapply pressure as often as necessary.

(8) Wheelbarrowing. On landing, take care not to allow the nose wheel of a nose wheel equipped aircraft to touch the ground first, or simultaneously with the main wheel, if compensating for drift in a cross-wind. The nose wheel is not structured to bear the landing impact load nor accept major surface irregularities it may encounter at the high touchdown speed. If the nose wheel is steerable it may be cocked to one side when compensating for drift and if it is allowed to contact the runway at touchdown speed in this position, the aircraft may develop a swing and/or the nose wheel may be damaged. Nose wheel-type aircraft are normally landed using a procedure in which the nose wheel is held off the ground as long as practical unless any difficulty is experienced in maintaining direction. Nose wheel-type aircraft should not be flown onto the runway with excess speed, but under gusty and turbulent conditions the nose wheel may be lowered to the ground sooner than usual to prevent the aircraft from skipping or lifting off again.

Touching down on the runway with the nose wheel before the main wheels may also produce wheelbarrowing. You may remember that wheelbarrowing is a condition encountered when the main wheels are lightly loaded or clear of the runway and the nose wheel is firmly in contact with the runway. This causes the nose gear to support a greater than normal percentage of weight while providing the only means of steering. In the extreme condition, a loss of directional control may ensue at a very critical point in the landing procedure. Wheelbarrowing may occur if the aircraft is allowed to touch down with little or no rotation and the pilot tries to hold the aircraft on the ground with forward pressure on the elevator control. This often occurs as a result of the use of excessive approach speeds, particularly in a full flap configuration. In a cross-wind the aircraft in this situation tends to pivot (yaw) rapidly about the nose wheel, in a manoeuvre very similar to a ground loop in a tail wheel-type aircraft. Other indications of wheelbarrowing are wheel skipping and/or extreme loss of braking effect when the brakes are applied.

Wheelbarrowing incidents have occurred during cross-wind landings in aircraft equipped with nose wheel steering when the "slip" technique for cross-wind correction is being used. On most training aircraft the nose wheel steers when rudder is applied; for this reason, such landings require careful rudder operation just prior to and during touchdown.

Corrective Action (Wheelbarrowing). Corrective action must be based on a number of factors, i.e., degree of development of the condition, the pilot's proficiency, remaining runway length, and aircraft performance. After considering these factors, you should initiate the following corrective measures:

(1) Close the throttle, relax forward elevator pressure to aft of the neutral position to lighten the load on the nose gear, and return steering and braking to normal. If the flaps can be retracted safely, additional braking will be obtained on dry runways.
(2) If control can be regained and adequate aircraft performance and runway are available, abort the landing and go around again.

A *ground loop*, generally associated with tail wheel equipped aircraft, is defined as: "A violent uncontrollable turn resulting from failure to correct (or overcorrecting) a swing on landing (or take-off)." An undesirable turn during the ground operation of an aircraft is generally referred to as a *swing*. A swing may be caused by any of the following:

(1) Touching down while crabbing into wind
(2) Touching down when the aircraft is drifting sideways

(3) A cross-wind acting on the fuselage and rudder, causing an aircraft to weathercock into wind
(4) Allowing the upwind wing to rise, which combined with weathercocking effects on the tail causes a swing into wind
(5) Failing to control a wheel landing properly: when the tail settles onto the runway, heading control changes from rudder to tail wheel and during the transition period, a ground swing can develop
(6) Incorrect recovery action for drift after a bounce, which has the same effect as landing with drift.

To prevent a swing from developing into a ground loop in a tail wheel aircraft, you must take immediate action. Keep the control column fully back and apply opposite rudder. If rudder alone is insufficient to stop a high-speed swing, open the throttle fully to make the rudder more effective. The application of power has the secondary advantage of pulling the aircraft forward, and helps to resist the turning moment.

Never attempt to realign the aircraft with the runway until you have regained positive control. If the landing is doubtful, or if you are starting to get into trouble, open the throttle and go around again, as long as you are positive there is adequate runway or open space to do so. In gusty cross-wind conditions, retract the flaps as soon as the aircraft is firmly on the ground. Flaps provide more surface for a cross-wind to act upon; therefore if they are retracted there will be less swing effect.

Wheel Landings

As you gain experience, you may carry out wheel landings in tail wheel-type aircraft in high winds and gusty conditions. The approach should be normal with or without power, to the point where the descent is checked. Then slow the airspeed to the point at which the aircraft settles. As the wheels contact the runway, apply some forward pressure to hold the wheels on the ground and to decrease the angle of attack of the wings, so as to prevent "ballooning" due to wind gusts. The aircraft should be held on the wheels in a nearly level attitude until it has slowed sufficiently to ensure full control in a three-point attitude under existing conditions. Due to the relatively low wing loading, it is frequently difficult to keep a light aircraft on the ground after a wheel landing, and as a general rule normal three-point landings should be made.

As speed gradually decreases in the landing roll, a transition point is reached in tail wheel aircraft at which the rudder ceases to provide adequate directional control. At this point the tail wheel must be positively and firmly on the ground so that the aircraft may be directionally controlled by the action of the steerable tail wheel. Keep the control column well back until the aircraft is clear of the runway and in the taxiing mode.

Landing Irregularities

If in any doubt of the safety of a landing, the best remedy is to overshoot and carry out another circuit. However, if you are positive that a safe landing can be made it is permissible to take recovery action.

(1) Bounce. Due to touching the runway prematurely the aircraft may bounce into the air again. Take action as follows:

(a) If airspeed is high and the bounce is small, release some of the backward pressure on the control column, allow the aircraft to descend, then, at the correct height, flare out into the landing attitude again.
(b) If the airspeed is low, and/or the bounce is high, apply power to assist in the round-out to prevent the aircraft from stalling.

(2) High Flare. If the flare is premature or too sudden the aircraft may start to climb and be too high. Check the backward pressure on the control column and allow the aircraft to descend to the correct flare altitude. If airspeed is low or the distance above ground very high, apply enough power to complete a proper flare. Close the throttle before attempting to regain the landing attitude, then flare out into the landing attitude again.

(3) Drift. The recovery action for bounce or ballooning has probably eliminated any original correction for drift, therefore drift correction must be reintroduced.

Overshooting

The decision to overshoot because of a poor approach or landing rests with the pilot. Occasionally, however, the control tower may ask you to go round again.

As soon as the decision to overshoot has been taken, apply full power, accelerate to a safe climb speed in level flight, reduce flap extension as required according to type, and raise the nose to the climbing attitude. Keep straight as the throttle is opened, and roughly trim off the pressure on the control column. Start the climb, and when you have firm control of the aircraft, raise the flaps, adjust the climbing speed, and retrim.

If a bad approach, flare or landing is the cause of the overshoot, and the remaining portion of the run-way is clear of other aircraft, it is permissible to climb straight ahead. However, if you have been forced to overshoot for some reason while on the approach, it is difficult to see ahead and below. Move over to the right side of the runway centre-line, fly parallel to the runway, and while climbing out keep a look-out for other traffic.

It is a general rule that if carburettor heat is in the "on" position during the approach to landing, it should be placed in the "off" position as soon as possible after power is applied on the overshoot procedure. However, be guided in this matter by the aircraft flight manual and/or the rules of the training authority.

Wake Turbulence

Wake turbulence, generated by preceding large heavy aircraft, should be avoided by lighter aircraft at all times but especially during approaches and landings.

Since vortices are subject to many variable factors (size, weight, and speed of the aircraft and air conditions) it is not possible to forecast their presence accurately. However, it should be remembered that the vortices are carried by the ambient wind and have a downward movement imparted to them when they are shed, and an outward movement near the ground, due to cushion effect.

(1) When it is necessary to operate behind a large heavy aircraft, remain above the flight path of that aircraft.
(2) When preparing to land remember that wake turbulence from any preceding aircraft will be maximum:
(a) just before the point of touchdown for a landing aircraft; and
(b) at the point of take-off for a departing aircraft.
(3) On landing, wake turbulence can best be avoided:
(a) if following an aircraft that just departed, by planning your approach to land near the approach end of the runway so as to be down before reaching the point where the preceding aircraft took off
(b) if following an aircraft that has just landed, by planning your approach so as to stay above the flight path of the preceding aircraft and to touch down beyond the point where the preceding aircraft touched down (Fig 2-55).
(4) Remember, even though a clearance for take-off or landing has been issued, if you believe it is safer to wait, to use a different runway, or in some other way to alter your intended operation, ask the controller for a revised clearance.

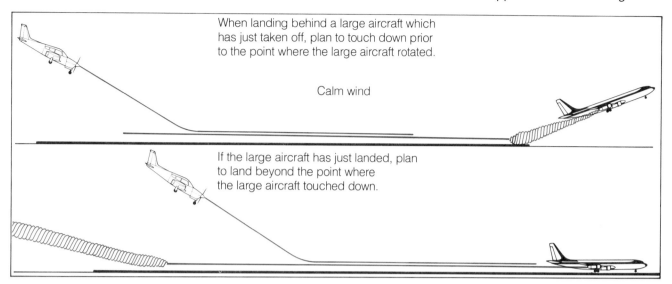

When landing behind a large aircraft which has just taken off, plan to touch down prior to the point where the large aircraft rotated.

Calm wind

If the large aircraft has just landed, plan to land beyond the point where the large aircraft touched down.

Figure 2-55   Landing behind a Large Aircraft

Visual Illusions

Visual illusions are frequently mentioned by accident investigators as contributing factors in approach and landing accidents. How do these illusions occur? Recent research has thrown light on these little understood phenomena.

In approaching a runway, you will customarily adjust your glide path in accordance with what you see. You are used to a visual relationship between the altitude and the position of the aircraft and the width of the runway below. When other visual references are scarce — at night, for example — you will tend to rely heavily on that spatial relationship. If you are accustomed to landing on runways of similar width, you may be deceived in your visual approach to a runway of a different width — especially if the length-width proportions of that runway appear to be much the same early in the approach.

If you are used to a runway 100 feet wide, when you approach a runway (say, 50 feet wide) the smaller target may give the illusion that you are higher than you should be, thereby influencing you to descend to a lower than normal altitude before round-out. If the error is not corrected in time, this could result in "driving the aircraft into the ground," or impacting the runway before flaring out (Fig 2-56).

Conversely, if the unfamiliar runway is significantly wider (say, 150 feet wide), you may experience the illusion of being lower than you actually are. This would influence you to make a higher than normal round-out, possibly resulting in stalling out over the runway (Fig 2-57).

Another deception may be created by the slope of the runway which, in mountainous country, may amount to as much as three to six degrees from level. A sloping runway can mislead you into flying an approach that also may be too high or too low for safety. When setting up your approach, you are guided in part by the angle at

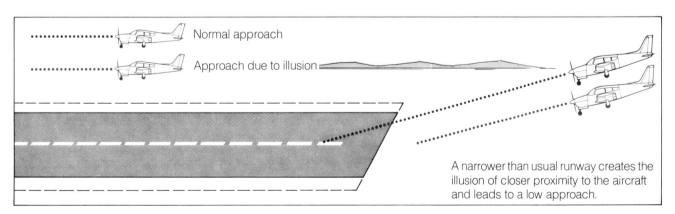

Normal approach

Approach due to illusion

A narrower than usual runway creates the illusion of closer proximity to the aircraft and leads to a low approach.

Figure 2-56   Illusion Caused by a Narrow Runway

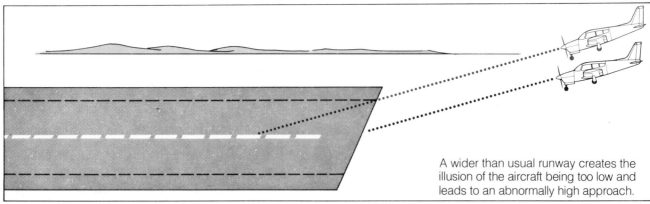

A wider than usual runway creates the illusion of the aircraft being too low and leads to an abnormally high approach.

Figure 2-57   Illusion Caused by a Wide Runway

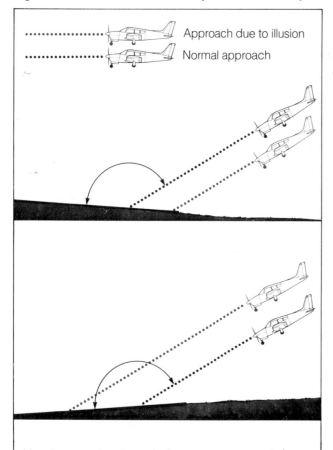

Approach due to illusion

Normal approach

Visual approaches to upsloping runways appear to be steeper than normal because the angle between the glide path and the runway is smaller than usual. With a downsloping runway, the angle formed to a normal approach path is greater and the pilot may compensate by flying a higher approach.

Figure 2-58   Illusions Caused by Sloping Runways

which you view the runway. Even a relatively small upslope can give the illusion that you are higher than you should be, thereby misleading you into making a lower than normal approach. Because of the upslope, extra pitch change is required during round-out, and deceleration is more rapid (Fig 2-58).

Similarly, when the ground slopes away from your landing aircraft, the angle of descent will appear more obtuse than normal, so you may fly a higher than normal approach and consequently find yourself coming in fast and high over the threshold. Sloping runway problems are accentuated at night when runway lights may provide the only visible reference to the ground.

To avoid the visual illusions created by sloping runways or variable runway width in making visual approaches to unfamiliar airports, note the size and terrain conditions of destination airports when planning the flight. Plan to take advantage of visual aids such as VASI lights (where available) or other visual references. A little preparation may be all you need, although it is sometimes helpful to overfly an unfamiliar field before making an approach to land. However, such things as the slope of a runway cannot be accurately judged from the air: that information should be tucked away in your head or written down before you begin the flight.

Air Density

The aircraft flight manual usually contains tables indicating the effect that airport elevation and ambient temperature have on the length of the landing run. *Density altitude* is the key term in determining the length of landing run required; it may be reviewed by referring to Exercise 16.

The required landing run length of an aircraft is based on its performance in standard atmosphere — i.e. 29.92 inches of mercury and an ambient temperature of 15 degrees Celsius. Rules of thumb of the effect of temperature and pressure varying from standard are:

(1) If the air is warmer the landing run will be longer.
(2) If the aerodrome is higher the landing run will be longer.
(3) If the air is warmer and the aerodrome is higher the landing run will be even longer.

Landing Clearance

At a controlled airport, you must receive clearance to land from the control tower; normally this clearance is forthcoming without being asked for but on occasion it must be requested. If a clearance is not received by radio, signal light, or pyrotechnic, do not land. Unless an emergency exists which can be fully substantiated, overshoot. After a landing, vacate the active runway without delay; quite often the control tower will request that this be expedited to make way for other approaching traffic. When a control tower makes this request, co-operation is being solicited, nothing more; the request does not require any action considered unsafe by the pilot-in-command. Until a landing aircraft has cleared the runway no other aircraft may land or take off on that runway.

Clearance to taxi after vacating the runway is the prerogative of the control tower. The tower will probably clear you to ground control, or, if this service/frequency is not available, to taxi, somewhere between the landing roll and the point where you stop the aircraft to carry out the after-landing cockpit check. If the clearance has been apparently overlooked, call the tower for taxi instructions to your destination on the airport.

Touch-and-Go

To save flight time *touch-and-go* landings are frequently resorted to during various stages of training. In this manoeuvre a take-off is executed while the aircraft is still in its landing roll. This means that the essential components of a pre-take-off cockpit check must be carried out while the aircraft is moving along the runway. Before attempting the cockpit check be sure that the aircraft is under complete control in the landed mode. The essential components of touch-and-go pre-take-off actions are:

(1) Flaps up (or set for take-off)
(2) Trim set for take-off
(3) Carburettor heat "cold"
(4) Power "full" (or take-off setting).

When operating at a controlled airport a standard landing clearance presumes that you will land and exit from the runway. If a touch-and-go landing is intended you must obtain clearance to do so from the control tower. Their clearance will most likely be: "cleared for touch-and-go."

First Solo

The first solo is a landmark in your flying career. You will never forget it and it is quite normal to look forward to it, but do not exaggerate its importance. It is not so much when you solo but rather what you know and what you can do correctly at this period of training that is important. Soloing is merely another step in the orderly process of flight training, bringing you to the stage where learning really begins.

The amount of dual instruction required to solo need not be a reflection on your ability. Everyone varies in capacity to learn, and very often the pupil who is a little slow to learn ultimately makes the better pilot.

Before being permitted to take your first solo flight you will have to satisfy your flight instructor that you are able to:

(1) Correct a potentially poor landing but be capable of judging when it is necessary to go around again
(2) Recognize whether you are overshooting or undershooting and take early corrective action
(3) Operate the radio competently where airport traffic control is in effect, and in the event of communications failure know the emergency procedures to follow and the light signals that may be directed to you from a control tower
(4) Realize the importance of keeping an alert look-out for other aircraft now that you are the sole occupant of the aircraft
(5) Handle normal emergencies, and
(6) Properly adjust your circuit pattern in the event of a change of runway in use after you take off.

As pilot-in-command you are responsible for the operation and safety of the aircraft during its flight time when on solo flight. However, for this first solo your instructor will ensure that suitable conditions exist and precautions are taken. For example:

(1) **Sufficient Fuel.** Be sure the aircraft has sufficient fuel for the intended solo flight, with adequate reserve for possible delays or overshoots.

(2) **Light.** Sufficient daylight must remain for successful completion of the anticipated flight, allowing a liberal margin for possible additional circuits due to traffic congestion, overshooting, etc.

(3) **Weather Conditions.** The first solo flight should not be considered unless suitable weather conditions exist and are forecast to continue.

(4) **Traffic Conditions.** At airports where unusually heavy traffic conditions are encountered at some periods of the day, it may be advisable to avoid a first solo flight at such times.

(5) **Pilot Fitness.** After a lengthy session of dual instruction you may be so fatigued that it is inadvisable to consider a first solo flight, even though you are performing satisfactorily.

Securely fasten the seat belt in the empty seat.

On a solo flight, the take-off will be much quicker and the climb more rapid due to the absence of the instructor's weight. Many students have remarked that this was the outstanding feature of their first solo flight: they were not fully prepared for the suddenness with which the aircraft became airborne.

Since the aircraft is relatively lightly loaded, it will require less power to maintain a desired rate of descent. Also, after the flare for landing, the aircraft will tend to "float" longer before touching down and it may be more sensitive to gusts during the initial stage of the landing roll, after contact with the runway is made.

New manoeuvres and procedures will be added as progress permits, and further solo periods planned and authorized. Specific practice on older procedures as well as new will be included. When authorized solo to do specific manoeuvres, it is important to practise the specific work diligently; there will be ample time for sightseeing or pleasure cruising when flight training is finished. Perfection of technique as early as possible is your objective; therefore, after the first solo, subsequent solo flights must be devoted to attaining greater precision, co-ordination, orientation, and judgment.

Illusions Created by Drift—Low Flying

There are times when it may be necessary to manoeuvre an aircraft relatively close to the ground, such as during a forced landing, when carrying out precautionary landing procedures or because of deteriorating weather. On these occasions it is very important that you recognize and understand illusions created by drift (Fig 2-59).

Once an aircraft becomes airborne it enters a medium of movement almost unrelated to any it encounters on the ground. As soon as the wheels leave the surface there is no wind in the sense that we normally associate with the word. Instead, the aircraft enters a body of air, and while airborne its movement is directly related to the speed and direction of movement of that body of air.

In flight at normal operating altitudes the movement of the aircraft relative to the ground appears to be comparatively slow even when the airspeed is quite high. However, when the aircraft is flown closer to the ground, movement in relation to the ground becomes more apparent and in strong winds illusions are created. If misinterpreted, they can develop into potentially dangerous flight conditions.

In conditions of good visibility, flight below normal operating altitudes can be at normal cruising speed, but if it is necessary to fly near the ground in reduced visibility it is usually advisable to reduce speed. The flaps should be partially extended when flying at lower speeds near the ground. This will allow a lower operational speed, a smaller turning radius to avoid obstacles, and a better view, owing to the lower position of the nose. The increased power required with flap extension will also improve control, due to the additional slipstream over the elevators and rudder.

To demonstrate illusions created by drift, your instructor will choose a day when the wind is strong enough for the effects to be easily discerned. Flying upwind the reduction in ground speed is noticeable. Flying downwind the increased ground speed is very noticeable, sometimes to the extent that there is a temptation to reduce airspeed, which if carried to extremes could lead to a stalled condition. Flying cross-wind, the sideways drift over the ground is very apparent, especially when the aircraft is aligned with a straight road or section line.

In a turn from upwind to downwind, because of the drift over the ground the aircraft seems to be slipping inwards, even though the turn is accurate and well co-ordinated. This impression is an illusion and you must not use the rudder in the attempt to correct it. A quick glance at the centred ball of the turn-and-bank indicator will confirm that no slip is occurring. However, the drift itself is very real and plenty of room must be allowed when turning from upwind to downwind if there is an obstacle on the inside of the turn. Similarly, in a turn from downwind to upwind the aircraft seems to skid outwards, although the ball is centred. This too is an illusion, but again the drift is real and ample room must be allowed between the aircraft and obstructions on the outside of the turn.

Remember, the lower the airspeed, the greater the illusion of skid and slip with a given wind velocity.

The closer you are flying to the ground, the greater the illusory effect. At such times, little attention can be given to the flight instruments. Therefore, it is most important to understand the false impressions that can be created by the deceptive appearance of the ground. An alert watch must be maintained not only for other aircraft but also for high obstacles on the ground, which under the circumstances add considerably to the hazard. Continual vigilance is essential.

Since the aircraft's altimeter indicates the height of the aircraft above sea level and not its height above the ground, it is most important to watch the ground contours carefully and learn to estimate the height above the ground. Heights can be more easily judged by looking well ahead.

Map Reading. When an aircraft is flown at lower than normal altitudes, map reading becomes more difficult due to the reduced area of ground visible and the shorter time available for identifying landmarks.

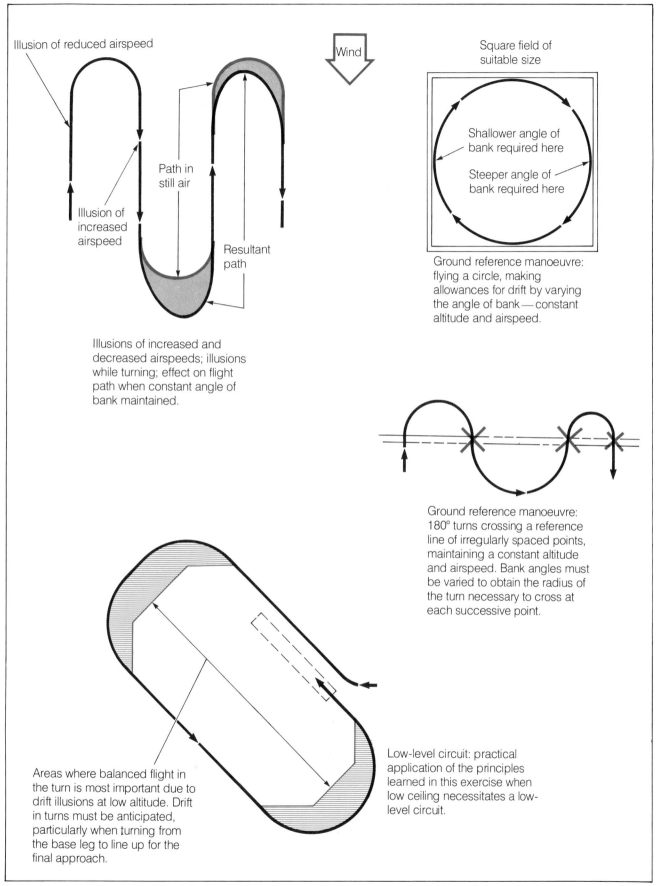

Illusion of reduced airspeed

Illusion of increased airspeed

Path in still air

Resultant path

Wind

Illusions of increased and decreased airspeeds; illusions while turning; effect on flight path when constant angle of bank maintained.

Square field of suitable size

Shallower angle of bank required here

Steeper angle of bank required here

Ground reference manoeuvre: flying a circle, making allowances for drift by varying the angle of bank — constant altitude and airspeed.

Ground reference manoeuvre: 180° turns crossing a reference line of irregularly spaced points, maintaining a constant altitude and airspeed. Bank angles must be varied to obtain the radius of the turn necessary to cross at each successive point.

Areas where balanced flight in the turn is most important due to drift illusions at low altitude. Drift in turns must be anticipated, particularly when turning from the base leg to line up for the final approach.

Low-level circuit: practical application of the principles learned in this exercise when low ceiling necessitates a low-level circuit.

Figure 2-59   Examples of Illusions and Effects of Drift in Turns during High Wind Conditions

Points to Remember

When flying close to the ground:

(1) Maintain a safe airspeed.
(2) Turn accurately in spite of the illusory effect of drift.
(3) Maintain a safe height above ground contours.
(4) Keep a good look-out.
(5) Do not turn too steeply.
(6) Do not annoy others or frighten livestock.

Never practise this exercise unless there is an authorized flight instructor on board the aircraft. The height and suitability of the area should be governed by local restrictions.

Precautionary Landings

The term *aircraft movement* signifies a take-off or a landing at a recognized civil aerodrome or airport. Over 6,000,000 such movements occur in Canada in the course of one typical year. It is further estimated that an additional 350,000 aircraft movements take place in the same typical year at places other than at aerodromes or airports. Relatively few of these movements were occasioned by true emergency situations. These off airport movement estimates point out two important factors: (1) when a flight is planned from A to B in a conventional landplane, B does not necessarily have to be an aerodrome or an airport as such; and (2) emergency landings, although extremely low in number by comparison to the overall movement picture, do occur. It follows, therefore, that training in the correct flight procedures for a precautionary landing is important not only in the event of an in-flight emergency, but also to increase the functional flexibility of the aircraft.

In the text that follows, procedures are described which many pilots may never have to carry out during their flying career, that is, to make a landing on an area other than a prepared runway. Pilots who have never ventured from paved or other well maintained aerodromes should know and apply the procedures for a precautionary landing when planning to land on an unfamiliar surface, or site. Even though the site may be used by other aircraft, it should be closely inspected in the recommended manner for flight obstructions and a suitable landing surface. The planned flight to visit a "farm strip" that you noticed during training, routine operations to remote unprepared strips, and a requirement to land at an abandoned or unfamiliar aerodrome are examples of when this procedure would be used.

Precautionary landing procedures will invariably have to be combined with one or more of the other special procedures included in this text, such as those for taking off and landing in short and/or soft fields, and if the circuit is at a lower altitude than usual, for dealing with illusions created by drift. These procedures also presume that the pilot has reasonable time to be selective in the choice of a safe landing area (which will also be satisfactory for the subsequent take-off), or even the option of not having to make a landing at all. Some emergency reasons for executing precautionary landings are:

(1) Mercy flights
(2) Weather deterioration
(3) Fuel shortage
(4) Aircraft malfunction
(5) Partial loss of engine power
(6) Being lost
(7) Approaching darkness
(8) Illness aboard.

For training purposes it is presumed that you are unfamiliar with the landing areas available, or if you are familiar with them, that special procedures are called for nonetheless. The most pressing problems are:

(1) Estimating the wind velocity
(2) Selecting an apparently suitable landing area
(3) Inspecting the landing area
(4) Deciding on the type of approach and landing to use
(5) Keeping the landing area in sight
(6) Manoeuvring the aircraft to a proper position for final approach.

Wind Velocity

Smoke gives the best indication of wind velocity. Grass and grain fields ripple in the direction of the wind and dust is blown with the wind. The calm areas on the upwind side of lakes or bodies of water are also an indication. If it is impossible to determine wind velocity, land in the direction of the wind at the time of take-off.

Landing Area

A landing area should be:

(1) Sufficiently long, preferably into wind, for both landing and take-off
(2) Smooth, firm, and free of obstructions
(3) As level as possible
(4) Free of high obstacles at the approach and overshoot ends
(5) Close to transportation or communication.

Field Inspection

When conducting field inspections and the final approach to a landing, any variation from a normal circuit and approach procedure should be dictated by existing special conditions. The speed used for the field inspection should be not less than that stipulated in the aircraft flight manual or pilot operating handbook, or if this is not given, not less than the normal approach speed. Should special conditions require a lower speed for field inspection, flight safety would dictate that the speed used should be significantly above that required for maximum endurance. In any case, the flight configuration, speed, and altitude selected should be such as to require minimum attention from the pilot, thus allowing more time for effective inspection of the intended approach and landing path.

Preliminary Inspection. Once a field has been chosen as a potentially suitable landing area, make a preliminary inspection circuit at about 500 to 1000 feet, or higher if conditions warrant. This circuit is to identify the field relative to prominent landmarks, to provide information on the approach path, confirm the gradient, and select reference points which can be used to

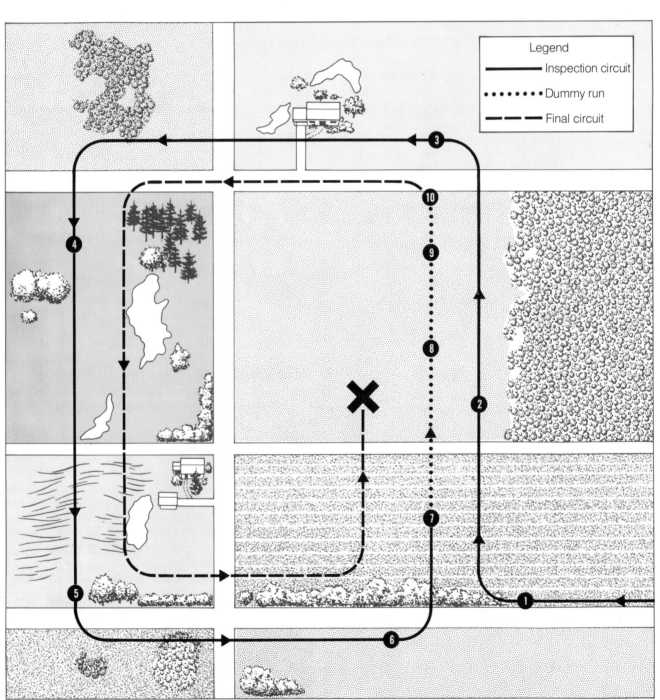

Figure 2-60   Precautionary Landing Procedure

determine turning points in the actual landing circuit or serve as guides in the event of poor visibility.

Final Inspection. Fly over the landing area at a height low enough to inspect the surface, but not so low that it is necessary to avoid obstacles. Make sure that the landing path is reasonably level and firm and that approaches are suitable. Look for hidden obstructions and rough or swampy ground. It is best if this inspection flight is made parallel to the landing path but slightly to the right of it, and into wind to keep ground speed as low as possible. If there is any doubt and conditions permit, make another inspection run.

Type of Approach

The inspection run will determine the type of approach to be made. If there is any doubt in this regard, with no alternate field or plan available, consider the field short, its surface soft, and plan your final approach and landing accordingly.

Figure 2-60 illustrates the typical circuits involved in precautionary landing procedures. The circled numbers indicate where certain actions should take place, as follows:

(1) Selection of Field. How long is the run into wind for landing and take-off? Is the field free of obvious obstacles?

(2) Preliminary Inspection. What are the relative landmarks? The general condition of the field, the approach path, etc. (Altitude 500 to 1000 feet above ground.)

(3) Cross-Wind Reference Point. Find a prominent landmark line — features for subsequent cross-wind leg, i.e. fence line, road, line of trees, etc.

(4) Downwind Reference Line and Cockpit Check. Is there a line of trees, fence, field(s) with prominent features (rock strewn, ploughed, etc.)

(5) Downwind/Cross-Wind Reference Point. Locate prominent landmarks, i.e. buildings, oddly shaped trees or group of trees, etc.

(6) Cross-Wind/Final Reference Point. Same as (5).

(7) Positioning for Final Inspection. Line up to open side of final approach at safe altitude — note obstacles on approach end and lead-in references — note heading.

(8) Overshoot Area. Are there obstacles on overshoot end? If the suitability of field is in doubt, make another close inspection or choose another field.

(9) Final Inspection. Make a close inspection for hidden obstacles, rough or swampy ground, rocks, stumps, slopes, ditches, hollows, etc., not identifiable on preliminary inspections. Note surface wind and drift — confirm type of approach.

(10) Start of Final Circuit. Get orientated with the field by "checking off" reference points selected on preliminary inspection circuit.

During the final inspection flight, a reduced airspeed is to be preferred. However, this and the use of flap at this point should be determined by the circumstance which made the precautionary landing necessary in the first instance. While carrying out this low level flight, you should also be alert to illusions created by drift.

If possible, the final circuit should be a normal circuit, at the circuit height in effect at your base aerodrome, so that all actions and manoeuvres are done at places and heights familiar to you. It is amazing how important this seemingly simple matter can be. If weather does not permit circuit height, maintain the highest altitude allowable under the circumstances.

Under the pressure of a situation or by being preoccupied with the approach, do not neglect the pre-landing cockpit check. Until the aircraft comes to a safe stop after landing, special conditions exist which may require the aircraft to be in the best possible condition in case of an overshoot. If you have not already done so, this would be a good time to communicate with a ground station and advise of circumstances, location, and intention.

Even if the field has been used by aircraft before, remember that it may not have been maintained. Unless only a few hours have elapsed since you used it last, it is a good policy to presume that the field is short, that the surface is soft, that brakes will not be as effective as usual, and that mobile or other obstacles may be present.

During the latter stages of the approach until just prior to touchdown, you need much concentration to manoeuvre the aircraft properly. Nevertheless, study the intended path continually for obstacles and surface conditions. A power or telephone line which was easily discerned during the flypast may become almost invisible on approach; farm animals which looked stationary may now be moving quite rapidly toward the intended landing path, perhaps having been flushed into the open by the aircraft itself during the inspection run.

After the aircraft has landed, if any reassessment was made of the condition of the surface during the landing, give some immediate thought to the possibility of complications arising due to indiscriminate taxiing at this point. A very soft surface may require that the aircraft be quickly manoeuvred to high ground before it sinks to a point of immobility. On the other hand, by taxiing too presumptuously you may manoeuvre the aircraft from a good surface to a poor one. If you have any doubt as to the condition of the surface of the manoeuvring area, stop the engine and make an inspection on foot. This is particularly important in the case of long lush grass, which tends to obscure the actual surface.

Take-off precautions are as important as those for landing. There is, however, one distinct added advantage to planning the take-off which should always be exploited fully — prior to take-off the pilot-in-command is in a position to inspect and select the best take-off surface on foot. Unless you are thoroughly familiar with the field under all conditions, a pre-take-off inspection of the intended take-off run is a necessary precaution.

If there are compelling reasons why a pre-take-off inspection of the field cannot be made, use the ground run path made by the aircraft on landing as a guide to selecting an acceptable take-off area. The tire impressions of a landing run will remain clearly visible for several hours on a grassy surface. There are documented cases of aircraft making successful precautionary landings and then coming to grief on the take-off run, when the pilot erroneously presumed that the entire field was as suitable as the area he had landed on.

A good general statement on the selection of a precautionary landing area for routine purposes is: "A pilot is not at liberty to use an area indiscriminately for landings and take-offs." There are many reasons why this statement must always be borne in mind; to cite a few, such operations may be contrary to:

(1) The Air Regulations
(2) Provincial, municipal, or local statutes and by-laws
(3) The right of a property owner to "quiet enjoyment" of his property.

Although some fields may offer good manoeuvring surfaces for an airport, landing and take-off can do considerable damage to crops during the growing season. Likewise, the low flight of an aircraft over a fur farm can cause the death of many of the young animals. These points must be given careful consideration when a routine landing and take-off are being considered.

In the case of wheel equipped aircraft, probably the most difficult field to assess for a precautionary landing, and one that can also give the most trouble on take-off, is one that is slush or snow-covered. The major problem is that even if the general depth of the slush or snow is not a ruling factor, snow drifts, not readily seen until the aircraft is almost upon them, are normally present.

Country snowdrifts being relatively free of dust and commercial soot, the lack of contrast makes them almost impossible to see, even on foot. When the wheels break through a crusted snowdrift, an aircraft's forward progress is abruptly arrested by the immense horizontal strength of the crust. A take-off under these conditions becomes highly improbable and a landing carries the risk of nosing over, damaging the propeller and/or the nose wheel. Nor can the assessment of a snow surface by a "landsman" be considered with too much credence. A hard-packed snow surface which will support the weight of a person without even cracking will most likely collapse under the weight of an aircraft, especially during the latter half of a landing run. If there is any doubt, and a safe alternative is available, don't land.

Ditching

The possibility of a single-engined landplane having to make an emergency landing in open water is extremely remote. However, should there be no other choice open, follow the procedures in the aircraft flight manual or pilot operating handbook. In the absence of manufacturer's data, there are general procedures you can use for the sake of the welfare of the aircraft's occupants.

Unless the landing is made into a fairly strong wind with reasonably calm surface conditions, experience has shown that fixed landing-gear aircraft will invariably receive major damage and might nose over when the landing-gear contacts the water.

Land into the wind if the water is smooth, or smooth with a very long swell. Waves generally move downwind except close to the shoreline, but swell does not bear any relation to the wind direction. Wind lanes (streaks upon the water) may be apparent, the streaked effect being more pronounced when looking downwind. Gusts may ripple a smooth surface and indicate the wind direction. Water appears from the air to be calmer than it really is; if possible, fly low over it and study its surface. When near the surface of the water the aircraft's drift will give a good indication of wind direction.

In some situations it may be advisable to land parallel to the swell, and across the wind, if the swells are of short spacing. The danger of nosing into large waves or swell is greater than the danger of landing cross-wind.

The value of power for slow approach flight is so great that a pilot faced with landing in water should land while he still has fuel available. In addition, with power the water surface can be studied carefully to help decide upon the best landing direction.

The airspeed and rate of descent on approach to a

water landing with a landplane must be as low as possible consistent with safe handling. Adopt a tail-down attitude when making contact with the water by "holding off" until excess speed is lost, to minimize the shock of impact to whatever extent is possible.

Extend partial flap on low wing aircraft and full flap on high wing aircraft.

Unless the landing-gear is fixed, it must be retracted.

Where in-flight door or canopy opening is permitted, consideration should be given to cracking the door and wedging it if necessary and to opening the canopy. Fasten the seat belts and secure loose objects. Be pre-pared for a double impact, the first when the tail strikes and the second, and greater, as the nose hits the water. The aircraft may also swing violently to one side if one wing touches the water before the other. Release seat belts when certain the aircraft has stopped and evacuate the cabin as quickly as possible.

If the doors cannot be opened immediately, do not panic. It may be necessary for a considerable amount of water to enter the cabin before the pressure equalizes and the doors can be opened. Meanwhile, unless it is badly damaged, the aircraft will not sink immediately.

Forced Landings

It is an interesting and comforting fact that in comparison to the millions of miles flown annually by single-engine aircraft in North America, engine failures in this type of aircraft are remarkably few. However, the fact that engines can fail for structural and other reasons makes it extremely important that you become proficient in the execution of forced landing procedures.

A forced approach to landing is the special procedure made necessary as a result of a total, or near total, loss of engine power. The procedure involves the approach only, since in a real situation the actual landing would be appropriate to the variety of governing conditions existing at the site selected for landing.

During earlier training you learned gliding for range and how to estimate the point of touchdown by reference to the terrain ahead of you. By additional application of this knowledge you learned to determine the "radius of glide" from your aircraft's position over the ground, making due allowance for the effect of the wind. During practice landings you also learned how to choose a point in relation to the touchdown point where the throttle could be closed and a successful power-off approach and landing made. In forced landing training and practice this knowledge and skill is developed further.

Those who believe that a successful forced landing is difficult to achieve are reminded that every landing made by student glider pilots must be a successful forced landing and they develop this skill very rapidly, since the average student glider pilot reaches licensing standard in less than 8 hours total flight time. This is the skill that the pilot of an aircraft must develop in order to make a successful landing in the event of an in-flight engine failure.

In essence, when an engine failure occurs, the aircraft must be manoeuvred so that it will be at that air position from which a continuation of the glide will result in a successful approach and landing, exactly as it did when you were practising power-off approaches and landings at your home base. That position can be called a key position, and can be "located" on either the left or right-hand base leg (Fig 2-61). Planning the approach is the key to execution of a successful forced landing. You must draw on all the skills that you have already attained and put them to use; there is actually nothing new to learn. It is strictly a matter of practical and methodical application of what you already know.

Wind Velocity

The direction and speed of the wind are important during any landing but especially so during a forced landing, since they affect the gliding distance of the aircraft, the flight path over the ground, and in the case of an actual landing, the ground speed at which the aircraft contacts the ground and the distance it will roll after landing. All these things must be considered when selecting a field.

All landings should be made with the aircraft headed into the wind. However, this cannot be a hard and fast rule in the case of a forced landing, since many other factors may make it inadvisable. Some of these factors are:

(1) Altitude may be inadequate for manoeuvring around into wind.
(2) Obstacles can make an into wind approach impractical by shortening the effective length of the field.
(3) A suitable into wind field is not available.
(4) The best field may run downhill into wind at such an angle that an uphill downwind landing is preferable.
(5) The nature of obstacles can be such that judging how to clear them may be tricky and dangerous. This is particularly true in the case of power lines.

Experience must be gained in determining the direction of the wind and estimating its speed by observing the windsock at an airport, smoke from factories and houses, dust, brushfires, windmills, wind lines on lakes and ponds, etc., and constantly checking them while in flight. An ability to sense wind direction and speed from the drift of the aircraft must be developed at an early stage.

Altitude

The altitude available is usually the controlling factor in the successful accomplishment of a forced landing. This emphasizes the need for establishing and maintaining the best gliding attitude.

The Field

Regardless of the importance of other factors, the objective is to land the aircraft safely. Therefore the terrain of the field selected must be suitable. A field of stumps, stones, or one containing irrigation ditches and the like would be a poor choice even if other factors were favourable. An alternative field with more reasonable terrain, even if downwind and downhill, may be better. Avoid fields with contour plowing, deep ditches, or any features that reduce their suitability. Try to pick a field near houses, or at least near a road.

Take the field's length into account. If there is a strong wind the normal landing roll will be comparatively short, but if it is imperative that you land downwind the landing roll may be very long. Similarly, the existence of a slope affects the length of the landing roll. But length is not the only factor. Ideally, the chosen field will be wide enough to allow for correction of errors in altitude and distance, which can be affected by varying the cross-wind leg and the point of turn onto the final approach.

The importance of landing into wind has already been stressed. However, should an into wind field be of marginal length (or width), good airmanship may dictate that another field of adequate size be used, even though this may require landing in a cross-wind or a slight tail wind. The strength of the wind is a major factor under such circumstances.

Since up to this point most of your airwork has been at circuit height, it is difficult at first to assess the factors affecting a forced landing when the procedure is initiated at altitudes above normal circuit height. Drift is less apparent and altitude tends to make all fields appear flat and smooth.

When the aircraft does get down to a more familiar altitude where the selected field can be better judged, it is often too late to choose a more suitable one. Then again, with the larger choice of fields visible at altitude, there is greater difficulty in making a selection and the delay can result in a loss of valuable height. Regardless of altitude, in practising forced approaches great effort must continually be put into acquiring the habit of decisive and correct field selection, by developing a keen sense for recognizing and assessing all

influencing factors. An alert pilot is constantly on the look-out for suitable landing fields and for indications of surface wind.

Point out the field you have selected to the instructor and then plan and fly a pattern for a forced approach to the field selected. This affords the instructor an opportunity to indicate any errors in the total plan, including constructive comment on the field selected. However, if during the descent you realize that a poor selection has been made and that a better field is still available, you will usually be permitted to change your plan. Regardless of the final outcome of the forced approach, the instructor will point out the hazards, such as abrupt manoeuvring at low altitudes, which last-minute decisions can create.

Gliding Speed

A constant gliding speed must be maintained, for a reason other than preserving height. Fluctuations in gliding speed and attitude interfere with accurate judgment of gliding distance and the proposed touchdown position. (Proper use of trim will help you keep the correct attitude and speed.)

Is a Forced Landing Necessary?

Many actual forced landings need not have occurred at all, since the failure or near failure of the engine was caused by something within the pilot's power to remedy. For this reason, forced landing training includes emergency and vital actions carried out during the descent. These actions should be committed to memory, and each check item spoken aloud with the fingers physically touching or pointing out the item to be checked. There are various cockpit items which if mishandled accidently or carelessly, or simply neglected, can make an engine fail. Turbulence or even an over-curious passenger can contribute towards a switch or a control being in the wrong position.

Vital Actions

The vital action power loss check should be made on the descent following engine failure, immediately after the correct glide attitude has been established and the aircraft is headed towards the manoeuvring area selected. Items to be checked may vary according to aircraft type but a typical list is:

(1) Mixture. Check that the control is in "full rich" position; it could have been accidently moved into "idle cut-off" or left in "lean" during a descent.

(2) Throttle. Reduce the throttle setting. An engine suffering a fuel flow malfunction may cease firing completely at a high throttle setting, but deliver enough power at a lower one to be of considerable value if a forced landing must be made.

(3) Carburettor Heat. If a total engine failure occurs due to carburettor icing, it could be too late to restore power with carburettor heat, since the system depends on heat from the engine. However, there may still be enough heat left in the system. Pull on full carburettor heat and reduce the throttle setting to about one-third normal power until the engine begins firing, then open the throttle gradually. If only a partial loss of power occurs, pull on full carburettor heat, leaving the throttle at about cruise setting until the engine begins to recover.

(4) Fuel Tank Selector Lever. Check that it has not been knocked to the "off" position. If it is already selected to a tank indicating full, reselect another tank known to have fuel in it. Gauges may be faulty.

(5) Primer. Check that it is in and securely locked.

(6) Fuel Booster Pumps. Place the switch for the booster pump in the "on" position, since there may be a failure in the regular fuel feed system.

(7) Magneto Switches. Check that the switches are in the correct position. If the engine continues to run roughly, select left and right positions to determine if it will function smoothly on one magneto.

(8) Starter. If the propeller has stopped turning, operate the starter. The engine may have stopped due to sustained idling at low speeds, as in practising stalls. The starter should not be operated if it is obvious that a major mechanical failure has occurred, because additional damage may result.

(9) Propeller Pitch. In aircraft with constant speed propellers, place the pitch control into the low RPM position. At lower airspeeds some aircraft can barely sustain flight with the propeller set at the high RPM position because of the resulting drag.

As you do this check, call out each action taken, in a loud voice.

When a landing appears imminent, endeavour to communicate with a ground or air station advising of the situation and geographic position, fasten seat belts firmly, and take action to secure the aircraft. A suggested security check, which may vary as to aircraft type, is:

(1) Magneto switches — off

(2) Mixture control — off ("full lean")
(3) Parking brake — off
(4) Fuel selector valve — off
(5) Gasoline cabin heater — off
(6) Fire extinguisher — locate and secure
(7) Secure loose objects
(8) Jettison emergency exits, or unlatch doors
(9) Just prior to or at touchdown, master switch — off.

Simulate the security check by pointing to or touching items to be checked while calling out the name of each item in a loud voice.

Methods for losing excess height include the use of flaps, turns across final approach, side-slipping, etc. In turns across the final approach, be careful to avoid crowding the field. Develop a sense of the need for any of these methods and when to use them, recognizing that they usually compensate for errors in judgment. Planned loss of height or changing of the glide angle at a specific point in the approach by the use of flap, slipping, etc., is not considered an error in judgment if the main objective is consistently realized thereby. The key word, of course, is "planning."

In giving way to an eagerness to "get down," airspeed may be overlooked and the aircraft will arrive at the edge of the selected field going too fast to permit a landing in the limited distance available. Unless airspeed is carefully monitored, there will be a tendency to keep lowering the nose, if the aircraft has excessive height, as the approach end of the field is neared. Finally, the aircraft is almost dived into the field at a speed which precludes any landing, let alone a safe one.

Approach Height

The objective in making a forced landing is to have the aircraft touch down at the most desirable point in the field. Therefore, it is good airmanship to arrive on the final approach with more height than judged necessary so that you have more freedom of choice in this regard.

Another consideration is that in a real forced landing the gliding angle with the propeller windmilling is likely to be steeper than the usual gliding angle with the engine throttled back.

Who Has Control?

When engine power is applied by either the student or the instructor after a practice forced approach procedure has been completed, no doubt should exist as to who has control of the aircraft. Many near accidents have occurred because each party erroneously thought that the other had control.

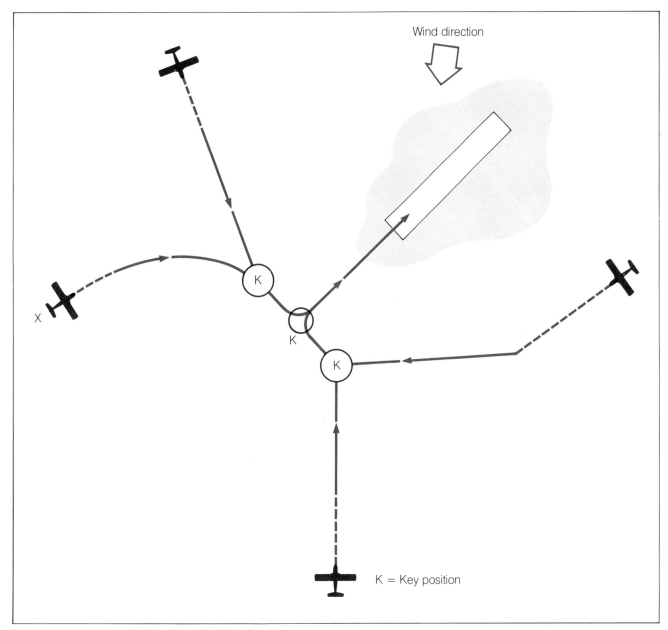

Figure 2-61   Forced Landing Approach

Executing the Forced Landing

When a forced landing becomes necessary, the procedure for gliding for range is followed and applied to the forced landing procedure (Fig 2-61) as outlined below:

(1) Assume the gliding attitude and determine the distance the aircraft will glide (range).
(2) Determine the direction of wind.
(3) Select the most suitable field within gliding distance and decide on a landing path.

(4) Proceed to a selected (key) position on the final approach side of the field. From this position three choices of action are available:
   (a) If height and position are correct, make a normal approach, losing excess height on base leg or final approach by using flaps or side-slipping.
   (b) If too close or too high, widen the base leg by side-slipping away from the field. This will increase distance from the field while losing height. If height is excessive, make another glide across the approach end.
   (c) If height available is critical, make a direct

approach to the field, dispensing with the base leg.

It is clear that the first thing to do is get downwind of the field, but keep well within gliding distance. While getting into this position, try to find the cause of the failure by carrying out a vital actions check. If the failure cannot be rectified, communicate with a ground facility, fasten seat belt(s) firmly, and secure the aircraft.

The approach should be judged in the same way that any approach is judged — that is, by the angle at which the pilot is looking down at the field.

If it is necessary to lose a great deal of height after reaching the downwind side of the field, while keeping the proper distance downwind lose the height in a carefully planned manner, making any necessary turns in the direction of the field so that the approach can be made straight in, overshooting slightly. Bear in mind that in an actual forced landing it may be better to risk colliding with obstacles at taxiing speed near the end of the landing roll than to risk this at flying speed on the approach end. However, when it is obvious that a glide approach to a landing can be made into the first third of the selected field, use flaps or side-slip to eliminate excess altitude, thus making all the field available for the landing run (provided the surface is suitable). Judge the approach in the same way as any approach — that is, by the angle at which you are looking down at the field.

Keep within easy gliding distance while losing excess height and plan to arrive in the correct position for a straight-in approach. Use only medium gliding turns unless a steeper turn is obviously necessary and always turn towards the field, to keep it in view and to judge distance lost through drift. Look for any obstacles or obstructions in or around the field, then decide on the landing path. The strength of the wind will be indicated by the drift of the aircraft. In a strong wind the whole approach must be closer to the field than in a light wind.

Flaps should not be extended until you are sure of reaching the field. Without flaps the glide slope is flat, the speed comparatively high, and the view of the field poor. The more the flaps are extended the steeper the glide slope, the lower the safe gliding speed, and the better the forward view.

When you are absolutely sure of reaching the field, lose any excess height on the final approach so that touchdown can be made at the most desirable point on the field. After landing (in an actual forced landing), use brakes to the fullest safe extent. It may be necessary to make a turn on the ground to avoid an obstacle.

Practise forced landings as often as possible so that in the event of a real one you will be fully confident of possessing the judgment and skill to execute the procedure successfully.

Vary your practice areas. When a designated field is habitually used for forced approach practice, it is easy to fall prey to the idea that the "key position" is a particular landmark, such as a certain tree, cross-roads, water tower, or other ground fix. This develops a mechanical conception of the procedure, and if it becomes ingrained, will result in a feeling of total loss when these familiar objects are not present. Therefore, when practising forced approaches, vary both altitude and geographical location as much as possible to eliminate any false conception of the key position.

Engine Failure

Low Altitude

Time is the all-important factor when engine failure occurs at a low altitude. Common sense must dictate the priority for the actions and checks to be carried out in the available time, since the primary aim is to land with the least danger to you and your passengers. Causing the least damage to the aircraft is desirable but a secondary consideration.

On the Runway

If partial or complete engine failure is encountered on take-off while the aircraft is still on the runway, close the throttle and apply the brakes. If it is obvious that the aircraft cannot be stopped before it runs off the runway, you should consider doing an intentional ground loop.

After Take-off

If the engine fails immediately after take-off you may only have time to close the throttle, pick a landing path which will require only minor changes in heading, attain a gliding speed, and concentrate on a good landing. Remember that the aim of a successful forced landing is to land without injury to yourself or your passengers. Do not become so engrossed in doing checks that you jeopardize the chances of making a good approach and landing.

There are numerous examples of fatalities or injuries in accidents resulting from attempting to turn back to land on the runway following an engine failure after take-off. As altitude is at a premium, the tendency is to try to hold the nose of the aircraft up during the turn without any consideration for airspeed. These actions have a remarkable similarity to those of procedures used for entering a spin. The height from which a successful 180 degree turn back to the runway can be made depends on several considerations:

(1) Altitude
(2) The glide ratio of the aircraft
(3) The length of the runway
(4) Wind strength
(5) Experience of the pilot
(6) Experience on type.

As a rough guide, a 180 degree turn can be successfully made from about 800 feet. However, the glide ratio of the aircraft is a very important factor, and only your instructor can advise you from what height a successful 180 degree turn can be made. Another item to be considered is the ground speed which may be encountered when landing downwind after a 180 degree turn. Considerably more damage could result than if a landing had been made straight ahead.

In the Circuit

When flying a normal circuit, it is highly probable that you can complete a forced landing successfully on the runway in use, or on one of the other runways more suited to your position.

Simulated Engine Failure

When practising forced landings, there are several ways to simulate a power failure but only one right way for a particular aircraft. The correct procedure may be found in the owner's manual or the aircraft flight manual, or outlined by the flight instructor.

You must not allow the engine to get too cold or it may fail to respond properly when power is applied. Cruising power should be applied for a few seconds at 500 foot intervals during descent. This keeps the temperature normal and prevents the spark plugs from oiling up through prolonged idling of the engine. Many aircraft require carburettor heat before reducing power.

With the exception of those approaches made on an aerodrome, all practice forced landings outlined must be practised in a pre-defined area, and only to the minimum altitude as specified by the training unit.

Pilot Navigation

One significant advantage that an aircraft has over most surface transportation is that it is capable of proceeding more or less directly to its destination at a constant and relatively high speed. To use this capability effectively, however, it is essential to be proficient in cross-country navigation. The first stage of this skill is a combination of practical navigation and map reading called *pilot navigation*. This involves the capability of piloting an aircraft a reasonable distance over relatively unfamiliar territory with a minimum of apprehension and a maximum of pleasure.

You must demonstrate competence in solo cross-country flight in order to be issued a pilot licence, but this will be preceded by dual instruction on all phases of the exercise. The success or failure of a cross-country flight hinges upon the ability to:

(1) Plan the flight, taking into account present and anticipated weather, terrain, distance involved, and your level of competence as a pilot
(2) Establish and maintain a planned heading and altitude
(3) Recognize the effect of drift, and competently estimate new headings to regain and maintain the desired track, or fly direct to your destination
(4) Calculate ground speeds accurately and revise estimated times of arrival (ETA's)
(5) Read charts and identify physical features on the ground, and more specifically, correctly identify predetermined and new check-points
(6) Recognize the need to divert from a planned route and estimate a heading and ETA to an alternate aerodrome with a minimum of delay or confusion.

The foregoing points are difficult to put into any set order of importance, since changing situations would force a change in that order. For example, when a flight is conducted over terrain or in weather conditions which make map reading extremely difficult, an ability to hold a heading accurately and correctly calculate ETA's becomes of overriding and vital importance either in continuing the flight or diverting to an alternate.

Preparing for the Flight

The success and enjoyment of a navigation flight depends greatly on systematic preparation and planning. There are several factors to consider which may vary with the conditions under which the flight has to be conducted. The weather, terrain, landing, and fuel facilities, together with the availability of en route check-points, may influence decisions and we recommend that you carry out itemized preparation, study, and calculations for the flight, in the following order:

(1) Weather
(2) Route selection
(3) NOTAM and field condition reports
(4) Aeronautical chart preparation
(5) Flight log preparation
(6) Filing of flight plan or flight notification.

Weather

Pilot navigation flights must not be conducted unless VFR weather prevails and is forecast to prevail over the selected route. Therefore you must obtain adequate weather information. The best way to do so is by means of a direct briefing from an aviation weather specialist, either in person or by telephone. Failing this, aviation area, terminal, and upper wind forecasts, together with hourly weather reports, are available from Transport Canada Flight Service Stations. Be sure to check the actual reports against the forecast weather for aerodromes at which you intend to land and along the selected route. Pay particular attention to the surface winds. The strength of the wind and/or its cross-wind factor may preclude a safe landing at these sites. Weather conditions are always subject to change; therefore, regardless of meteorological forecasts, in preparing for a cross-country flight, plan the possibility of having to divert to an alternate airport. This may be done by listing all the suitable alternate aerodromes along the route in chronological order on the flight log form. They may also be circled on the navigation chart.

Charts

The chart used almost exclusively for pilot navigation is the Transverse Mercator Projection, with a scale of 1:500,000. With this scale, 1 inch on the chart represents 500,000 inches on the ground (approximately 8 miles to the inch). Other scales you may encounter are 1:1,000,000 (approximately 16 miles to the inch) and 1:250,000 (approximately 4 miles to the inch). For fine detail, the 1 mile to the inch chart can be used. This chart even shows individual buildings, and is particularly useful for float flying operations. The 1:500,000 statute mile scale does not exactly correspond to 8 miles to the inch, which is 1:506,880. For short distances the differences may be ignored.

The Route

Once you have determined that the weather for a flight will be satisfactory, all pertinent factors must be analysed and a route decided upon. The most direct route may not be the most desirable, as it may be largely over water beyond gliding distance from land, over a prohibited or danger area, or perhaps over poor terrain (such as sparsely settled areas) for map reading.

In selecting routes, try to avoid those which include extended periods of flight over areas where map reading is difficult or impossible. The ability to read maps is a very important part of pilot navigation; if a route does not reasonably afford this opportunity, it should not be selected. The objective is to get there safely and comfortably. "As quickly as possible" is an aim which can be sacrificed for this objective.

A check–point, or pin-point, is a prominent feature or group of features along or close to the route, used to establish the position of the aircraft and for other purposes such as in-flight calculation of ground speed and revisions to the ETA.

Main highways, rivers, railroads, and lakes afford excellent and readily identifiable check-points for pilot navigation. To take full advantage of the aircraft, and for other purposes, a route should be chosen which will encompass most of them. For example, if a prominent highway or railroad runs from a city adjacent to the airport of departure to a town near the destination airport, draw the track line from the city to the town. Then set heading over the city and, at the end of the trip, navigate the short distance from the destination town to the destination airport. It is often undesirable to arrive

directly over an airport, especially an unfamiliar or busy one. Make any adjustments to routing that are required to maintain the flight over good map reading terrain. To do this it may be necessary to make one or two dog-leg tracks to achieve point B from A. In the event of any situation which requires diverting from the original flight plan, a pilot strengthens his hand considerably when he knows exactly where he is at the time the diversion must be made.

It is important that the aeronautical chart used is up to date and not so dog-eared from use that important details are obscured. Many experienced pilots augment aeronautical charts with information from current automobile road maps, since the latter invariably include more secondary roads and greater bridge and highway detail. Remember, however, to use road maps only as a secondary source of information, as distance scales and physical land features are not always displayed accurately.

Preparing the Chart

Once you have selected the appropriate current aeronautical chart(s) and decided on the route, draw the "required track" lines from the point of setting heading through immediate points to the destination, and determine the true tracks and distances. The required track lines should be drawn in a way that makes them easily distinguished from printed chart detail and yet does not hide chart features. A yellow-tipped pen can be used to emphasize the track line drawn on the chart. If the yellow is not too intense the track line shows through, and is readily distinguishable from other lines.

Determine distances, then examine the route carefully and note the following:

(1) Elevation of terrain, with particular attention given to hills, peaks, and other obstructions
(2) Danger and prohibited areas
(3) Other airports and fields suitable for an emergency landing
(4) Location, availability, and distances between check points.

To assist in assessing in-flight deviations from track and making corrections, drift lines should be drawn on the chart. These are lines drawn on the chart at 10 degrees each side of the required track line from both the set heading and destination points. They are described in detail later in this text, but can be seen drawn on the chart in Figure 2-62. A preferred set-heading point is an easily identifiable or known landmark, such as a railway or road intersection, a bend in the river, a tower, or a

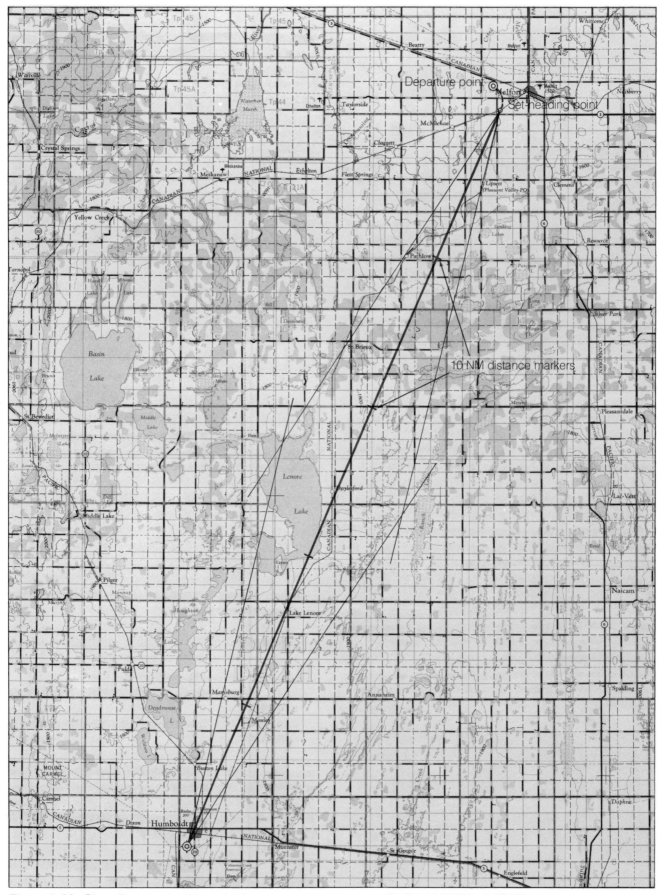

Figure 2-62 Chart Preparation Using 10 Degree Lines

small village or lake, to which the pilot can "eye ball" his way to set heading. In Figure 2-62 the intersection of two railway lines has been chosen. Climbing to a height over the departure airport is not only inherently dangerous, due to the increased traffic density around some airports, but also a waste of time. However, if no suitable and readily identifiable landmark exists, there is no alternative to setting heading over the airport. Accuracy on setting heading is essential. Setting heading from the downwind leg is not acceptable if the track line originates from the centre of the airport symbol on the chart, as a half to 1 mile track error exists from the start.

For rapid distance calculations, the track line drawn on the chart should also be marked into 10 mile intervals (Fig 2-62). With the track divided into 10 mile intervals there should be no need to "scale" distances in flight. Another method is to strike a line across the quarter-, mid-, and three-quarter-way points of each track segment to aid mental time, distance, and track error calculations.

The Flight Planning Form

As information relating to the proposed flight is accumulated, enter it in the appropriate sections of a flight planning form. Figure 2-63 shows how the planned flight from Melfort to Humboldt would be entered. The cruising altitude of 4,500 feet, and true airspeed, track, and wind velocity can be entered, and the remaining figures can be added as they are obtained through measurement or calculation. Other pertinent information, particularly weather and landing runway details, can be added for current and future use.

FLIGHT PLANNING FORM													(√)
							Distances/speeds in					kts.	✓
												mph	
From — To	Alt.	IAS	TAS	Track (T)	W/V	Hdg. (T)	Var.	Hdg. (M)	G/S	Dist.	Time	Fuel Req'd
MELFORT - CHECK PT #1	↗	90	-	135			17E	118		2	2	
CHECK PT #1 - HUMBOLDT	4500	115	120	204	290/20	214	17E	197	117	43	22	8
											24	8

Weather Forecast

YXE/YPA

50 SCT 70 OVC 6-8 RW-
OCNL GUSTS 30
3 - 290/20 +10
6 - 310/30 +6

En Route Station Reports

En Route Radio Frequencies
and Navigation Aids

YPA VOR 113.0
YXE VOR 116.2
TWR 118.3

315' TOWER 1 MILE N OF
HUMBOLDT

Destination Information

YXE 40 SCT OCNL 6 RW-

Forecast W/V 275/20 +25

Runway   09-27 1900' TURF
1865' ASL

Cross-wind component   10° 6 KT.
HUMBOLDT - 072° RADIAL YXE VOR
PHONE YXE FOR WX 306-665-4265
FLIGHT PLAN YXE 306-242-8227

Figure 2-63   Flight Planning Form

Track Line Measurement

One of the properties of a Transverse Mercator Projection is that scale can be considered constant all over the chart. Because of this, the meridians of longitude, or the vertical lines, converge at a point above the top of the chart, and for that reason a straight line drawn on the chart meets each meridian at a slightly different angle. To offset these differences, place the protractor at the midpoint of the track line when measuring that angle. This is particularly important when the track line is long and runs parallel to the parallels of latitude.

Airspeed Corrections

True Airspeed (TAS) is used for navigation computations since *Indicated Airspeed* (IAS) varies with temperature, pressure, and altitude. Conversion of IAS to TAS (or vice-versa) can be done very rapidly on your circular navigation computer.

Wind Velocity (W/V)

In aviation terminology, the term *wind velocity*, usually abbreviated to w/v, implies both the direction of the wind and its speed. Wind velocities normally change with altitude, and in planning a cross-country flight this must be taken into account when preparing the flight planning form. Many factors affect the selection of the altitude(s) at which a flight will be conducted and w/v is a major one.

Navigation Log

With the w/v selected for the altitudes to be flown, calculate headings, ground speeds, and times, then fill out the navigation log (Fig 2-69). Itemize all tracks, headings, distances, speeds, times, etc., pertinent to the flight. This provides an organized record and schedule for the flight and minimizes the possibility of forgetting important data and having to compute problems in flight. Fuel requirements should be calculated, and while en route these calculations should be checked against actual consumption to determine if the calculated reserves will be available at the destination. There are various forms of flight planning forms and navigation logs, each designed for a particular purpose. The training organizations' forms will be supplied by the flight instructor, who will also assist in their preparation.

Flight Plan or Flight Notification (Air Traffic Control)

It is mandatory that a flight plan, flight notification, or flight itinerary be filed prior to flying 25 nautical miles or more from the airport of departure. Among other things, this ensures that the appropriate authorities are alerted should the aircraft become overdue. Air searches can involve considerable time and expense. It is imperative that the pilot close his flight plan by notifying the appropriate agency when the intended or alternate destination is reached.

General Technique

In this text, we do not intend to discuss all the details involved in conducting a pilot navigation flight, since the training unit will provide appropriate instruction by means of a dual navigation exercise. However, the following are some general points applicable to any cross-country flight.

Magnetic Compass

When you read about vagaries of the compass later in this chapter, you will note that this navigation instrument may be unreliable while the aircraft is being turned, banked, accelerated, or decelerated. Therefore, in order to maintain the all-important heading of an aircraft by means of a magnetic compass, the aircraft must be held straight and at a constant airspeed.

Compass Turns

Since compass readings are unreliable when the aircraft is turning, accurate compass turns from one heading to another can only be made by timing the turn. In a co-ordinated standard rate turn, an aircraft turns at the rate of 3 degrees per second. For example, to alter heading from 090 degrees to 270 degrees (a change of 180 degrees), the aircraft would be held in a standard rate turn to the right or left for one minute. Dependent upon individual aircraft design, a turn of more than, or a fraction of, 90 degrees can be estimated by using the angle between the nose of the aircraft and the wing tips as a guide. For example, a turn of 100 degrees to the left can be made by turning on to a reference point which lines up with the trailing edge of the left wing.

Heading Indicator

Although the heading indicator is not entirely free of speed and altitude change errors, these errors are so slight that they may be ignored for all practical purposes. However, the heading indicator must be set manually by the pilot to the magnetic compass and reset about every 15 minutes, since this instrument is subject to precession errors. It is important to set the heading indicator accurately just prior to setting heading.

Altimeter

Atmospheric pressure varies from time to time and place to place; therefore the pilot must reset the altimeter to compensate for these variations. Current altimeter settings may be obtained on request from control towers and Flight Service Stations, or by tuning in to Automatic Terminal Information Service (ATIS) broadcasts.

Map Reading

The generally accepted term to describe navigation by means of a chart is *map reading*, although the publication used is more correctly called a chart than a map. You will begin to gain experience in map reading during earlier air exercises and learn it progressively, first by identifying highways, railroads, or rivers and relating them to other prominent features on the ground, such as towns, airports, powerlines, etc. Then, as your ability increases, a specific compass heading should be maintained while reading a chart.

Arrange charts so that both the charts and the controls of the aircraft may be easily managed at the same time. A chart should be folded so that the section being used is readily available, with a minimum of refolding or handling in the air. If more than one chart is to be used, they should be pre-arranged in the order in which they will be required. Align the chart so that the required track on the chart will be parallel to and pointing in the same direction as the track being flown.

The recommended practice in navigation by map reading is "from watch to chart to ground," in other words, noting the time, studying the chart, and anticipating what is to be seen on the ground. There are times, however, such as when you are lost, when the reverse procedure is more valuable — i.e., relating features on the ground to features on the chart. A great deal of practice with both methods is required at varying altitudes and on different headings.

Estimating

To become proficient in pilot navigation you must develop the ability to estimate. This can only be done through practice and more practice. While in flight, estimate the bearing and distance the aircraft is from an airport or town or check-point; observe the natural signs of surface winds and estimate their direction and strength; estimate the size of objects on the ground and the distance they are from each other. When passing near a field that you could consider for an emergency landing, estimate its length and width. Look quickly at a chart and estimate the distance that a certain lake is from the aircraft, what heading will be required to fly to it, and how long it will take to get there.

The more you know about the subject of navigation, the easier and more accurate estimating will be. However, the pilot of a light aircraft does not have the time, facilities, or need to practise precise navigation, therefore the accuracy of estimating must be developed to as high a level as possible.

Track Errors and Corrections

Owing to inaccuracies in the forecast wind and in flying the aircraft, errors often occur that require alterations of heading to bring the aircraft to the destination. Before corrections are discussed, the following terms must be defined:

(1) Required Track. The proposed path of the aircraft over the ground.

(2) Track Made Good. The actual path of the aircraft over the ground.

(3) Track Error. The angle between the required track and the track made good, measured in degrees, and always expressed as being left or right of the required track.

(4) Opening Angle. The angle between the required track and the track made good.

(5) Closing Angle. The angle between the old required track and the new required track to arrive at the destination.

Ten Degree Drift Lines

In Figure 2-62, 10 degree drift lines are shown opening up from the set-heading point and closing down to the destination. These lines enable the pilot to estimate

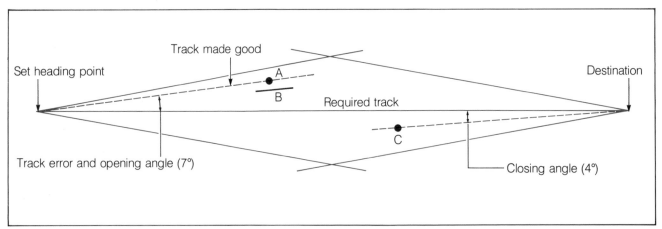

Figure 2-64A   Track Errors and Opening and Closing Angles

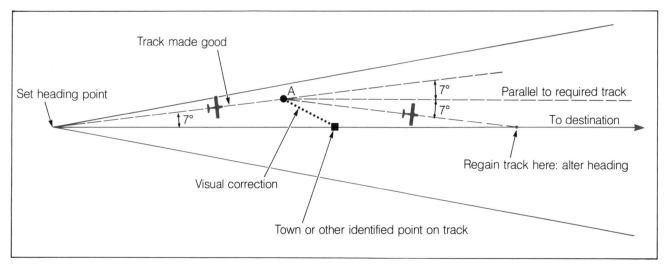

Figure 2-64B   Double Track Error Method

track errors and required heading changes with reasonable accuracy.

Point A in Fig 2-64 indicates a point on the track made good which is 7 degrees to left of the required track, indicating an opening angle of 7 degrees. The angle can be estimated more accurately by imagining or physically making a mark at the mid-angle at 5 degrees (line B) and establishing the pin-point in relation to that mark. Closing angles may be determined in the same manner, using the 10 degree drift lines which converge on the destination. The angle between the required track and a line joining Point C to destination indicates a closing angle of 4 degrees.

Heading Corrections

Once you have established the position of the aircraft accurately, and provided it is not on the required track, decide upon the best course of action. Normally, approximately 10 to 25 miles should be flown before attempting to estimate any track error, because errors over a short distance are magnified considerably. The heading of the aircraft can be changed so as to either return to the required track, or else fly directly to the destination. This will depend on the position of the aircraft. It is usually more desirable to return to the required track since the route study has been concentrated on that area and, in addition, a line already drawn on a chart is much easier to follow.

Provided the aircraft has not passed the half-way point, the double track error method or the visual alteration method can be used. If the aircraft is beyond the half-way point, you can still use the visual alteration method, or alternatively, the opening and closing angle method. Each method will be discussed in detail later in this text but first some basic geometry may help.

The key to understanding how these various methods work lies in the fact that if the aircraft heading is altered in the direction of the required track by a number of degrees equal to the track error or opening angle, the resulting heading will produce a track parallel to the required track. The desirable thing now is to get us back over track so that we can fly that heading. Some orderly

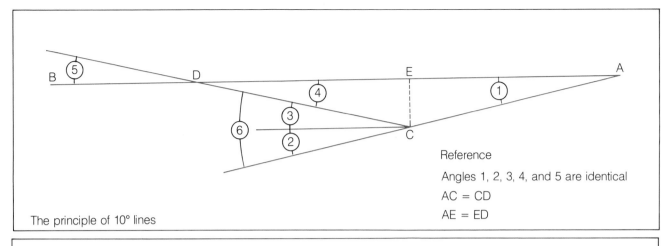

Reference

Angles 1, 2, 3, 4, and 5 are identical

AC = CD

AE = ED

The principle of 10° lines

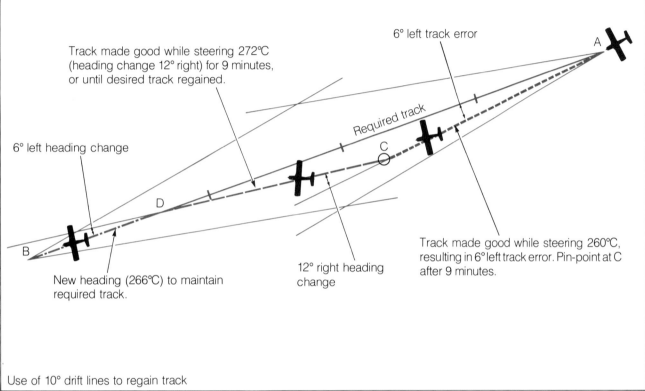

6° left track error

Track made good while steering 272°C (heading change 12° right) for 9 minutes, or until desired track regained.

Required track

6° left heading change

Track made good while steering 260°C, resulting in 6° left track error. Pin-point at C after 9 minutes.

New heading (266°C) to maintain required track.

12° right heading change

Use of 10° drift lines to regain track

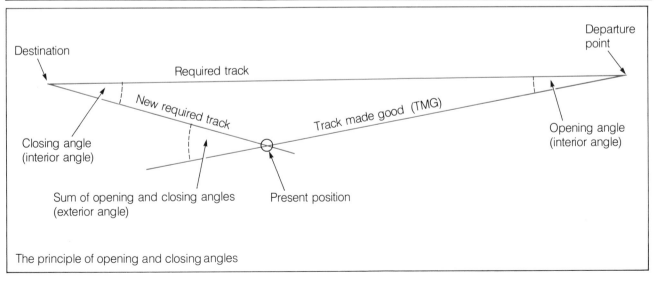

Destination

Departure point

Required track

New required track

Track made good (TMG)

Closing angle (interior angle)

Opening angle (interior angle)

Sum of opening and closing angles (exterior angle)

Present position

The principle of opening and closing angles

Figure 2-65A Methods of Making Track Corrections

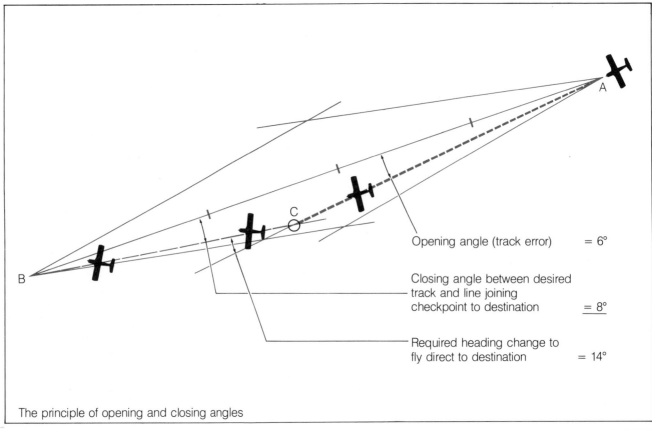

Opening angle (track error)   = 6°

Closing angle between desired
track and line joining
checkpoint to destination   = 8°

Required heading change to
fly direct to destination   = 14°

The principle of opening and closing angles

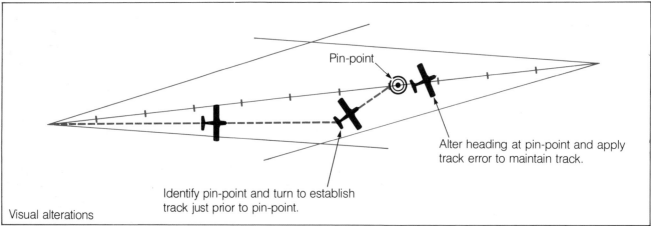

Pin-point

Alter heading at pin-point and apply
track error to maintain track.

Identify pin-point and turn to establish
track just prior to pin-point.

Visual alterations

Figure 2-65B

method must be followed to take the aircraft from its present position off track to a point on the required track. Once this is accomplished we can then take up and fly the new corrected heading. Alternatively, we have the chance of flying direct from the position off track to the destination.

Using the 10 degree drift lines in Figure 2-65, it can be seen that the track made good is widening out from the required track by an angle of 7 degrees. By altering the heading 7 degrees to the right, we now have the heading which produces a track parallel to the required track and is the heading to steer when the required track is regained. (This is not strictly true, because in either

method mentioned below the new heading calculated to keep the aircraft over track may not be exactly correct, due to the fact that the direction of the wind relative to the new heading is altered and drift may not remain what it was before. Yet for most practical purposes the change of drift caused by such a small alteration in heading can be neglected.)

If you decide to return to the required track, the primary method is the double track error method. Simply double the amount of track error or opening angle, and apply this to the original heading in the direction of the required track: the aircraft will regain track in approximately the same period of time as it took to drift off track and the required track will be intercepted again at a distance along track equal to twice the distance from set heading point to the point where the heading change is made (Point A in Figure 2-65). On regaining track it is necessary to subtract half the correction applied to the original heading to obtain the heading to keep the aircraft over the required track.

If a positively identified landmark on the required track can be seen, the visual alteration method can be used. Once again the key fact is the heading change, which would produce a track parallel to the required track. After determining the opening angle and applying it to the heading which produced the error, we now have a heading which we can fly once we are back on the required track. By simply flying visually from the present position (A in Fig 2-65) to the positively identified landmark, the new heading can now be flown and the aircraft should remain on the required track. Now let's look at a practical example of these two methods in Figure 2-66.

We take off from Chilton airport and set heading at 1000 hours over the point where the railway line crosses the Carter River, at the town of Chilton. Our calculations have indicated that we must steer a compass heading 065 degrees on our trip to Twin Cities Airport, 148 miles distant. After 14 minutes (1014 hours) we pin-point ourselves at the north end of Harker Lake, and using the 10 degree drift lines determine that we are 7 degrees to right of track. A heading change of 7 degrees (058 degrees) left would result in a heading whereby we would parallel the required track. But as we wish to regain track using the double track error method, we alter heading to 051 degrees (065 degrees - 14 degrees

= 051 degrees). This new heading is held for an additional 14 minutes and we regain track just south of the bend in the Lisson River at 1028. At this time we alter heading 7 degrees right and steer 058 degrees. Any physical features near or along the track line which will confirm that the track has been regained will be helpful, but if none are available, the heading should be altered at the calculated time. Revised ETA's can be made while flying towards the required track. If we had decided to use the visual alteration method, we could have flown visually to Allerton, which is right on track and easily identifiable, and then steered 058 degrees (065 - 7 = 058) which should keep the aircraft on track.

Some flights are carried out over featureless terrain, and may be more than half completed before a reliable pin-point is located. This is where the opening and closing method can be used, or again the visual alteration method. As we have already discussed the visual alteration method, let's have a look at the principle behind the opening and closing method. Go back a few pages and study the definitions of opening angle and closing angle. By going back to basic geometry again and consulting Figure 2-67, it can be seen that by altering the heading by an amount equal to the *sum* of the opening and closing angles, we should track to destination.

In Figure 2-67 the line A-B passes through Point C where the heading change is made, and is parallel to the required track. At Point C, which is 4 degrees to left of track, a 4 degree right heading change would parallel the track. Angle X equals Angle Y (the closing angle) and using the 10 degree drift lines we can determine that Angle Y equals 7 degrees. Therefore at Point C, an

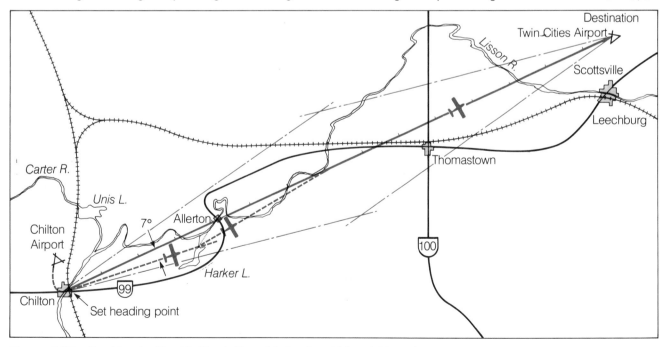

Figure 2-66 Tracking by Double Track Error Method and Visual Alterations

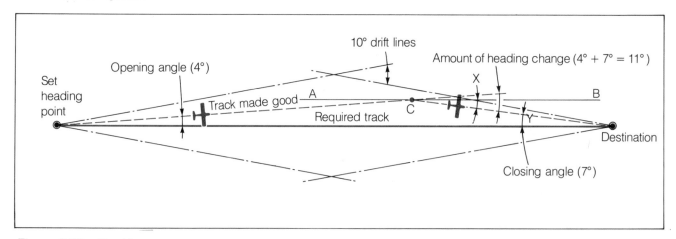

Figure 2-67   Tracking

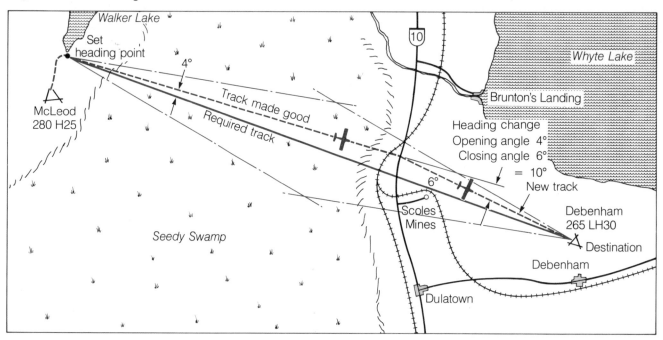

Figure 2-68   Tracking: A Practical Application

11 degree right heading change (4 degrees + 7 degrees = 11 degrees) should permit the aircraft to track directly to destination.

Now let's look at a practical application. In Figure 2-68 the calculated heading to fly from McLeod Airport to Debenham Airport was found to be 105 degrees Compass.

Set-heading time was 0900. No reliable pin-point was available until 35 minutes later, close to where the north-south railway crosses Highway 10, 82 miles along the track. Using the 10 degree drift lines we find the opening angle to be 4 degrees and the closing angle to be 6 degrees. Therefore, in order to fly direct to Debenham Airport, a 10 degree right heading change (4 degrees + 6 degrees = 10 degrees leads onto a heading of 115 degrees (105 + 10 degrees). As the ground speed is found to be 141 knots and there are 49

miles left to go, the revised ETA would be 0956. It should be understood at this time that the opening and closing method can be employed at any distance along the required track, and is not limited to use after passing the half-way point. Alternatively, a visual correction could have been made to the point where the original required track meets the curve in the railway line at Scoles Mines, where a heading of 109 degrees (105 degrees + 4 degrees opening angle) taken up at the time would have kept the aircraft on the track to Debenham.

The Drift Compensation Method

Experienced pilots often establish heading by constantly compensating for drift as the flight progresses. When the heading to maintain a desired track is established by this method, drift angle can then be easily computed if you need it. Visibility must be such that enough check-points are visible to maintain an accurate track.

Select at least two prominent check-points a sufficient distance apart (5 to 10 miles or more, depending on the terrain), on the desired track ahead of the aircraft. Maintain a heading which keeps the nearer check-point aligned with the farther one. When the aircraft and the check-points remain on the same line, the heading indicated on the compass will be the heading which, provided there is no wind change, should keep the aircraft on the track required for the remainder of the flight. To continually compensate for wind effect, select another check-point on track in the distance before the nearer check-point is reached; then repeat the alignment and drift compensation procedure. Calculate ground speed by time and distance between check-points to keep ETA's accurate.

The Flight

Setting Heading

After take-off, establish the aircraft on the desired compass heading for the first leg, either over the airport or over a convenient prominent check-point. Note the time and enter it in the flight log and calculate the ETA for the destination and the first check-point. Remember, to ensure accuracy in determining the actual amount of drift, it is necessary to begin the navigation exercise directly over the planned set-heading point. Immediately after you are established on the first heading, check the chart and pin-points on the ground to confirm that the aircraft is in fact heading in the correct direction.

It is important to bear in mind that the objective of the pilot navigation cross-country exercise is to practise navigation by maintaining accurate headings, calculating and making corrections for drift, and calculating accurate ETA's. Accurate map reading for exact determination of aircraft position is essential to provide the necessary information for calculation of heading and ETA corrections when required.

En Route. Provided the set-heading procedure is properly completed, you can then concentrate on accurate flying, identifying check-points, and maintaining a good look-out. A prior knowledge of ETA over check-points along the route will allow you to anticipate and thereby identify them easily as the flight progresses. However, look-out for other traffic must not be sacrificed to the navigation of the aircraft. Also perform normal in-flight checks at the prescribed intervals.

The Navigation Log

The pilot navigator has little time for log keeping in the air (Fig 2-69), but the following are some of the items that must be recorded:

(1) Each compass heading (use 3 digits — i.e., 037)
(2) The time the aircraft sets out on each compass heading
(3) ETA at destination and planned turning points
(4) Time over or by check-points and turning points
(5) New ground speeds and revised ETA's.

ETA Revisions

At the first positive pin-point, ideally between 10 and 25 miles from the departure point, the ground speed should be calculated and ETA's revised if necessary. Rely on the navigation instruments in the aircraft, rather than inexperienced personal judgment. It is most important to maintain a steady planned heading and airspeed. If you cannot at once recognize the track being made, do not suspect the compass of unreliable behaviour. Continue to hold a steady heading until you reach a recognizable check-point. If a heading indicator is being used, verify its heading frequently with the magnetic compass and reset it as necessary.

Check-Points and Pin-Points

Time is one of the essentials of navigation, so acquire the habit of calculating ETA's for en route check-points. This will help locate check-points by preventing the habit of looking for specific places on the ground too soon or too late. It is imperative that a reliable watch or clock be on board the aircraft during cross-country flights. The number of pin-points on a leg varies according to the length of the leg. Usually one pin-point every 10 minutes is sufficient, but more may be used if necessary. Once the aircraft has passed the pin-point, immediately begin to anticipate the next check-point in the same manner as the previous one was anticipated.

Do not fly a zigzag path from check-point to check-point when the check-points can be readily identified from a position on or near the required track. There is no disgrace in not arriving directly over a check- or turning point. Alteration in heading should be deliberate and aimed at flying in as straight a line as possible.

Diverting to an Alternate Destination

One of the skills required of the pilot navigator is the ability to rapidly estimate a new heading to an alternate

NAVIGATION LOG

From — To	Alt.	IAS	Track (T)	W/V	Hdg. (M)	kts. mph / Dist.	(√) ✓ / D.R. time
			Distances/speeds in				
MELFORT - CHECK PT. #1	↗	90	135	290/20	→	2	2
CHECK PT. #1 - HUMBOLDT	4·5	115	204	290/20	197	43	22
						45	24

FLIGHT LOG

Time	Hdg. (C)	Observations	Actual G/S	E.T.A.
1255	118	OFF MELFORT		
1300	195	OVER CHECK PT. #1 S/HEADING	117	1322
1307		2 MILES E. OF ST. BRIEUX (6°R)		
1307	183	A/HDG TO REGAIN TRACK (2 x 6°) = 12°L		
		G/S 14 MILES IN 7 MIN.	120	1322
1314	189	REGAIN TRACK N. OF LAKE LENORE		
1322		HUMBOLDT		
1327		LAND		
1330		SHUT DOWN		

Figure 2-69 Navigation Log

destination when for various reasons continuation of the flight is impracticable. Computation of headings, speeds, distances, and ETA's in flight involves the same basic procedures as those used in pre-flight planning. However, because of space and time limitations, and having to operate the aircraft simultaneously with computations, the pilot must take advantage of all possible short-cuts. It is rarely practical to actually plot a line on a chart and mark check-points and distances as in pre-flight planning.

With a little practice, headings to alternates can be determined quickly with reasonable accuracy, by interpolation and mental transposition of airways and air routes on the chart or the azimuth information on the compass rose encircling VOR stations. These all have the advantage of already containing the magnetic variation for the general area. Use a pencil or the hand (on edge) as a straight-edge. If airways or a compass rose are not close enough on the chart to be used, an angle may be estimated as being a fraction of the 90 degree angle between the meridians of longitude and parallels of latitude found on the chart. If possible, draw a line freehand on the chart from the divert point to the alternate destination.

Distances can be estimated accurately enough for diversion purposes by using the thumb and index finger as "dividers" applied against the scale on the chart, or easier still, against the mileage lines which were marked along the original track before the flight began. The compass rose circles around VOR stations are all approximately 35 statute (30 nautical) miles in diameter on Canadian 1:500,000 aeronautical charts.

When diversion to an alternate destination becomes necessary, the decision to change to a new heading should be made as early as possible. First consider the distances to all available and suitable alternates, select the one most appropriate, then estimate the heading to the alternate chosen. Turn the aircraft to the new heading and then more accurately estimate drift correction, distance, speed, compass heading, and ETA while proceeding towards the alternate. Under the circumstances it may be advantageous to "hold" over a known check-point while computations are made.

If a suitable choice is available, always divert to the airport which offers the easiest route to follow, such as a highway, river, powerline, etc. This is particularly important if visibility is a factor. If low level navigation is required due to low ceilings keep a careful look-out for obstructions. Diversion is often synonymous with emergency: this is not time to test your pure navigation skills if you don't have to.

To compensate for the wind, which can often be an unknown factor in diverting to an unplanned alternate, establishing a heading by means of drift compensation may be the best expedient. The forward landmarks should be readily identifiable and, if visibility is a factor, they should also be reasonably close to the desired track. Again, rely on the instrument indications and any new heading established by drift compensation will be fairly close to the heading originally estimated for the diversion track.

In-Flight Mental Calculations

Mental arithmetic can be sometimes difficult when flying, and you may add to the following suggestions as your experience increases. When the distance and time is known, finding the ground speed is much easier if the "time" part is a fraction of 60 minutes. 25 NM covered in 12 minutes is 125 kts. We know that 12 minutes multiplied by 5 equals 60; thus, by multiplying the distance covered by 5, the ground speed can be easily determined. Another example is: 40 NM covered in 20 minutes is 120 kts (40 x 3). If a distance marker on a track line coincides with a check-point, the time at the distance marker twice the distance away will be twice the elapsed time.

If You Are Uncertain of Your Position

The danger of jumping to the wrong conclusion is very real when you cannot recognize expected landmarks. There are times when you will be uncertain of your position, but then all pilots experience the same feeling sooner or later. Such moments require calm reasoning and a recognized procedure. The recognized procedure is as follows:

(1) Hold a steady heading and check the heading indicator against the compass.
(2) Check all previous calculations by studying your chart and log.
(3) Check for a possible wind shift.
(4) Draw a circle of uncertainty.
(5) Try to get a bearing using radio aids.

Usually you can establish your position within a short time and continue the flight. You must never assume, however, that you are in a certain position. Check for a possible shift in the wind by drawing a *circle of uncertainty*.

To do this, draw a circle on the chart around the position you would be in if you were on track and on time. The radius of the circle should be 10 per cent of the estimated distance flown since the last confirmed position. Check within the circle of uncertainty for any prominent physical features you have noted on the ground, and when you have positively identified one or more landmarks, fix your position. Remember, positive identification of a distinctive landmark is the only way to get back on track. If you decide that you are definitely lost, do not exhaust your fuel in aimless wandering from one heading to another trying to pick up a landmark. Always work to plan. Notify ATC by radio that you are lost, or try to contact any other control agency. When you have established radio contact, transmit your general position, the amount of fuel remaining in the tanks, ask for whatever assistance you need, and indicate the action you propose to take.

Usually you will have a rough idea of the direction of home base and can turn towards it, while continuing to search for prominent landmarks. "DF steers" are available from ATC in many areas and provided you are within radio range a heading to fly will be freely offered. Do not be too proud or afraid to ask for assistance.

In an extreme emergency you should broadcast a MAYDAY distress message on 121.5 MHz giving the aircraft type, the nature of the emergency, the amount of fuel left, the assistance required, and your immediate intentions. Listen out on the same frequency for instructions. If you have no idea of the direction to fly, set up a triangular pattern at endurance power settings, at the highest practical altitude, to alert the radar network.

If shortage of fuel is becoming a problem, save enough to complete the precautionary landing procedures you have been taught. Pick a suitable field, near habitation if possible, and concentrate on making a good landing.

If no help is available and you have to rely on map reading to find your position, you should proceed as follows:

(1) Fly for maximum range if no landmark is visible.
(2) Using your circle of uncertainty, estimate a heading to home base or the nearest airfield, and fly that heading until you sight a prominent landmark.
(3) Reduce speed to permit more effective observation, and fly a pattern on cardinal headings around this landmark until you can identify it on the chart. You should read from the ground to the chart.
(4) When you have established your position, estimate a new heading to base, calculate your ETA, check the heading indicator, and fly normally, pin-pointing your position as you go along.

Reciprocal Track

For one reason or another, such as a diversion to an alternate, it may be necessary to calculate a track to take you over the route you have just flown. An easy method for mentally calculating the reciprocal of a heading is to add 200 to headings less than 180 degrees and then subtract 20. For headings of more than 180 degrees subtract 200 and then add 20.

Once on the reciprocal track, the allowance for wind will be opposite to that used outbound. If 10 degrees was added to the outbound track to allow for drift, it will now be subtracted from the reciprocal track to obtain a compass heading. This heading should be adequate until a new and more accurate one is calculated. Turn the chart 180 degrees, map read back to a known fix, and then resume normal navigation either back to the point of departure or to an alternate destination.

Low Level Navigation

There may be an occasion, during the cross-country flight, that will necessitate low level navigation. Some of the flying on your private pilot flight test may also be done at low level. Special mention is therefore made now of low level map reading.

The greatest difference in navigating at cross-country altitudes lower than usual is the restricted field of view at low level, which becomes extremely limited when flying over rough or hilly terrain. This, combined with the greater attention that must be given to handling the aircraft, cuts down the time you have to positively identify your landmarks and check-points as they come up. Since you cannot hope to continually compare your check-points with the chart to assist identification, you must pick unique, easily recognizable features. Line features, such as railway lines or roads, that run 90 degrees to the track are used as check-points, and those that run to the turning point are used as lead-in lines.

During low level navigation flight, you have to be on the look-out for obstacles such as TV and radio towers, power lines, factory chimneys, and sharply rising ground. The set-heading procedure should be carried out if possible, before descending to the low level altitude, and navigation should be strictly confined to map reading. Log keeping should be limited to essential items, because of the urgent need to keep a good look-out. When making log entries, check outside frequently if altitude is critical, to avoid flying into the ground. If you become uncertain of your position, if possible climb as high as necessary to give yourself an extended field of view and try to identify a landmark.

Remember that when you are doing cockpit checks you must not bury your head in the cockpit. Complete the first item and then pause to have a thorough look around; complete the next item and look around again; continue in this way until the check has been fully covered. If your low level navigation technique is to be a success, you must develop good handling habits, so that most of your time can be devoted to checking your position and to look-out.

Vagaries of the Magnetic Compass

Vagary means wild motion, eccentricity, freak, wandering about, etc. It suitably describes the actions of the magnetic compass under some conditions of flight.

The mechanical and other reasons for the eccentric behaviour of this instrument will not be discussed here. What is important to know at this time is that the magnetic compass can be relied on only when the aircraft is flying straight, and at a constant airspeed.

When an aircraft on a northerly heading executes a turn, the compass card remains stationary on its pivot or momentarily turns in the opposite direction. This falsely indicates less than the real amount of turn. The compass may be said to lag in turns from a northerly heading.

When an aircraft on a southerly heading executes a turn, the compass card turns faster than the aircraft, instead of remaining stationary on its pivot. This falsely indicates more than the real amount of turn. The compass may be said to lead in turns from a southerly heading.

When an aircraft is maintaining an easterly or westerly heading, changes of speed will cause the compass to falsely indicate a turn; deceleration will indicate a turn to the south and acceleration will indicate a turn to the north.

Weather

Weather conditions should be constantly observed during a cross-country flight. Any sign of deteriorating weather must be seriously assessed and appropriate action taken without delay to keep well clear of it. When you encounter or are about to encounter bad weather, avoid haphazard changes of heading looking for a path through it, as this may disorient you. The navigation exercise then breaks down into a confused search for a way out of the weather. If any doubt exists concerning the weather ahead, to avoid it and keep the navigation of the aircraft intact turn the aircraft completely around and fly the reciprocal of the original required track. Do this by making a standard rate turn through 180 degrees, which should take one minute if the turn is being timed.

Common Sense

Like any other worthwhile endeavour, pilot navigation requires the application of common sense. For example, approximate direction can be verified by such things as the sun, rivers, lakes, the location of prominent landmarks, etc. If the aircraft is equipped with radio, communicate briefly with as many ground stations as reasonably possible. It is sound practice to let flight progress be known and it is always good insurance to have the current weather for the destination and intermediate points, which may be provided by some ground stations. When the flight is apparently going well, do not be lulled into false security and abandon map reading for long intervals. Continually take mental note of fields and other areas on the route which would be suitable for emergency landings. Should something occur which appears to affect the safety of the flight, evaluate the situation carefully; the most prudent action may be to land at the first suitable airport.

When alone in an aircraft it is good practice to refrain from smoking. It would be difficult to fly the aircraft and attempt to retrieve a lighted cigarette that has fallen beyond reach or to cope with a fire that had started from an improperly extinguished match. Do not hold charts or other pilot navigation material too near open windows, as there is a strong suction at such points which can easily snatch light articles out of an aircraft in flight. Last but not least, make sure that more than one serviceable writing instrument is available.

Instrument Flying

Instrument flight is a key factor in extending the utilization of an aircraft. Since a great number of general aviation aircraft now have this capability and their numbers continue to increase, more and more pilots are choosing to broaden their own competence to include control of an aircraft by reference to flight instruments alone. When you begin instrument flight training, you will be no stranger to the instruments nor to their indications for any flight attitude or manoeuvre. What will be strange at first is that these same instruments, which have always been predictable during visual flight, now seem to become unruly and frequently indicate flight attitudes with which your normally reliable senses do not agree.

Of all our senses, vision is probably the one we rely upon the most. Other senses can be trying to tell us something but it is vision we depend upon to help us make decisions. However, take normal vision away and we suddenly become prone to believing information given by other senses which, in the case of flight by instrument references alone, can be completely false. In spite of what our senses insist on telling us, when the turn needle of the turn-and-bank indicator shows a turn in a certain direction, the aircraft is turning in that direction; when the nose of the miniature aircraft is below the horizon bar of the attitude indicator, the nose of the real aircraft is below the real horizon. When the airspeed indicator shows a steady increase in speed during normal cruise flight, the instrument hasn't suddenly become unserviceable; speed is increasing and the aircraft is most likely in an undesired nose-down attitude. During instrument flight you must put complete faith in the instrument indications and never react to a bodily sensation, no matter how strong it is. The sooner you accept this fact, the more quickly and deeply the learning process develops.

It may help if you lower the pilot's seat so that the view of the instruments is unstrained and natural. For example, you will find that when you look at the attitude indicator with as little downward slope as possible, the instrument simulates the real horizon more convincingly.

If the aircraft is equipped with arm rests, full use should be made of them, especially in the case of the left arm, since it is the one generally used to manipulate the control column. This allows the application of the required control pressures without having to constantly make allowances for the weight differential of the arm. Arm rests also provide a sense of unity with the aircraft. The seat belt should be fastened snugly; when the body is too free to move about in the seat, false sensory impressions become more acute and believable.

There are several methods for learning instrument flight, but in this text groups of instruments will be presented as they relate to control function as well as aircraft performance. Instruments will therefore be grouped as follows:

(1) Pitch Instruments.
    (a) Attitude Indicator
    (b) Altimeter
    (c) Airspeed Indicator
    (d) Vertical Speed Indicator
(2) Bank Instruments.
    (a) Attitude Indicator
    (b) Turn-and-Bank Indicator
    (c) Heading Indicator
(3) Power Instruments.
    (a) Tachometer
    (b) Airspeed Indicator

Those instruments which provide the most pertinent and essential information for a particular manoeuvre will be referred to as primary instruments and others as supporting instruments. The pitch, bank, and power supporting instruments necessary to maintain straight and level flight at a constant airspeed are:

(1) Altimeter. Provides the most pertinent altitude information and is therefore primary for pitch.

(2) Heading Indicator. Provides the most pertinent bank or heading information ("banking" normally

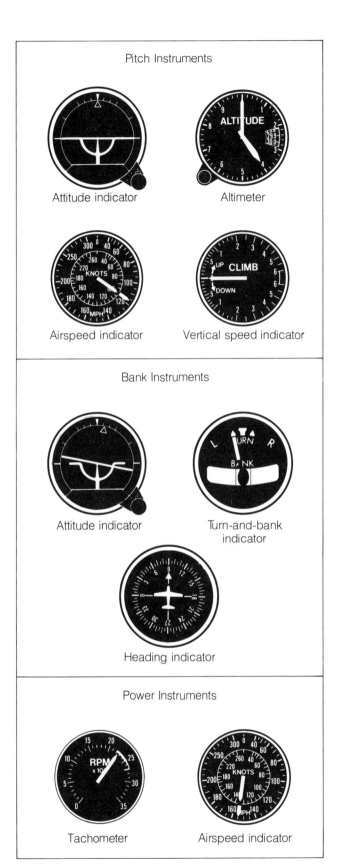

Figure 2-70   Instruments

means "turning") and is therefore primary for bank.

(3) **Airspeed Indicator.** Provides the most pertinent information concerning performance in terms of power output (in level flight) and is therefore primary for power.

The concept of primary and supporting instruments does not lessen the value of any particular instrument. The attitude indicator is the basic attitude reference. It is the only instrument which instantly and directly portrays the actual flight attitude, and when available should always be used in establishing and maintaining pitch and bank attitudes.

The terms "direct indicating" and "indirect indicating" will be used concerning certain instruments. A "direct" indication is the instantaneous reflection of pitch and bank by the miniature aircraft relative to the horizon bar of the attitude indicator. The airspeed indicator, altimeter, and vertical speed indicator give "indirect" indications of pitch attitude at a given power setting. The heading indicator and turn needle give "indirect" indications of bank attitude.

Fundamental Skills

During instrument training, three fundamental skills are involved in all instrument flight manoeuvres: instrument cross-check, instrument interpretation, and aircraft control. A measure of proficiency in instrument flying will be your ability to integrate these skills into unified, smooth, positive control responses to maintain any prescribed flight path.

Cross-Check

Cross-checking is the continuous and logical observation of instruments for attitude and performance information. In instrument flying, the pilot maintains an attitude by reference to instruments which when combined with power will produce the desired result in performance. Due to human error and differences in aircraft performance under various atmospheric and loading conditions, it is impossible to establish an attitude and have performance remain constant for a long period of time. These variables make appropriate changes in aircraft attitude.

The following cross-check faults are frequent problems:

(1) *Fixation,* or staring at a single instrument, usually occurs for a good reason but with poor results; for

instance, you stare at an altimeter which reads 200 feet below assigned altitude and wonder how the needle got there. Meanwhile a heading change occurs unnoticed and more errors accumulate.

(2) *Omission* of an instrument from cross-checking is another likely fault. It may be caused by failure to anticipate significant instrument indications following attitude changes: for example, you roll out from a 180 degree turn referring to the attitude indicator alone and neglect to check the heading indicator for constant heading information.

(3) *Emphasizing* a single instrument, instead of the combination of instruments necessary for attitude information, is an understandable fault during initial stages of training. But it is poor technique. One can maintain reasonably close altitude control with the attitude indicator, but the altitude cannot be held with precision without including the altimeter in the cross-check.

Instrument Interpretation

The second fundamental skill, instrument interpretation, requires the most thorough study and analysis. It begins with the understanding of each instrument's operating principles. Then comes the application of this knowledge to the performance of the aircraft, the particular manoeuvres to be executed, and the cross-check and control techniques applicable to that aircraft and the flight condition in which it is operating. For example (Fig 2-71), if full power is used in a light aircraft for a 5 minute climb from near sea level, the attitude indicator shows the miniature aircraft 2 bar widths (twice the thickness of the miniature aircraft wings) above the horizon bar. The aircraft is climbing at 500 feet per minute as shown on the vertical speed indicator, and at an airspeed of 90 knots, as shown on the airspeed indicator. With the power available in this particular aircraft and the attitude selected by the pilot, the performance is shown on the instruments.

Now set up the identical picture in a jet aircraft. With the same aircraft attitude as in the first example the vertical speed indicator in the jet reads 2,000 feet per minute, and the airspeed indicates 300 knots. As you learn the performance capabilities of an aircraft, you will interpret the instrument indications in terms of the attitude of the aircraft. If the pitch attitude is to be determined, the airspeed indicator, altimeter, vertical speed indicator, and attitude indicator provide the necessary information. If the bank attitude is to be determined, the attitude indicator, turn-and-bank indicator,

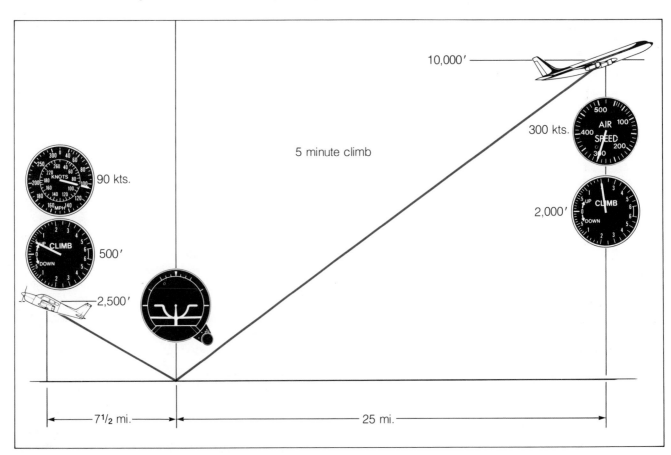

Figure 2-71   Power + Attitude = Performance

and heading indicator must be interpreted.

For each manoeuvre, a combination of instruments must be interpreted in order to control aircraft attitude during the manoeuvre.

Aircraft Control

The third fundamental instrument flying skill is control. With the instruments substituted for outside references, the necessary control responses and thought processes are the same as those for controlling aircraft performance by means of outside references. Aircraft control has four components: pitch control, bank control, power control, and yaw control.

(1) Pitch Control. Pitch control is controlling the rotation of the aircraft about the lateral axis by movement of the elevators. After interpreting the pitch attitude from the proper flight instruments, control pressures must be exerted to effect the desired pitch attitude.

(2) Bank Control. Bank Control is controlling the angle made by the wing and the horizon. After interpreting the bank attitude from the appropriate instruments, the necessary pressures must be exerted to move the ailerons to effect the desired bank attitude.

(3) Power Control. Power Control is used when interpretation of the flight instruments indicates a need for a change in thrust.

(4) Yaw Control. Yaw control is controlling the movement of the aircraft about the normal (vertical) axis. Yaw control is used when interpretion of the instruments indicates a need to improve the flight balance of the aircraft. In all normal attitudes and flight configurations, the ball of the turn-and-bank indicator is always the primary instrument for balance.

Trim is used to relieve all possible control pressures after a desired attitude has been attained. An improperly trimmed aircraft requires constant control pressures, produces tension, distracts attention from cross-checking, and contributes to abrupt and erratic attitude control.

Pre-Flight Check

Before any flight make a thorough check of all instruments and equipment in the aircraft. The aircraft flight manual lists the items to be checked. They may vary as to sequence and content from the checks shown below.

Before Starting Engine

(1) Appropriate documents and charts
(2) Radio equipment — off
(3) Suction gauge — proper markings
(4) Pitot cover — removed
(5) Airspeed indicator — proper reading
(6) Turn-and-bank indicator — needle centred, tube full of fluid
(7) Vertical speed indicator — zero indication
(8) Magnetic compass — full of fluid
(9) Clock — wind and set to the correct time
(10) Engine instruments — proper markings and readings.

After Starting Engine

(This text presumes that power to operate the gyro wheels of gyroscopic instruments is derived from a mechanical source. If the power source is a venturi tube, instruments may be summarily checked for operation after the engine is started but they cannot be considered as operationally reliable until the aircraft is well established in flight.)

(1) Suction Gauge or Electrical Indicators. Check the source of power for the gyro instruments. If the gyros are electrically driven, check the generators and inverters for proper operation.

(2) Pitot Head. Heat checked.

(3) Magnetic Compass. The compass must move freely on its pivot and the bowl must be full of fluid. Check its accuracy by comparing the indicated heading against a known heading (a runway heading, for example).

(4) Heading Indicator. Allow 5 minutes after engine start for the gyro rotor of vacuum operated instruments to attain normal operating speed. Before taxiing out, set the heading indicator to correspond with the magnetic compass heading. Before take-off, recheck the indicator. If the magnetic compass and deviation card are accurate, the heading indicator reading should be approximately that of the runway heading when the aircraft is aligned with the runway centre-line.

Electric gyros should also be set and checked against known headings. Allow 3 minutes for the electric gyro to attain operating speed.

(5) Attitude Indicator. Allow 5 minutes for the gyro wheel to attain normal rotor speed. If the horizon bar erects to the horizontal position and remains at the correct position for the attitude of the aircraft, or if it begins to vibrate after this attitude is reached and then slowly stops vibrating altogether, the instrument is operating properly. If the horizon bar fails to remain in the horizontal position during straight taxiing, or tips in excess of 5 degrees during taxi turns, the instrument is unreliable.

Adjust the miniature aircraft with reference to the horizon bar for the particular aircraft while on the ground. For some tricycle-geared aircraft, a slightly nose-low attitude on the ground will give a level flight attitude at normal cruising speed.

(6) Altimeter. With the altimeter set to the current altimeter setting, note any variation between the field elevation and the altimeter indication. Normally, the maximum acceptable tolerance is plus or minus 50 feet.

(7) Turn-and-Bank Indicator. Check the turn needle for right and left deflection and for positive return to the centre position. The check can be made by noting the indications during taxi turns. The ball should move freely in the tube and no bubbles should appear in the fluid.

(8) Vertical Speed Indicator. The instrument should read zero. If it does not, tap the panel gently. If it stays off the zero reading and is not adjustable, the ground indication will have to be interpreted as the zero position in flight.

(9) Engine Instruments. Check for proper readings.

Taxiing

While taxiing to the take-off point you have an opportunity to check some of the instruments. Turns in either direction will permit testing of the heading indicator, ADF, turn-and-bank indicator, and attitude indicator.

Straight and Level Flight

Straight and level flight is related to cruise attitude, except that in straight and level flight, power settings and airspeeds may vary according to operational requirements. In the case of cruise attitude this power

setting (and subsequent airspeed) is specified so as to establish a fixed reference datum to which all other attitudes may be related.

Pitch Control

The pitch instruments are the attitude indicator, the altimeter, the vertical speed indicator and the airspeed indicator.

In level flight, the pitch attitude varies with airspeed. At low cruising speeds, the level flight attitude is nose-high (Fig 2-72, left); at high cruising speeds, the level flight attitude is nose-low (Fig 2-72, middle). Figure 2-72 (right) shows the attitude at normal cruising speeds.

The attitude indicator gives a direct indication of pitch attitude. The desired pitch attitude is attained by raising or lowering the miniature aircraft in relation to the horizon bar by means of elevator control. This corresponds to the way pitch attitude is adjusted in visual flight by raising or lowering the nose of the aircraft in relation to the natural horizon.

When practising pitch control by means of the attitude indicator only, first restrict displacement of the horizon bar to 1 bar width (up or down) then progress to 2 and 3 bar widths.

Remove the instrument training hood from time to time and visually compare the indications on the attitude indicator with the aircraft's position with respect to the natural horizon. Note that pitch attitude changes for corrections to level flight by reference to instruments seem much smaller than those commonly used for visual flight. Note especially that with the aircraft correctly trimmed for level flight, the elevator movement and the control pressures necessary to effect these standard pitch changes are usually very slight.

It is important to learn to relax while flying by instruments. First, you cannot feel control pressure changes with a tight grip on the controls. Relaxing and learning to control with your eyes and your head instead of your muscles usually takes considerable conscious effort during early stages of instrument training. It may

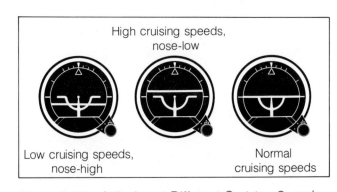

Figure 2-72   Attitudes at Different Cruising Speeds

help if you visualize the attitude of the aircraft, as well as any movements taking place which will change the attitude. Second, make the pitch changes smooth and small, yet with a positive pressure. Third, with the aircraft properly trimmed for level flight, momentarily release all pressure on the elevator control when you become aware of tenseness. This will remind you that the aircraft is stable and strives to maintain level flight by itself.

At a constant thrust, any deviation from level flight (except in turbulent air) must be the result of a pitch change. The altimeter, therefore, gives you an indirect indication of the pitch attitude in level flight, assuming constant power. Since the altitude should remain constant when the aircraft is in level flight, any deviation from the desired altitude shows the need for a pitch change. If you are gaining altitude the nose must be lowered. How much? And how can it be done by reference to the altimeter alone?

The ratio of movement of the altimeter needle is as important as its direction of movement in maintaining level flight without the use of the attitude indicator. An excessive pitch deviation from level flight results in a relatively rapid change of altitude, while a slight pitch deviation causes a slow change. Thus, if the altimeter needle moves rapidly clockwise, presume a considerable nose-high flight attitude. Conversely, if the needle moves slowly counter-clockwise to indicate a slightly nose-low attitude, presume that the pitch correction necessary to regain the desired altitude is small. As you add the altimeter to the attitude indicator in the cross-check, learn to recognize the rate of movement of the altimeter needle for a given pitch change as shown on the attitude indicator.

When first practising control of pitch in an aircraft without an attitude indicator, make small pitch changes by visual references and note the rate of movement of the altimeter. Note the pitch change giving the slowest steady rate of change on the altimeter. Then practise small pitch corrections until you can control them by interpretation of the rate of needle movement.

Your instructor may demonstrate an excessive nose-down deviation (indicated by rapid movement of the altimeter needle) and then show the result of improper corrective technique. The normal impulse is to make a large pitch correction in a hurry, but this inevitably leads to overcontrolling; the needle slows down, then reverses direction and finally indicates an excessive nose-high deviation. The result is erratic and increasingly extreme control movements. The correct technique, which is slower and smoother, will return the aircraft to the desired attitude more quickly, with positive control and no confusion. When a pitch error is detected corrective action should be taken promptly, but with light control pressures and with two distinct changes of attitude. First is a change of attitude to stop the needle movement; second is a change of attitude to return to the desired altitude.

When altimeter needle movements are observed, apply just enough elevator pressure to slow down the rate of needle movement. If it slows down abruptly, ease off some of the pressure until the needle continues to move, but slowly. Slow needle movement means that the aircraft attitude is close to level flight. Add a little more corrective pressure to stop the direction of needle movement. When it stops moving and remains stationary the aircraft is in level flight; therefore relax control pressures carefully, continue to cross-check, and then adjust the pitch attitude with elevator pressure for the rate of change of altimeter needle movement required to return to the desired altitude.

Practise predetermined altitude changes using the altimeter alone, then in combination with the attitude indicator. As a rule of thumb, for corrections of less than 100 feet use a half-bar width correction; for corrections of more than 100 feet use a full bar width correction.

The vertical speed indicator gives an indirect indication of pitch attitude and is both a trend and a rate instrument. As a trend instrument, it shows the initial vertical movement of the aircraft which, disregarding turbulence, can be considered a reflection of pitch change. To maintain level flight, use the vertical speed indicator in conjunction with the altimeter and attitude indicator. Note any "up" or "down" trend of the needle from zero and apply a very light corrective elevator pressure. As the needle returns to zero, relax the corrective pressure. If control pressures have been smooth and light, the needle will react promptly and slowly and the altimeter will show little or no change of altitude.

Used as a rate instrument, the vertical speed indicator's *lag* characteristics must be considered. Lag refers to the delay involved before the needle attains a stable indication following a pitch change. Lag is directly proportional to the speed and magnitude of a pitch change. If a slow, smooth pitch change is initiated, the needle will move, with minimum lag, to a point of deflection corresponding to the extent of the pitch change and then stabilize as the aerodynamic forces are balanced in the climb or descent. A large and abrupt pitch change will produce erratic needle movement and also introduce greater time delay (lag) before the needle stabilizes. Take care not to "chase the needle" when flight through turbulent conditions produces erratic needle movements.

In using the vertical speed indicator as a rate instrument and combining it with the altimeter and attitude indicator to maintain level flight, keep this in mind: the distance the altimeter has moved from the desired altitude governs the rate at which you should return to that altitude.

A rule of thumb is to make an attitude change that will result in a vertical speed rate that is approximately double the error in altitude. For example, if off altitude 100 feet, the rate of return should be approximately 200 feet per minute. If off more than 100 feet, the correction should be correspondingly greater but should never exceed the optimum rate of climb or descent for the aircraft at a given airspeed and configuration. While returning to an altitude, the vertical speed indicator is the primary pitch instrument.

The airspeed indicator presents an indirect indication of the pitch attitude. At a constant power setting and pitch attitude, the airspeed remains constant. If the pitch attitude lowers, airspeed increases and the nose should be raised. If the pitch attitude rises, airspeed decreases and the nose should be lowered. A rapid change in airspeed indicates a large pitch change, and a slow change of airspeed indicates a small pitch change. The apparent lag in airspeed indications with pitch changes varies among different aircraft and is due to the time required for the aircraft to accelerate or decelerate when the pitch attitude is changed. There is no appreciable lag due to the construction or operation of the instrument.

Pitch control in level flight is a question of scanning and interpretation of the instrument panel for whatever information the instruments present that will enable you to visualize and control pitch attitude. Pilots should use the instruments that give the best information for controlling the aircraft in any given manoeuvre and also check the other instruments to aid in maintaining the primary instruments at the desired indication.

The primary instrument is the one that gives the most pertinent information for any particular manoeuvre. It is usually the one that you should hold at a constant indication. Which instrument, for example, is primary for pitch control in level flight? This question should be considered in the context of specific aircraft, weather conditions, operational conditions, and other factors.

Attitude changes must be detected and interpreted instantly for immediate control action in high performance aircraft. On the other hand, a pilot in a slower aircraft may rely on the altimeter for primary pitch information, especially if too much reliance on the attitude indicator fails to provide the necessary precise information. Whether to regard the altimeter or the attitude indicator as primary is a question of which approach best helps to control attitude. In this text, the altimeter is normally considered as the primary pitch instrument during level flight.

Bank Control

The *bank attitude* of an aircraft is the angle between the lateral axis of the aircraft and the natural horizon. To maintain a straight and level flight path, keep the wings of the aircraft level with the horizon (assuming that the aircraft is in co-ordinated flight). Any deviation from straight flight resulting from bank error should be corrected by co-ordinated aileron and rudder pressure.

The instruments used for bank control are the attitude indicator, the heading indicator, and the turn-and-bank indicator (Fig 2-73). The attitude indicator shows any change in bank attitude directly and instantly. On the standard attitude indicator, the angle of bank is shown pictorially by the relationship of the miniature aircraft to the attitude indicator bar, and by the alignment of the pointer with the banking scale at the top of the instrument. On the face of the standard instrument, small angles of bank can be difficult to detect by reference to the miniature aircraft, therefore the position of the scale pointer is a good check against the apparent miniature aircraft position. Disregarding precession error, small deviations from straight co-ordinated flight can be readily detected on the scale pointer. Until you become accustomed to the use of the instrument, you may be bothered by the fact that the scale pointer moves in a direction opposite to the direction of bank shown by the miniature aircraft. A bank indication of 30 degrees to the right of the zero, or nose position, indicates a 30 degree left banking attitude.

One advantage of the attitude indicator is that it offers an immediate indication of both pitch and bank attitude in a single glance. Even with the precession errors associated with many attitude indicators, the quick attitude presentation requires less visual effort and time for positive control than do the other flight instruments.

The bank attitude of an aircraft in co-ordinated flight is shown indirectly on the heading indicator, since banking results in a turn and change in heading. A rapid movement of the heading indicator in co-ordinated flight indicates a large angle of bank, whereas a slow movement reflects a small angle of bank, assuming the same airspeed in both instances. When you note deviations from straight flight on the heading indicator, make the correction to the desired heading by using an angle of bank no greater than the number of degrees to be turned. In any case, limit bank corrections to a bank

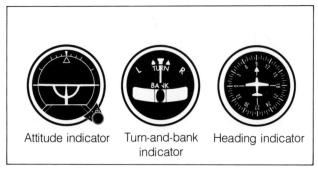

Attitude indicator   Turn-and-bank   Heading indicator
                       indicator

Figure 2-73   Instruments Used for Bank Control

angle no greater than that required for a standard rate turn. Use of larger bank angles normally results in overcontrolling and erratic bank control.

The turn needle of the turn-and-bank indicator gives an indirect indication of the bank attitude of the aircraft. When the turn needle is exactly centred, the aircraft is in straight flight. When the needle is displaced from centre, the aircraft is turning in the direction of the displacement. Thus, if the ball is centred, a left displacement of the turn needle means the left wing is low and the aircraft is in a left turn. Return to straight flight is accomplished by co-ordinated aileron and rudder pressures.

In turbulent air the turn needle oscillates from side to side. Therefore you must interpolate or "average" the fluctuations. When the deflection is greater on one side of centre than the other, the aircraft is turning in that direction. The adjustment of the turn needle can be checked by placing the aircraft in straight flight by reference to the other bank instruments; if the turn needle indicates a deflection, interpret this position of the needle as the centre position. Abrupt or unco-ordinated use of aileron and rudder, as well as flight in turbulent air, causes oscillation of the turn needle, making if difficult to interpret. When using the instrument to maintain straight flight, apply control pressures very lightly and smoothly to avoid overcontrolling and oscillation of the needle.

The ball of the turn-and-bank indicator is actually a separate instrument, conveniently located under the turn needle because the two instruments are used together. This instrument is best used as an indication of balance or "quality" rather than as a direct indication of attitude. When the ball is centred within its glass tube the manoeuvre being executed is, from a co-ordinated bank and your viewpoint, balanced. However, if the ball is out of its centre location the aircraft is either slipping or skidding and the side to which the ball has rolled indicates the direction of the slip or skid. For example, if the ball is to the left of centre, the aircraft is slipping or skidding to the left; if it is to the right of the centre, the aircraft is slipping or skidding to the right.

To differentiate between a slip and a skid consider the following:

(1) Side-slip. If the needle is centred and the ball is displaced from centre, the aircraft is side-slipping (Fig 2-74, left).
(2) Skid. If the ball is displaced to one side and the needle is displaced to the opposite side (Fig 2-74, middle), the aircraft is skidding.
(3) Slip. If both the needle and ball are displaced to the same side of centre (Fig 2-74, right), the aircraft is slipping.

It is good policy in instrument flight to use the ball

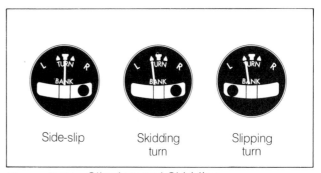

| Side-slip | Skidding turn | Slipping turn |

Figure 2-74 Slipping and Skidding

primarily to determine the quality of a manoeuvre. For example:

(1) In the slipping turn shown in Figure 2-74 (right), the needle shows that the aircraft is turning at a standard rate which would normally be (for illustration purposes) about 17 degrees of bank. However, since the ball is also displaced to the same side, the angle of bank during this particular turn would actually be much more than 17 degrees.
(2) In the skidding turn shown in Figure 2-74 (middle), the needle again shows a standard rate turn which normally requires an angle of bank (depending on airspeed) of about 17 degrees. However, since the ball displacement is opposite to that of the needle, the angle of bank will be much less than 17 degrees.

When the needle of a turn-and-bank indicator is displaced from centre, assuming non-turbulent air, the aircraft is positively turning in the direction indicated; however, regardless of its direction of displacement, the wings may be banked either right or left. The ball imparts no positive attitude or performance information by itself. The ball can be left of centre while the aircraft is turning left or right, or vice versa; it can be displaced to the right of centre with the aircraft banked either to the right or left. But so long as the ball is kept centred the needle of the turn-and-bank indicator positively shows direction of bank and direction of turn.

Since under most instrument flight conditions the ball of the turn-and-bank indicator should be properly centred, how is this latter controlled? If the ball is displaced to the left it may be centred by right aileron pressure, but this may introduce an undesirable bank and turn to the right (or vice versa). The ball may be centred by appropriate rudder pressure but this too may introduce unwanted yaw and subsequent turning.

The answer to controlling and trimming an aircraft in straight and level flight by means of the turn-and-bank indicator requires a return to basic control principles — i.e., control yaw with the rudder and keep the wings level with aileron. Therefore, when flying straight and level using the turn-and-bank indicator for bank attitude control, prevent yawing with appropriate rudder pressure, and keep the wings level (and the ball centred) with appropriate aileron pressure. The needle will remain centred; it will not deflect while heading is constantly maintained, since no turn exists.

However, if you have some reason to feel that the needle and the ball require separate actions, control the ball with rudder, since the ball moves parallel to a plane passing through the rudder pedals, and control the needle with aileron, since the ailerons are the primary controls for bank and bank is primary to turning (the needle indicates direction and rate of turn).

The problem associated with the "separate action" theory is that although the ball will positively indicate that the aircraft is slipping or skidding, just which one of these the aircraft is doing can only be determined by reference to the needle. Furthermore, the needle will not positively indicate a banked attitude. An aircraft could be in a banked attitude and yet the needle could remain centred or indicate a turn in the opposite direction, if controls are not co-ordinated.

When flying solely by reference to instruments in a single-engine aircraft, there is no reason for uncoordinated use of the controls. If the ball is kept centred the needle will always positively indicate two of the most important facets of instrument flight: the direction in which the aircraft is turning and the rate at which it is turning. If angle of bank information is important, under the circumstances it may be interpolated readily.

Power Control

Power control must be related to its effect on altitude and airspeed, since any change in power setting results in a change in the airspeed or the altitude of the aircraft. At any given airspeed, the power setting determines whether the aircraft is in level flight, in a climb, or in a descent. If you increase the power while in straight and level flight and hold the airspeed constant, the aircraft will climb. If you decrease the power while holding the airspeed constant, the aircraft will descend. On the other hand, if you hold altitude constant, the power applied will determine the airspeed.

For changes in airspeed in straight and level flight, pitch, bank, and power must be co-ordinated in order to maintain constant altitude and heading. When power is changed to vary airspeed in straight and level flight, a propeller-driven aircraft tends to change attitude around all axes of movement. Therefore, to maintain constant altitude and heading you will need to apply various control pressures in proportion to the change in power. When you add power to increase airspeed, the pitch instruments will show a climb unless you apply forward elevator control pressure as the airspeed

changes. When you increase power, the aircraft tends to yaw and roll to the left unless you apply counteracting aileron and rudder pressures.

Power control and airspeed changes are much easier when you know in advance the approximate power settings necessary to maintain various airspeeds in straight and level flight. Consider the example of an aircraft which requires 2300 RPM to maintain a normal cruising airspeed of 120 knots and 1900 RPM to maintain 90 knots. While the basic attitude is maintained on the attitude indicator, to reduce airspeed in straight and level flight, specific pitch, bank, and power control requirements are detected on the following primary instruments:

(1) Altimeter — Primary Pitch
(2) Heading Indicator — Primary Bank
(3) Airspeed Indicator — Primary Power

Supporting bank instruments are the turn-and-bank indicator and the attitude indicator; supporting pitch instruments are the vertical speed indicator and the attitude indicator. The supporting power instrument is the tachometer.

As you make a smooth power reduction to approximately 1900 RPM the tachometer becomes the primary power instrument. As the thrust decreases be ready to apply rudder, elevator, and aileron control pressure the instant the pitch and bank instruments show a deviation from altitude and heading. Assuming smooth air, as airspeed decreases a proportionate increase in pitch attitude is required to maintain altitude. Similarly, effective torque control means maintaining heading with co-ordinated rudder and aileron pressures.

As the power is reduced, the altimeter is primary for pitch, the heading indicator is primary for bank, and the tachometer is momentarily primary for power. Control pressures should be trimmed as the aircraft decelerates. As the airspeed approaches the desired airspeed of 90 mph, the tachometer is adjusted to 1900 RPM and becomes the supporting power instrument.

Practising airspeed changes in straight and level flight provides an excellent means of developing increased proficiency in all three basic instrument skills, and brings out some common errors to be expected during training. Having learned to control the aircraft in a "clean" configuration, increase proficiency in cross-check and control by practising speed changes while extending or retracting the flaps. While practising be sure to comply with the airspeed limitations specified in the aircraft flight manual for flap operation.

Pronounced attitude changes may be necessary in order to maintain straight and level flight as the flaps are lowered. In some aircraft the nose tends to pitch down and lift increases momentarily (at partial flap settings), followed by a marked increase in drag as the flaps approach their maximum extension. Control technique varies according to the lift and drag characteristics of each aircraft. Accordingly, knowledge of the power settings and trim changes associated with different combinations of airspeed and flap configurations will reduce instrument cross-check and interpretation problems.

Common Errors

Heading Errors. These usually result from the following faults:

(1) Failure to cross-check the heading indicator, especially during changes in power or pitch attitude.
(2) Misinterpretation of changes in heading, with resulting corrections in the wrong direction.
(3) Failure to correct small heading deviations. Unless zero error in heading is your goal, you will tolerate larger and larger deviations.
(4) Correcting with improper bank attitude. If you correct a 10 degree error with a 20 degree bank correction, you can turn past the desired heading before you have the bank established, which means another correction in the opposite direction.

Pitch Errors. These usually result from the following faults:

(1) Improper adjustment of the miniature aircraft. Check the attitude indicator and make any necessary adjustment in the miniature aircraft for level flight indication at normal cruising airspeed.
(2) Insufficient cross-check and interpretation of pitch instruments.
(3) Failure to interpret the attitude indicator in terms of the existing airspeed.
(4) Late pitch corrections. When the altimeter shows a 40 foot error, there is a reluctance to correct it, for fear of overcontrolling. If overcontrolling is the error, the more you practise small corrections and find the cause of overcontrol, the closer you will be able to hold your altitude.
(5) Chasing the vertical speed indications. This tendency can be corrected by proper cross-check of other pitch instruments, as well as by increasing your understanding of the instrument characteristics.

Power Errors. These usually have the following causes:

(1) Failure to know the power settings appropriate to various airspeeds or drag configurations.
(2) Abrupt use of throttle.
(3) Failure to "lead" the airspeed when making power changes. For example, during an airspeed reduction in level flight, adjust the throttle to maintain the slower speed before the airspeed reaches the desired level.
(4) Fixation on airspeed or tachometer during airspeed changes, resulting in erratic control of both airspeed and power.

Trim Errors. These errors are usually caused by:

(1) Improper adjustment of seat or rudder pedals for comfortable position of legs and feet.
(2) Faulty sequence in trim technique. Trim should be used not as a substitute for controls, but to relieve pressures already held to stabilize attitude.
(3) Excessive amounts of trim. Use trim frequently and in small amounts.

Straight Climbs and Descents

Climbs

Details of the technique for entering a climb vary according to airspeed on entry and the type of climb (predetermined airspeed and predetermined rate) desired. (Heading and trim control are maintained as discussed under straight and level flight.)

Entries. To enter a predetermined airspeed climb from cruising airspeed, raise the nose of the miniature aircraft to the approximate nose-high indication for the predetermined climbing speed. Control pressures will vary as the aircraft decelerates. Power may be advanced to the climb setting simultaneously with the pitch change, or after the pitch change is established and the airspeed approaches climbing speed. If the transition from level flight is smooth, the vertical speed indicator will show an immediate trend upward, continue moving slowly, and stop at a rate appropriate to the stabilized airspeed and attitude.

Once the aircraft is stabilized in the climb at a constant airspeed and attitude, the airspeed indicator is primary for pitch and the heading indicator remains primary for bank. Monitor the tachometer to ensure that the climb power setting is being maintained. If the climb attitude is correct for the power setting selected, the airspeed will stabilize at the desired speed. If the airspeed is low or high, make an appropriate small pitch correction.

The technique for entering a predetermined rate climb is very similar to that used for a predetermined airspeed climb from climb airspeed. As power is increased to the approximate setting for the desired rate, simultaneously raise the nose of the miniature aircraft to the climb attitude for the desired airspeed and rate of climb. As the power is increased, the airspeed indicator is primary for pitch control until the vertical speed approaches the desired value. As the vertical speed needle stabilizes, it becomes primary for pitch control and the airspeed indicator becomes primary for power control.

Pitch and power corrections must be closely co-ordinated. For example, if the vertical speed is correct but the airspeed is low, add power. As the power is increased, lower the nose slightly to maintain constant vertical speed. If the vertical speed is high and the

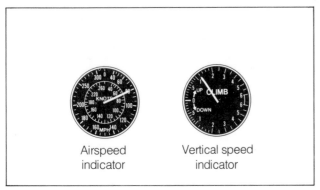

Airspeed indicator   Vertical speed indicator

Figure 2-75   Correcting Pitch and Power

airspeed is low (Fig 2-75), lower the nose slightly and note the increase in airspeed to determine whether or not a power change is also necessary. Familiarity with the power settings helps to keep pitch and power corrections at a minimum.

Levelling Off. To level off from a climb and maintain an altitude, it is necessary to start levelling off before reaching the desired altitude. The amount of lead varies with rate of climb. If the aircraft is climbing at 500 feet per minute (fpm), it will continue to climb at a decreasing rate throughout the transition to level flight. An effective practice is to lead the altitude by 10 per cent of the vertical speed shown (500 fpm/50 foot lead).

To level off at cruising airspeed, apply smooth, steady forward elevator pressure toward level flight attitude for the speed desired. The vertical speed needle will move slowly toward zero, the altimeter needle will move more slowly, and the airspeed will show acceleration. Once the altimeter, attitude indicator, and vertical speed indicator show level flight, constant changes in pitch control will have to be made as the airspeed increases. As the airspeed approaches cruising speed, reduce power to the cruise setting.

Descents

A descent can be made at a variety of airspeeds and attitudes by reducing power and adjusting the pitch to a predetermined attitude. Until the airspeed stabilizes at a constant speed, the only flight instrument providing a positive attitude reference by itself is the attitude indicator. Without the attitude indicator, as during a limited panel descent, the airspeed indicator, the altimeter, and the vertical speed indicator will be showing varying rates of change until the aircraft decelerates to a constant airspeed at a constant attitude. During the transition, changes in control pressure and trim, as well as cross-check interpretation, must be very accurate to maintain positive control.

Entry. The following method is effective either with or without an attitude indicator. First reduce power to give the desired descent airspeed, then lower the nose to maintain constant airspeed, and trim off control pressures.

During a predetermined airspeed descent, any deviation from the desired airspeed calls for a pitch adjustment. For a predetermined rate descent, the vertical speed indicator is primary for pitch control (after it stabilizes near the desired rate), and the airspeed indicator is primary for power control. Pitch and power must be closely co-ordinated when corrections are made.

Levelling Off. Levelling off from a descent must be started before reaching the desired altitude. The amount of lead depends upon the rate of descent and control technique. Assuming a 500 fpm rate of descent, lead the altitude by 100 to 150 feet to level off at an airspeed higher than descending speed. At the lead point, add power to the appropriate level flight cruise setting. Since the nose will tend to rise as the airspeed increases, hold forward elevator pressure to maintain the vertical speed at the descending rate until approximately 50 feet above the altitude, then adjust the pitch smoothly to the level flight attitude for the airspeed selected.

To level off from a descent at descent airspeed, lead the desired altitude by approximately 50 feet, simultaneously adjusting the pitch attitude to cruising attitude and increasing power to a setting that will hold the airspeed constant. Trim off the control pressure and continue with the normal straight and level flight cross-check.

Turns

It is important to repeat a caution previously mentioned in "Pilot Navigation" concerning the setting or resetting of the heading indicator from magnetic compass indications. It is impossible to obtain accurate readings from the magnetic compass unless the aircraft is well settled into a straight, wings level attitude at a constant airspeed. Students commonly roll into turns much too rapidly. During initial training in turns, there is nothing to be gained by manoeuvring an aircraft faster than your capacity to keep up with the changes in instrument indications. On the roll-in, use the attitude indicator to establish the approximate angle of bank, then check the turn needle for a standard rate turn indication. Maintain the bank for this rate of turn, using the turn needle as the primary bank reference and the attitude indicator as the supporting bank instrument. Note the angle of bank shown on the banking scale of the attitude indicator when the turn needle is directly under the standard rate index. During the roll-in, check the altimeter, vertical speed indicator, and attitude indicator for the pitch adjustments necessary as aerodynamic loading increases with increase in bank. If constant airspeed is to be maintained, the airspeed indicator becomes primary for power and the throttle must be adjusted as drag increases. As the bank is established, trim off the pressures applied during pitch and power changes (see Exercise 9, "Turns").

To recover to straight and level flight, if you strive for the same rate of roll-out used to roll into the turn, you will encounter fewer problems in judging the lead necessary to roll out on exact headings. Upon initiation of the turn recovery the attitude indicator becomes the primary bank instrument. When the aircraft is approximately level the heading indicator is the primary bank instrument, as in straight and level flight. Pitch, power, and trim adjustments are made as changes in aerodynamic loading and airspeed occur.

Some aircraft are very stable during turns. Others require constant cross-check and control to correct overbanking tendencies. Due to the interrelationship of pitch, bank, and airspeed deviations during turns, the cross-check must be constant to prevent an accumulation of errors.

Turns to Predetermined Headings

The roll-out to a desired heading must start before the heading is reached. The amount of lead varies. For small changes in heading, using an angle of bank not exceeding the number of degrees to be turned, lead the desired heading by one-half the number of degrees of bank used. For example, if you maintain the 10 degree bank during a change in heading, start the roll-out 5 degrees before reaching the desired heading.

Timed Turns

A timed turn is a turn in which the clock and the turn needle are used to change heading a definite number of degrees in a given time. For example, using a standard rate turn (3 degrees per second) an aircraft turns 45 degrees in 15 seconds; using a half-standard rate turn, the aircraft turns 45 degrees in 30 seconds. Use the same cross-check and control technique used to execute turns to predetermined headings, but substitute the clock for the heading indicator. The turn needle is primary for bank control, the altimeter is primary for pitch control, and the airspeed indicator is primary for power control. Start the roll-in when the clock second hand passes a prominent point, note the time and hold the turn at the standard rate indication on the turn needle (or half-standard rate for small changes in heading), and begin the roll-out when the computed number of seconds has elapsed. If the rates of roll-in and roll-out are the same, the time taken during entry and recovery need not be considered in the time computation; small corrections will invariably have to be made after roll-out to obtain the exact heading desired.

Steep Turns

Enter a steep turn the same way as any other turn, but prepare to cross-check rapidly as the turn steepens. Because of the greatly increased aerodynamic loading, pitch control is usually the most difficult aspect of this manoeuvre. Unless immediately noted, and corrected with a pitch increase, the added loading results in rapid movement of the altimeter, vertical speed, and airspeed needles. The faster the rate of bank change, the more suddenly the load changes occur. If your cross-check is fast enough to note the immediate need for pitch changes, smooth, steady back elevator pressure will maintain constant altitude (Fig 2-76). However, if you overbank to excessively steep angles without adjusting pitch as the bank changes occur, pitch corrections require increasingly stronger elevator pressure and the increase in wing loading finally reaches a point at which further application of back elevator pressure tightens the turn without raising the nose.

How do you recognize overbanking and a low pitch attitude and what should you do to correct it? If the vertical speed indicator and the altimeter indicate a rapid rate of descent, and the airspeed is increasing despite increased backward pressure on the control column, you are most likely in a spiral (Fig 2-77).

Figure 2-76   Steep Left Turn

Figure 2-77   Spiral Dive

Immediately level the wings with co-ordinated control pressures and, if the airspeed is still increasing, reduce power. Rapidly cross-check the attitude indicator, altimeter, vertical speed, and airspeed indicators. You will find that the elevator control is now effective in raising the nose; therefore restore the aircraft to straight and level flight and confirm that the gyroscopic instruments have not "toppled" before you attempt another steep turn (Fig 2-77).

If pitch control is consistently late on entries to steep turns, roll out immediately to straight and level flight and analyze your errors. Practise shallower turns until you can keep up with the attitude changes and control responses required, then steepen the bank angle as you develop more accurate control technique.

The power necessary to maintain a desired altitude and airspeed increases as the bank increases. Learn the power settings appropriate to specific bank attitudes and make adjustments without undue attention to airspeed and power instruments. During steep turns, as in any other manoeuvre, attend to first things first. If you keep pitch relatively constant, there is more time to cross-check, interpret, and control for accurate airspeed and bank.

During recovery from steep turns back to straight and level flight, elevator and power control must be co-ordinated with bank control in proportion to the changes in aerodynamic forces. Back elevator pressures must be released, and power decreased. The common errors associated with steep turns are the same as in any other turn; however, errors are more exaggerated and more difficult to correct.

Climbing and Descending Turns

To execute climbing and descending turns, combine the techniques used in straight climbs and descents with the various turn techniques. The load factor in turns must be considered in determining power settings, and the rate of cross-check and interpretation must be increased to control bank as well as pitch changes.

Change of Airspeed in Turns

Changing airspeed in turns is an effective manoeuvre for increasing proficiency in all three basic instrument skills, since it involves simultaneous changes in all components of control. Proper execution requires rapid cross-check and interpretation as well as smooth control. Proficiency in the manoeuvre will also contribute to confidence in the instruments during attitude and power changes involved in more complex manoeuvres. Pitch and power control techniques are the same as those used during changes in airspeed in straight and level flight.

The angle of bank necessary for a given rate of turn is proportional to the true airspeed. Since the turns are executed at standard rate, the angle of bank must be varied in direct proportion to the airspeed in order to maintain a constant rate of turn. During a reduction of airspeed, decrease the angle of bank and increase the pitch attitude to maintain a level standard rate turn.

The altimeter and turn needle indications should remain constant throughout the turn. The altimeter is primary for pitch control and the turn needle is primary for bank control. The tachometer is primary for power control while the airspeed is changing. As the airspeed approaches the new indication, the airspeed indicator becomes primary for power control.

Two methods of changing airspeed in turns may be used. In the first method, airspeed is changed after the turn is established; in the second method, the airspeed change is initiated simultaneously with the turn entry. Regardless of the method used, the rate of cross-check must be increased as you reduce power. As the aircraft decelerates, check the altimeter and vertical speed indicator for needed pitch changes and the bank instruments for needed bank changes. Adjust pitch attitude to maintain altitude. When the airspeed approaches that desired it becomes primary for power control, and the power setting is adjusted to maintain the desired airspeed. Trim is important throughout the manoeuvre to relieve control pressures. Frequent cross-check of the attitude indicator is essential to keep from overcontrolling and to provide approximate bank angles appropriate to the changing airspeeds.

Unusual Attitudes and Recoveries

Unusual attitudes can result from a number of conditions, such as turbulence, disorientation, confusion, preoccupation with cockpit duties, carelessness in cross-checking, errors in instrument interpretation, etc. Since unusual attitudes are not intentional manoeuvres during instrument flight except in training, they are often unexpected, and the reaction of an inadequately trained pilot to an unexpected abnormal flight attitude is usually instinctive rather than intelligent and deliberate. When an unusual attitude is noted on the cross-check, the immediate problem is not how the aircraft got there, but what it is doing and how to get it back to straight and level flight as quickly as possible.

Recognition

As a general rule, whenever you note an instrument rate of movement or indication other than those you associate with the basic instrument flight manoeuvres already learned, assume an unusual attitude and increase the speed of cross-check to confirm the attitude. Nose-up attitudes (Fig 2-78) are identified by the immediately recognizable indication of the attitude indicator (except in extreme attitudes), and the rate and direction of movement of the altimeter needle, vertical speed needle, and airspeed indicator needle. Nose-low attitudes are shown by the same instruments, but in the opposite direction.

Recovery

In moderate unusual attitudes, recovery can normally be made by establishing a level flight indication on the attitude indicator. However, you should not depend on this instrument entirely. If the attitude indicator is the

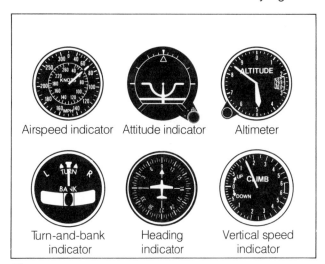

Figure 2-78   Nose-up Attitudes

type that can be toppled, its limits may have been exceeded. Even if it is the non-toppling type its indications are very difficult to interpret in extreme attitudes. As soon as an extreme unusual attitude is detected, initiate recovery primarily by reference to the airspeed indicator, turn-and-bank indicator, altimeter, and vertical speed indicator.

Nose-down Attitudes

If the airspeed is increasing, or is above the desired airspeed: (1) reduce power to prevent excessive airspeed and loss of altitude; (2) correct the bank attitude with co-ordinated aileron and rudder pressure to straight flight by referring to the turn-and-bank indicator; (3) raise the nose to level flight attitude by smooth back elevator pressure. All components of control should be changed simultaneously for a smooth, proficient recovery. However, during initial training a positive recovery should be made "by the numbers" in the sequence given above.

After initial control has been implemented, continue with a fast cross-check for possible overcontrolling, since the initial control pressures may be large. As the rate of movement of altimeter and airspeed indicator needles decreases, the attitude is approaching level flight; if the needles stop and then rotate in the opposite direction, the aircraft has passed through level flight attitude. As the indications of the airspeed indicator, altimeter, and turn-and-bank indicator stabilize, incorporate the attitude indicator into the cross-check. The attitude indicator, turn needle, and ball should be checked to determine bank attitude and corrective control pressures applied. The ball should be centred, since skidding and slipping sensations can easily aggravate disorientation and retard recovery.

Nose-up Attitudes

If the airspeed is decreasing or below the desired airspeed: (1) increase power in proportion to the observed deceleration; (2) apply forward elevator pressure to lower the nose and prevent a stall; and (3) correct the bank by applying co-ordinated aileron and rudder pressure to centre the needle and ball. The corrective control applications are made almost simultaneously, but in the sequence given above. As in the nose-low recovery, a level pitch attitude is indicated by the stabilization of the airspeed indicator and altimeter needles. Straight co-ordinated flight is indicated by the centred needle and ball of the turn-and-bank indicator.

The spin is the most critical unusual attitude of all, not necessarily because of the manoeuvre itself but because of the disorientation that usually accompanies it. It is not likely that light aircraft in common use will develop a spin on their own. Nevertheless, spins should be demonstrated on instruments to show how to recognize and recover from them.

The first requirement for spin recovery is to determine the direction in which the aircraft is spinning. The only reliable instrument for this purpose in the average elementary training aircraft is the turn needle of the turn-and-bank indicator. The needle will show a full deflection in the direction of the spin. The altimeter will show a rapid loss of height, and to distinguish the manoeuvre from a steep spiral the airspeed will be low (at or near the stalling speed) and constant.

Having determined the direction of the spin, disregard the ball instrument temporarily and perform the following actions strictly in the order set out:

(1) Close the throttle.
(2) Apply full rudder opposite to the direction of the turn (if the turn needle is full right apply full left rudder, etc.)
(3) Centralize the aileron control if necessary and ease the elevator control steadily forward. When the turn needle starts moving back to its centre position the spin has almost stopped.
(4) Centralize the rudder as the spin stops (needle at or near centre).
(5) Watch the airspeed indicator now and as the airspeed increases, apply back pressure on the control column to ease the aircraft out of the ensuing dive (see note).
(6) When the airspeed begins to decrease, decrease back pressure on the control column and apply engine power to resume normal cruising flight. Keep the turn needle and ball centred with co-ordinated control pressures.

Note: In the recovery from the dive, the turn needle of the turn-and-bank indicator may go over to one side. During this part of the manoeuvre the turn needle is sensitive to acute pitching motion and no turn actually exists. Once the pitching ceases, the needle will again function reliably. This action should be studied during visual spin demonstrations.

Common errors which may cause unusual attitudes to develop are:

(1) Failure to keep the aircraft properly trimmed. A cockpit interruption when you are holding pressures can easily lead to inadvertent entry into unusual attitudes.
(2) Disorganized cockpit. Hunting for charts, logs, computers, etc., can seriously detract from attention to the instruments.
(3) Slow cross-check and fixation. Resist the impulse to stop and stare when you note an instrument discrepancy.
(4) Attempting to recover by sensory sensations other than sight. Always trust the instruments.
(5) Failure to practise basic instrument skills once you have learned them. All of the errors noted in connection with basic instrument skills are aggravated during unusual attitude recoveries until the elementary skills have been mastered.

Basic Instrument Flight Patterns

A good way to continue practice once you have achieved a degree of proficiency on instruments is to simulate the basic flight patterns used in IFR (Instrument Flight Rules) procedures. Knowing the flight requirements of these procedures will also prove advantageous if you intend to extend your instrument flight instruction beyond the elementary stage. The actual procedures presume a "starting point" or "fix" such as an NDB (Non-Directional Beacon), a VORTAC (VOR combined with TACAN [Tactical Air Navigation]), etc.; however, for practice purposes an imaginary fix may be used, since at this stage timing, precision turns, and the maintenance of specific airspeeds and altitudes on instruments are the primary objectives.

The holding pattern outlined in Figure 2-79 is used to hold an aircraft in a specific and confined area for reasons of air traffic congestion, emergencies, weather, etc. It demands very accurate timing and instrument flying skill to stay within the bounds of the confined area at the assigned altitude.

The "procedure turn" shown and outlined in Figure 2-

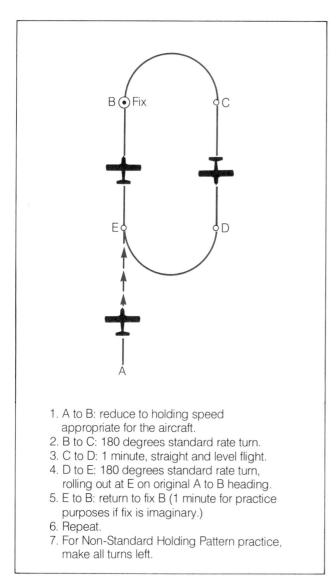

1. A to B: reduce to holding speed
   appropriate for the aircraft.
2. B to C: 180 degrees standard rate turn.
3. C to D: 1 minute, straight and level flight.
4. D to E: 180 degrees standard rate turn,
   rolling out at E on original A to B heading.
5. E to B: return to fix B (1 minute for practice
   purposes if fix is imaginary.)
6. Repeat.
7. For Non-Standard Holding Pattern practice,
   make all turns left.

Figure 2-79 Standard Holding Pattern (all turns right)

80 is typical of an instrument approach to landing. For non-standard procedures (and many airports have them), make the turn at B a right turn, all other turns left turns. For practice purposes, times on each leg have been liberally interpreted.

Automatic Direction-Finder

The automatic direction-finder (ADF) is a low frequency radio receiver which can be used for reception of non-directional radio beacons and commercial broadcast stations. The principal value of the system lies in its ability to provide continuous relative bearings or magnetic bearings, or both, to any radio facility within its frequency range of 200 KHz to 1750 KHz.

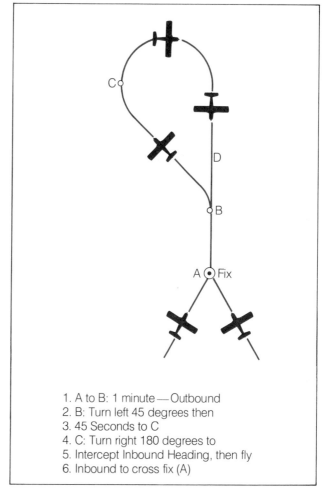

1. A to B: 1 minute —Outbound
2. B: Turn left 45 degrees then
3. 45 Seconds to C
4. C: Turn right 180 degrees to
5. Intercept Inbound Heading, then fly
6. Inbound to cross fix (A)

Figure 2-80 Procedure Turn

When radio beacons are used as a navigational aid, the morse code identifier signals can be readily used to identify the beacon, whereas if a broadcast radio station is used, it is essential to identify the station positively by listening for station announcements prior to using bearing indications. Compared with the static free qualities of VOR, radio static caused by lightning or any disturbance in the atmosphere is quite often a problem with the use of the ADF. Its main advantage is its range and the fact that it is not subject to line-of-sight transmissions. While many types of ADF's have a rotatable azimuth, in this text we will only discuss a fixed azimuth where the longitudinal axis of the aircraft is parallel to a line passing through the zero index (0 degrees) and 180 degrees, as illustrated in Figure 2-83. In this illustration the ADF needle is pointing to a beacon which is 45 degrees off the nose of the aircraft. Figure 2-84 shows a typical ADF installation.

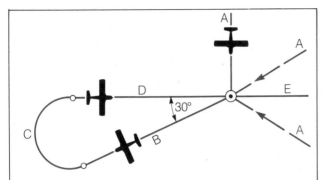

A: Approach fix ⊙ at published sector altitude,
B: Take up a heading 30 degrees "off" published
   outbound heading; maintain this heading
   for 1 minute, at procedure speed,
C: Standard rate turn; roll out on published inbound
   heading;
   As soon as heading is definitely inbound,
   "let-down" to published minimum altitude for *fix*,
D: Inbound heading; when fix is reached, "let-down"
   to published minimum altitude for the facility (E),
   at approach speed.

Note: Turns and timing must be adjusted to
   compensate for wind effect.

Figure 2-81   Tear-Drop Procedure Turn

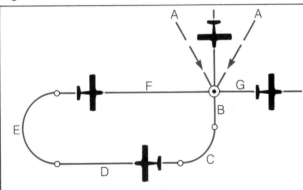

A: Approach ⊙ fix at published minimum *sector*
   altitude; cross fix,
B: Fly 90 degrees to outbound heading for
   30 seconds at procedure speed,
C: Standard rate turn; roll out on outbound heading,
D: Hold outbound heading for 1½ minutes,
   (reciprocal of published inbound heading),
E: Standard rate turn; roll out on published
   inbound heading and "let-down" to minimum fix
   altitude as soon as aircraft is on a definite
   inbound heading,
F: Inbound heading to fix; after crossing fix inbound,
   "let-down" to minimum facility altitude (G)
   at approach speed.

Note: Adjust all turns and timing to compensate
   for wind effect.

Figure 2-82   Parallel Procedure Turn (racetrack)

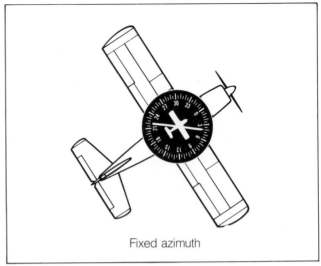

Fixed azimuth

Figure 2-83   Fixed Azimuth

Terms and Definitions

Before using the automatic direction-finder, you should
understand the following definitions (see Fig 2-85).

Relative Bearing. The angle formed by the intersection
of a line drawn through the centre-line of the aircraft and
a line drawn from the aircraft to the beacon. This angle is
always measured clockwise from the nose of the
aircraft. The relative bearing is indicated directly by the
ADF needle when the beacon is tuned in.

Magnetic Bearing. The angle formed by the intersection of a line drawn from the aircraft to the beacon and a
line drawn from the aircraft to magnetic north. For an ADF
radio with a fixed azimuth indicator, a magnetic bearing
to the beacon is obtained by adding the relative bearing,
shown on the indicator, to the magnetic heading of the
aircraft. If the total is more than 360 degrees, 360
degrees is subtracted to obtain the magnetic bearing.

Reciprocal Bearing. The bearing plus 180 degrees.
Reciprocal bearings are used when plotting fixes. A
reciprocal bearing (beacon-to-aircraft bearing) is
obtained by adding or subtracting 180 degrees from the
aircraft-to-beacon bearing. If the bearing is less than
180 degrees, 180 degrees is added to obtain the
reciprocal bearing. If the bearing is more than 180
degrees, 180 degrees is subtracted to obtain the
reciprocal bearing.

Homing. Homing to a beacon using the ADF in no-wind
conditions simply entails keeping the ADF needle on the
0 degree index. Even in a cross-wind condition this
method can be followed, resulting in a curved path as
shown in Figure 2-86, where the aircraft approaches the
beacon from a downwind position.

Courtesy Aviation
Training Systems

1. **Bearing Indicator** indicates the bearing to the station being received, relative to the nose of the aircraft.
2. **On/Off Volume Control Knob** turns the set on and controls the audio output.
3. **Frequency Selection Knobs** tune the desired frequency as indicated on the adjacent read-out.

4. **Function Selector Knob.**

BFO: (Optional) Used to identify CW (Continuous Wave) signals within frequency range of the system.

ANT: Operates as a standard communications receiver using sense antenna only.

ADF: This system functions as automatic direction-finder. Both loop and sense antenna signals are used.

TEST: (Optional) Verifies operation and signal reliability on the bearing indicator.

Figure 2-84   A Typical ADF Installation

Intercepting a Track to a Station

To intercept a desired ADF track, it is first essential to determine the aircraft's position relative to that track. When the aircraft is turned to the heading which parallels the desired track, the ADF needle will indicate the direction the aircraft must be turned to intercept that track. The closer the aircraft is to the station, the greater will be the number of degrees the needle is off 0 degrees. For example, if an aircraft was 1 mile to the right of a desired track 60 miles from the station, under no-wind conditions, the ADF would show 1 degree off 0 degrees (359 degree relative). At 30 miles it would be 2 degrees (358 degrees relative) and at 15 miles it would be 4 degrees (356 degrees relative). This figure builds up as the aircraft gets closer to the beacon, so that as the aircraft passes abeam the beacon at a distance of 1 mile, the needle would be 90 degrees off 0 degrees (270 degrees relative).

In order to determine the heading change required to intercept a desired track, a basic rule is to double the number of degrees that the needle is off the 0 degree index and make this the interception angle. If there is any doubt, use a 90 degree interception angle, but in this case take extra care to allow for the turn on to the desired track, or else the aircraft will fly right through it

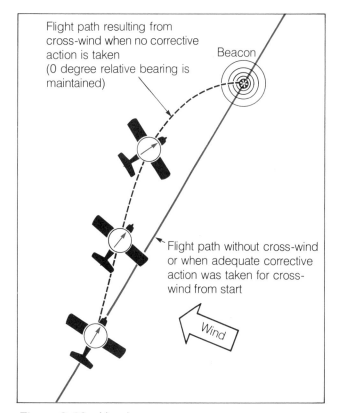

Figure 2-85   Bearings

Figure 2-86   Homing

and another interception will have to be made. Figure 2-87 shows a 30 degree angle of interception being used. Assuming the desired track to the beacon was 360 degrees, then a heading of 330 degrees should be flown on the heading indicator until the needle shows 30 degrees to the right of the 0 degree index, at which time the aircraft is over the track of 360 degrees to the beacon. It is essential for orientation purposes that the desired track be intercepted prior to passing over the beacon.

Check the ADF needle periodically for any deviation from the 0 degree index. Any deviation while maintaining the inbound heading shows that the aircraft is drifting. If if is, turn 30 degrees towards the desired track. Fly the new heading until the ADF needle opens to 30 degrees off the 0 degree index and then estimate the drift angle. Turn the aircraft back to the inbound heading plus or minus the estimated drift. If the drift angle has been correctly estimated, the ADF needle will remain steady and will be displaced from the 0 degree index an amount equal to the drift correction.

If you have not estimated the drift angle correctly a

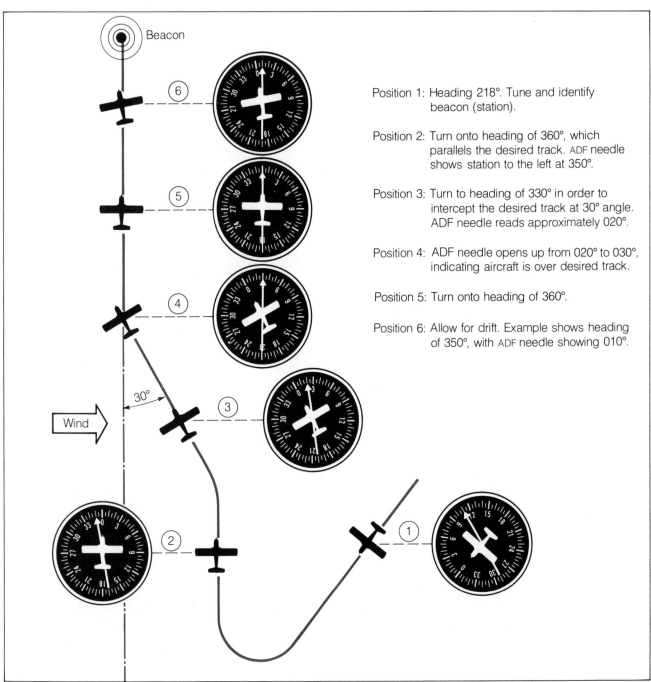

Position 1: Heading 218°. Tune and identify beacon (station).

Position 2: Turn onto heading of 360°, which parallels the desired track. ADF needle shows station to the left at 350°.

Position 3: Turn to heading of 330° in order to intercept the desired track at 30° angle. ADF needle reads approximately 020°.

Position 4: ADF needle opens up from 020° to 030°, indicating aircraft is over desired track.

Position 5: Turn onto heading of 360°.

Position 6: Allow for drift. Example shows heading of 350°, with ADF needle showing 010°.

Figure 2-87   Intercepting a Track Inbound

change in bearing will again become apparent and further adjustments to the drift angle will have to be made until the ADF needle remains steady.

Intercepting a Track Outbound

Unless an ATC clearance requires that the aircraft proceed to a desired track by the most direct route, there is no need for a large interception angle when tracking outbound. After beacon passage or after take-off, take up a heading which parallels the desired track, and hold this for a short time (2 to 5 minutes) to establish drift. In Figure 2-88 the aircraft has drifted west of track, with the needle reading approximately 170 degrees. For an interception angle of 30 degrees, a heading of 030 degrees would be required. The angle between the needle and the 180 degree index on the ADF will initially be greater than 30 degrees, but as the angle closes to a relative bearing of 150 degrees this indicates that the aircraft is over the desired track and the turn onto the desired heading of 360 degrees should be made in the usual manner. When a constant heading is being maintained, an opening or closing of the needle relative to the 180 degree index indicates that drift is present and must be allowed for. The correct allowance for drift will be evident when the number of degrees the needle is placed off the 180 degree index remains constant, with a constant heading being shown on the heading indicator.

Beacon Passage

Flight over the beacon is indicated by a sudden increase in activity of the needle, which will suddenly swing back and forth and will finally swing completely around to 180 degrees on the dial, indicating that the beacon is behind the aircraft.

Visual Omni-Range

One common means of radio navigation is the Visual Omni Range (VOR) or Very High Frequency Omnidirectional Range. This system consists of many strategically placed ground stations that transmit navigational signals in the VHF frequency range 112.10 to 117.95 MHz. An airborne VOR receiver converts these signals into visual indications which may be used by the pilot for accurate navigation. A typical airborne VOR installation is shown in Figure 2-89.

The greatest advantage of VOR is that it provides you with 360 different magnetic tracks (one for each degree in a circle) from which you can select the one which best suits your needs in order to fly to or track from a VOR station. These tracks are called *radials*. Examination of a navigation chart will show the VOR stations surrounded

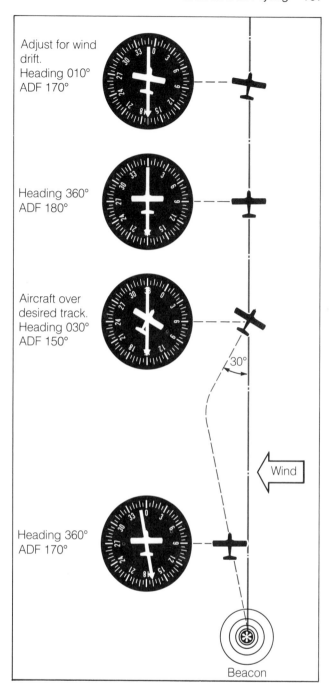

Figure 2-88 Intercepting a Track Outbound

by a compass rose which enables you to identify the desired track in degrees magnetic. L.E. (En route Low Altitude) charts have the VOR airways clearly indicated, enabling you to readily determine the "Victor Airway" to follow. As on a topographical chart, magnetic variation and convergence have an effect upon radials, and it will be noticed that the straight line (VOR airway) joining two VOR stations does not show the radials as being exact reciprocal numbers. All radials are identified as bearings *from* the station; for example, the 090 degree radial extends east of the station. Since the magnetic bearing of a VOR radial can be ambiguous, a sense

Communications side   Navigation side

Courtesy Aviation Training Systems

1. Communication Receiver-Transmitter Frequency Selector Knob selects communication receiver-transmitter frequency in 1 MHz steps.
2. Communication Receiver-Transmitter Frequency Dial.
3. Communication Receiver-Transmitter Fractional Frequency Selector Knob selects communication receiver-transmitter fractional frequency in 0.05 MHz steps.
4. Navigation Receiver Frequency Selector Knob selects navigation receiver frequency in 1 MHz steps.
5. Navigation Receiver Frequency Dial.
6. Navigation Receiver Fractional Frequency Selector Knob.
7. Ident Filter Switch selects identifier. At "ID" position, the filter is switched out of circuit and station identifier (Morse Code) signal is audible.
8. Navigation Receiver Volume Control Knob controls the volume of audio from the navigation receiver only.
9. Off/On Volume Control Knob turns the complete set on and controls the volume of audio from the communication receiver.
10. Squelch Control Knob controls the communication receiver squelch circuit. Clockwise rotation increases background noise (decreases squelch action): counterclockwise rotation decreases background noise.
11. Course Deviation Indicator (CDI) indicates the course deviation from the selected omni bearing or localizer centre-line.
12. Off/To-From (Omni) Indicator operates only with VOR or localizer signal. "Off" position (flag) indicates an unreliable signal. When the "Off" position disappears, the indicator shows whether the selected course is "To" or "From" the station.
13. Reciprocal Course Index indicates the reciprocal of the selected VOR course.
14. Course Selector (Omni Bearing Selector (OBS)) Knob selects the desired course to or from a VOR station.
15. Azimuth Dial.
16. Course Index indicates the selected VOR course.

Figure 2-89   NAV/COM Radio with VOR

indicator (TO-FROM) is used to indicate whether an aircraft is on a bearing towards or away from the VOR station. If the (TO-FROM) indicator reads "TO" with the course indicator centred, the bearing is towards the station from the aircraft. (In Fig 2-90 the aircraft is on the 090 degree radial flying a magnetic track of 270 degrees to the VOR.) If the TO-FROM indicator reads "FROM," the bearing is away from the station towards the aircraft. The stations are identified by a three letter code and a VHF frequency. (Toronto's VOR identifier is YYZ and the VOR transmits on 117.4 MHz.) The aircraft does not have to be flying the heading of the radial inbound or outbound in order for the course deviation indicator (CDI) to be centred. The receiver merely indicates that at that moment the aircraft is located on that radial regardless of the aircraft heading. It could be flying along it or crossing it at an angle (Fig 2-91).

Like all VHF signals, VOR signals are subject to line-of-sight transmission, hence the greater the height, the greater the range of the signal. For this reason, caution must be exercised when flying close to the ground or within mountainous regions. Line-of-sight range at 1000 feet AGL is approximately 39 miles; at 2000 feet AGL, 54 miles; at 3000 feet AGL, 66 miles; at 4000 feet AGL, 77 miles, etc.

Most large airports have a VOT, or omni-test frequency, which enables the pilot to determine the serviceability and accuracy of the receiver. To test the receiver, select the VOT frequency, and you should hear a rapid succession of morse code dots or the local ATIS broadcast. Turn the omnibearing selector (OBS) knob to 360 degrees, and a "FROM" indication should show in the sense meter. The CDI should be centred. If the OBS

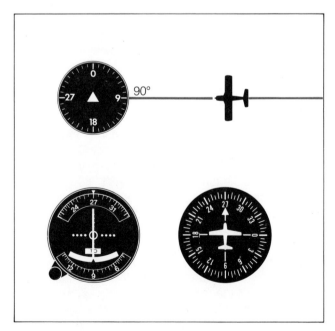

Figure 2-90   Aircraft on 090° Radial Flying a Magnetic Track of 270° to the VOR

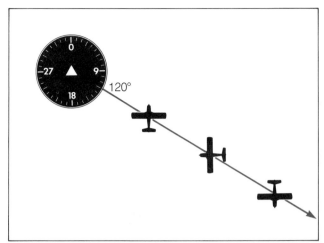

Figure 2-91   Aircraft on 120° Radial Regardless of Heading

indicator reading is within plus or minus 4 degrees, the receiver is acceptable for IFR navigation. Turning the OBS knob to 180 degrees produces a "TO" indication, and any error should be determined. Turn the OBS 10 degrees either side of needle centre and full deflection of the CDI should result.

Caution: You are not to correct for any "within limit" error when actually using the equipment. You must consider it either completely accurate or unusable. Any attempt to apply a degrees-off correction will

complicate VOR navigation procedures, and in fact can be hazardous because there is no guarantee that the error is the same throughout 360 degrees.

Tracking to a Station

While experienced pilots may develop their own method of intercepting a specific radial, there is one basic technique which may be used when you do not know the distance from the station. After identifying the station, use the OBS to determine the radial the aircraft is on at that time (060 degrees in Fig 2-92). By visualizing the compass rose you can then identify the position relative to the radial which is to be flown to the station. In Figure 2-92 a heading of 180 degrees will put the aircraft on the most direct route to the 090 degree radial. Because it is desired that you will be flying towards the station on the 090 degree radial, it will be necessary to turn the OBS to the reciprocal of the desired radial, which in Figure 2-92 would be 270 degrees, and fly the radial to the station, allowing for drift.

Follow this method if it is essential that a certain radial be flown to a station, such as in an ATC clearance or to avoid an obstruction. Normally, once the position of the aircraft is determined, it would only be necessary to turn the OBS to the reciprocal heading and to fly direct to the station. Visualization of the aircraft's position relative to

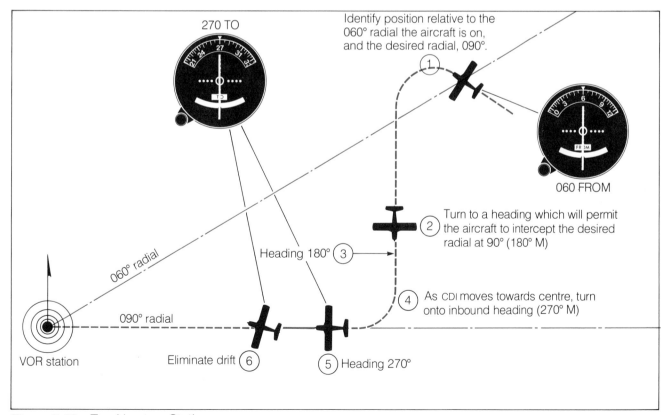

Figure 2-92   Tracking to a Station

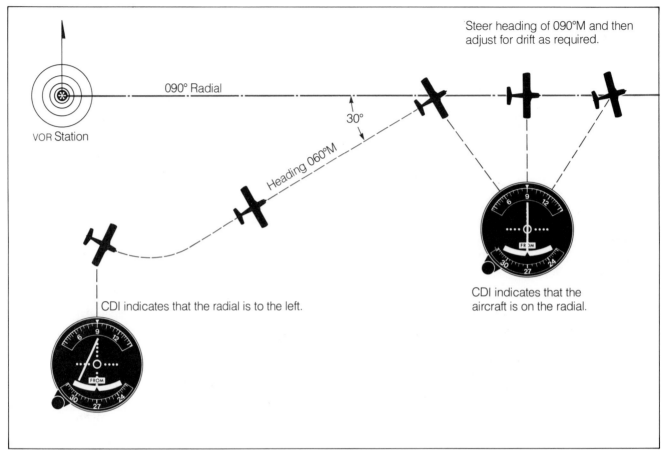

Steer heading of 090°M and then adjust for drift as required.

090° Radial

30°

Heading 060°M

VOR Station

CDI indicates that the radial is to the left.

CDI indicates that the aircraft is on the radial.

Figure 2-93   Tracking Away from a Station

the station and desired radial is the key to easy VOR navigation.

Tracking Away from a Station

Once airborne, tune in the frequency of the selected VOR station and identify it by the morse code signals, which are shown by letters and dots and dashes in the identification box of the station on the navigation chart. If you want to intercept and fly along a radial away from the station, turn to a heading parallel to the selected radial, check the CDI deflection, and then turn to follow the indications of the CDI. If it points left, turn left to a heading which will permit interception of the radial at a desired angle (usually 30 degrees to 45 degrees) and hold this heading until the CDI centres, signifying that the aircraft is on the desired radial. Then take up the desired heading, making corrections to compensate for wind drift, and keep the CDI centred (Fig 2-93).

Once you are established on a radial, it may be necessary to eliminate drift. If the wind direction is known, an allowance for drift may be made. Figure 2-93 shows the CDI indications that may be observed while following a radial. If the wind is not known hold a heading identical to the radial being flown; after a short time any

drift will be indicated by deflection of the CDI. The radial may be again intercepted, as in Figure 2-94, and the correct amount of drift then applied.

When flying along a Victor Airway between two VOR stations, tune in the frequency of the station ahead at approximately the half-way point and set the inbound radial bearing on the OBS. The CDI will not necessarily be centred when the new station is tuned, but it will indicate what direction to turn if necessary to intercept the new radial.

The position of an aircraft can be plotted on a chart by taking "FROM" bearings from two or more VOR stations. Because the aircraft is still moving ahead, the accuracy of these positions will depend on how quickly the bearings are taken. If the aircraft has two VOR receivers this is not a problem. Figure 2-95 shows how the aircraft's position may be plotted.

Station Passage

As the aircraft approaches a VOR station, the CDI becomes very sensitive. Hold the heading which has kept you on track along the radial until the aircraft has passed over the station. Station passage will be indicated by full deflection of the CDI to one side and

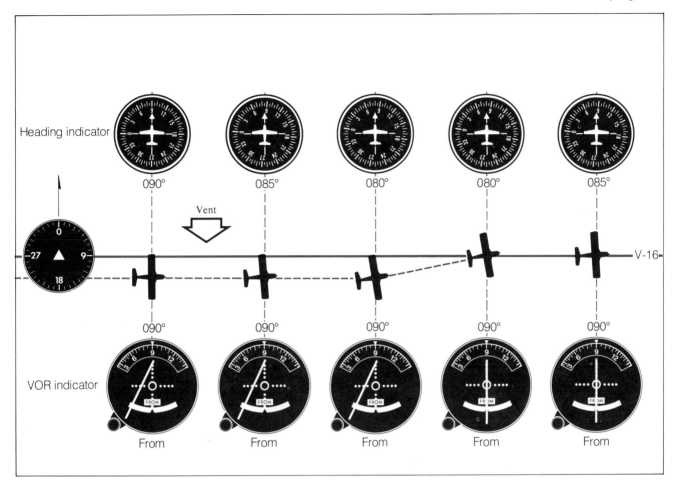

Figure 2-94   Correcting for Drift

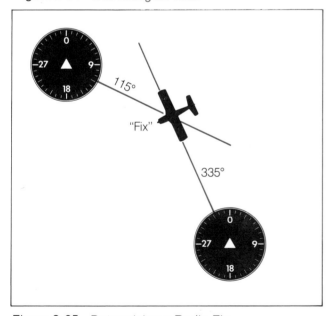

Figure 2-95   Determining a Radio Fix

then the other, with the sense meter changing from "TO" to "FROM." This is indicated in Positions 1 and 2 of Figure 2-96. If the aircraft is passing abeam the VOR station, the CDI and sense meter will record the fact as shown in Positions 3, 4, and 5 of Figure 2-96.

If a change of direction is desired after station passage, select the outbound radial on the OBS and use the CDI as before to indicate the direction to fly to intercept the new radial.

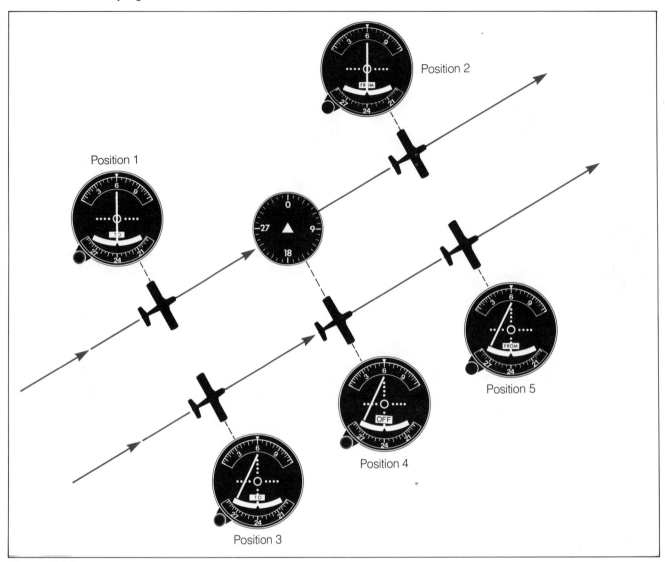

Figure 2-96 Station Passage

Night Flying

Night flying can be most enjoyable; in fact, many experienced pilots prefer it to flying by day. In summer, the lower temperatures at night make the air more dense, which improves aerodynamic and engine performance. Convection cloud tends to dissipate; therefore, air turbulence is much weaker and very often almost entirely absent. The air near the ground is generally more stable and good landings can be made with relatively less manipulation of the flight controls. Once accustomed to night flying, you will find that other aircraft in flight, which are generally less numerous than during the day, can be seen more readily.

Night flying does require that you readjust to a relatively different environment, especially outside the cockpit. Reference points such as the horizon, topographical features, and even the ground itself, all so vital in establishing aircraft attitudes by day, are indistinct, obscure, and sometimes invisible. Nevertheless, you will find that there is nothing mysterious or particularly difficult about night flying. The aircraft is flown by night in the same way as it is by day, though more frequent reference should be made to the instruments to verify attitude, airspeed, heading, etc. For this reason you must be adequately proficient in controlling the aircraft by reference to instruments.

You should become familiar with the airport lighting systems. Some of the names of these systems are: (1) runway lights, (2) runway threshold lights, (3) runway approach lights, (4) taxiway lights, (5) taxiway entrance lights, (6) airport rotating beacon, and (7) obstruction lights. Various colours are used: threshold — green, taxiway — blue, and obstruction — red. At many airports runway lights and approach lights can be varied in intensity. The intensity is usually controlled by the control tower or aeradio station and can often be varied at the pilot's request. It may have been some time since you have had to manoeuvre around an airport traffic circuit by means of light signals directed at you by the control tower. Review these signals so that you know what to expect and do in the event of a radio failure.

Before attempting a night flight, you must be thoroughly familiar with the operation of the aircraft's lighting system and its emergency equipment. Memorize the location of switches, circuit breakers, and fuses, so that no wild searches are forced on you in flight. Check that the required flashlight is working, that its batteries are strong enough, and that it is within easy reach. Cockpit lighting must illuminate vital instruments and equipment satisfactorily, but should not create a glare that interferes with the pilot's outside vision. Position lights, sometimes referred to as navigation lights, must be checked for serviceability and operation. Do not forget the importance of the generator or alternator charging rate, since the load imposed both by the radio and the aircraft lighting system now depend on it.

The position lights of an aircraft are coloured, and are located and visible through certain angles for the express purpose of indicating the relative position of an aircraft and the general direction in which it is moving. It is important that you know how to interpret the position lights of another aircraft to determine whether there is any possibility of a collision.

Allow enough time for your eyes to become accustomed to darkness after the bright lights of the pilot's lounge or air terminal. Most people require about a half-hour in darkness for their eyes to achieve maximum adaptation.

During the day there is little possibility of flying into a cloud condition accidentally. On a dark, overcast night, however, it can be done easily. Be alert to the possibility of the existence of cloud in the area. At night it may be detected or suspected by the otherwise unwarranted disappearance of lights on the ground and by a red or green glow adjacent to the position lights of the aircraft.

The Circuit

In preparation for the flight carry out all normal daytime checks before taxiing out, but in addition check your night flying equipment — such as landing lights, position lights, instrument and cabin lighting, the flashlight, and the alternator/generator charging rate.

Taxiing at night requires considerable extra care compared to taxiing in the daytime, for the following reasons:

(1) Distance at night is deceptive when judged by stationary lights, which are nearer than they appear to be.
(2) Speed is deceptive at night and there is a tendency to taxi an aircraft too fast. There are several reasons for this, but the major one is the lack of the customary visible ground objects which make speed apparent on the ground during the day.
(3) Careful look-out is required to avoid obstructions. They are made visible by the positioning of obstruction lights, which are sometimes mistaken for the lights of aircraft.
(4) It is difficult to determine slight movement of the aircraft on the ground at night, and care should be exercised to prevent the aircraft from creeping forward during the run-up.

During the briefing your instructor will already have prescribed the taxiing route to be used to the point of take-off and back after the final landing. At the take-off position keep the engine running fast enough to keep the generator/alternator charging.

Take-off

Complete a normal pre-take-off check. Correct trim is important. It is also good airmanship to put the landing lights on, if the aircraft is equipped with them. Obtain take-off clearance (or take the required precautions at uncontrolled airports), then line up the aircraft on the runway in use.

The take-off is basically similar to the daytime take-off. Direction is maintained first by reference to the runway lighting and later by other lighted objects ahead. If landing lights are not used there may be some difficulty in judging the aircraft's attitude, so take care to ensure that the normal nose-up attitudes for take-off and climb are not exceeded. It is essential that a safe climbing speed with a positive rate of climb be achieved just after lift-off. Thus, any temptation to lift the aircraft off the ground prematurely must be resisted.

Because of difficulty in judging the fore and aft attitude, on some tail wheel aircraft the control column is allowed to remain neutral during the take-off run and the aircraft allowed to assume the flying attitude of its own accord. To guard against settling back to the ground after lift-off, the aircraft is climbed at a gentle pitch-up attitude immediately it becomes airborne, until the

desired climbing attitude may be safely assumed.

When established in the climb you may have to augment directional control by reference to flight instruments, since visual references can often be obscured by the nose-up attitude. Do not start to turn until a height of 500 feet above ground has been gained, after which the aircraft should be put into a climbing turn in the direction of the circuit. Action in the event of engine failure after take-off is the same as by day, with the additional action of switching on the landing lights if they are not already on.

Regular circuit patterns are to be made, thus permitting completion of cockpit checks (and receipt of clearances) in accordance with the normal procedure on the various legs of the circuit. The circuit is flown principally by external references available in the form of lights on the ground, and the aerodrome lighting provides a means of monitoring the aircraft's position.

Your instructor will point out other aircraft in flight, and will also show you how to space your circuit pattern to avoid crowding on the approach.

Approach

A power assisted approach is normally used, but a low flat approach should be avoided.

It is an important principle of night flying that pilots be able to complete safe approaches and landings by reference to the runway lighting only. The normal aid to judgment is the appearance of the runway lighting as seen after turning in on the final approach. If the approach path is correct, the lights will appear to remain equidistant (longitudinally). If you are overshooting, the distance between the lights appears to increase; if undershooting, the distance appears to decrease. The aim, therefore, is to regulate the approach path so as to maintain the runway lights in the correct perspective (Fig 2-97). Ideally, the approach should be gauged so that the flare occurs over the beginning of the runway lighting.

Landing

The landing at night is made by visual reference to the approach lights and the runway lights. The appearance of the ground is deceptive: never attempt to refer to it as you do by day.

The normal but not invariable effect of night conditions on the pilot is to induce a tendency to flare too high. If you experience this difficulty early in instruction, it may be advisable to keep some power on until the touchdown is completed.

When the aircraft's landing lights are used you should not look directly down the beam, but ahead of it and

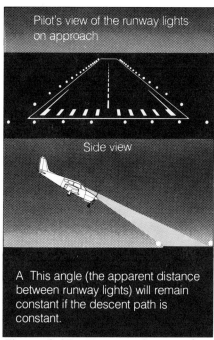

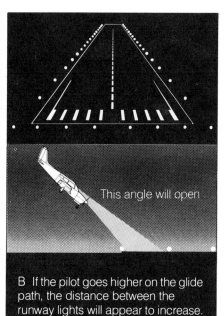

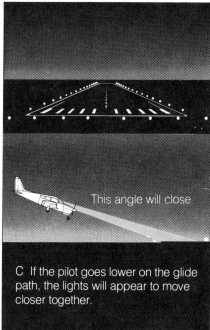

A This angle (the apparent distance between runway lights) will remain constant if the descent path is constant.

B If the pilot goes higher on the glide path, the distance between the runway lights will appear to increase.

C If the pilot goes lower on the glide path, the lights will appear to move closer together.

Figure 2-97   Runway Approach at Night

slightly to one side, in order to avoid losing perspective. Remember that the flare is still gauged by reference to the runway lights.

Executing a missed approach by night requires no special technique, but is conducted in the same manner as by day. Transition to instrument flight should be made before losing sight of the runway lights, if no reliable outside visual reference is available for attitude indication.

At night as during the day, you must keep an alert look-out for other air traffic and avoid keeping your head in the cockpit to read instruments for too long a period. As you gain experience in flying night circuits, it is a good idea to become familiar with the correct position of the flight instrument needles for various flight attitudes and airspeeds. It is not necessary to try to read the actual figures, a glance being sufficient to determine that reasonable accuracy is being achieved.

Cross-Country Flying by Night

The principles of pilot navigation by night are basically similar to those applicable by day, except that map reading at night calls for special techniques. The aircraft is navigated according to a predetermined flight plan, corrected from time to time by use of the radio and reliable visual aids.

The following points in pilot navigation by night call for special consideration:

(1) A complete weather briefing and pre-flight planning are essential. Pilot briefing should be conducted as usual and an ATC flight plan compiled and filed.

(2) For visual navigation greater stress should be placed on positively identifiable lighted landmarks or large lakes and rivers, rather than on the usual ground features.

(3) All compass headings should be accurately maintained and corrections made only when the position, fixed by check-points or by radio aids, is absolutely certain.

(4) Accuracy in time keeping is essential.

The route for initial night pilot navigation practice should be carefully chosen to include several landmarks which can be identified unmistakably at night. The feasibility of map reading will depend mainly on the weather and the moon. Ground features show up better when viewed against the moon. Aerodrome beacons are very useful fixes, but guard against the possibility of gross errors when judging distance to or from them. Avoid depending on small lights on the ground for fixes; the scattered lights around a small community can easily give the impression of a much larger town. At all times be aware of the approximate bearing and distance of a known prominent feature which you can divert to easily should anything occur to make continuation of the flight impossible or impracticable.

Airport Lighting

The floodlights illuminating most terminal building aprons are in many cases semi-blinding, but they cannot be dimmed or turned off except in emergencies. When taxiing in floodlit areas use extreme caution, since persons, vehicles, and other objects tend to "shadow" out or become invisible in these areas.

Blue lights are used to delineate taxiways and are necessarily of very low intensity. To assist aircraft exiting from a lighted runway, the exit is generally identified by an amber light adjacent to one of the runway lights on each side of the taxiway exit.

Runway and approach lighting systems are not restricted to night-time use. If visibility is poor, a landing is being made into the sun, or any other factor affects the safety of the aircraft in this regard, you should have no hesitation in requesting the control tower or the agency responsible for their operation to put the runway and approach lights on. These lights may also be adjustable in intensity; ask for that best suited to the circumstances.

Floatplanes

Most of the civil primary flight training aircraft which use water instead of land as a take-off and landing surface are conventional landplanes equipped with two floats instead of wheels. All aircraft capable of taking off or landing on water are termed seaplanes, including flying boats. For the purpose of this text, the subject aircraft is a floatplane, since we do not intend to include any of the operating procedures applicable solely to flying boats. For the most part, the subject will be referred to as an aircraft.

In the air a floatplane acts much like a landplane. It does not require as much use of the ailerons in a side-slip and is generally liable to be less stable directionally than a landplane. Otherwise, any normal manoeuvre that can be performed by a landplane can also be performed by a floatplane. Accordingly, no special instructions will be given here concerning operating of the aircraft in the air. The same applies, to a large extent, to familiarization with the aircraft itself.

The techniques for handling and manoeuvring a floatplane on the water are very different from those for handling a landplane, since besides airmanship the pilot must also acquire and apply knowledge in seamanship. A floatplane has no brakes and is affected by both wind and water currents. Whether the engine is stopped or running, left to its own devices the aircraft will always turn into the wind. Therefore, the stronger the wind the more difficult it is to manoeuvre a floatplane. Despite the additional problems, floatplanes can offer more pleasure and operational versatility than equivalent landplanes. In most areas of North America the floatplane has countless "aerodromes" with "runways" of unlimited length.

Performance

Due to the weight of the floats and other related equipment, the useful load of a floatplane is normally less than that of the same aircraft on wheels. The rate of climb and cruising speed are also reduced, due to

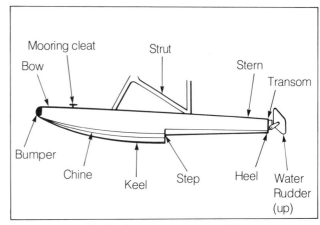

Figure 2-98   Major Components of a Float

increased drag produced by the floats and the float attachments.

Seamanship

Terms

(1) **Under Way.** An aircraft which is not moored or fastened to any fixed object on the land or in the water is *under way.* A floatplane under way must be moving forward, backward, or sideways upon the surface of the water, with its engine running or stopped, and may be taxiing, sailing, or stationary. "Under way," for this text, presumes that a properly authorized person is at the controls of the aircraft.

(2) **Sailing.** A floatplane which is under way and is being manoeuvred backwards or sideways solely with the wind or water currents providing the necessary force is *sailing.* The engine may be running or stopped.

(3) **Bilgewater.** All floats leak water to a varying

degree, adding to the overall weight of the aircraft and diminishing buoyancy. The water is removed by means of a bilge pump. It is essential that this be done as often as necessary to keep the floats dry, especially before the first take-off of the day or when the floats have been subject to a hard landing or other abuse. The centre of gravity will also be affected by water in the floats.

(4) Stationary. A floatplane under way which is being held in one position against wind or water currents by means of engine thrust is not taxiing, but is said to be *stationary.*

(5) Taxiing. A floatplane under way which is being manoeuvred in a forward direction by means of engine thrust is *taxiing.*

(6) Lines. Lengths of hemp, manila, or nylon rope, used for mooring a floatplane or securing it to a dock.

(7) Bridle. A Y-shaped configuration of lines used when mooring a floatplane to a buoy or when using an anchor. So that a floatplane may properly weathercock when moored to a buoy or anchored, the bridle must be equilaterally secured to the bow cleats of each float. The longer the "single" line of the bridle the less the aircraft will tend to drag the anchor or mooring (Fig 2-99).

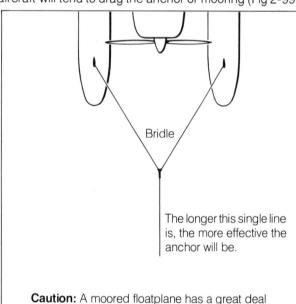

Bridle

The longer this single line is, the more effective the anchor will be.

Caution: A moored floatplane has a great deal of surface exposed to the wind and in strong winds and/or high waves the aircraft will exert considerable drag force upon its mooring line. Under these conditions, an anchorage which has proven satisfactory for relatively large pleasure boats may be found quite unsatisfactory for even a small floatplane.

Figure 2-99 Bridle

Equipment on Board

In addition to the items carried by any aircraft to meet operational requirements, a floatplane should also have on board the following equipment, in serviceable condition:

(1) an approved and readily accessible life-jacket for each occupant
(2) two or more 25 foot mooring lines
(3) a float bilge pump
(4) one or more paddles
(5) an anchor with its own 50 foot line
(6) a chamois for filtering gasoline when away from base.

General Considerations

Footwear. Floatplane pilots should wear shoes or boots which afford a good grip on the normally wet surface of the floats. Footwear with nails or cleats on the soles should not be worn, to avoid scratching or otherwise damaging the top surface of the floats.

Starting the Engine

Many variables apply to the actions immediately preceding the actual starting of the engine. If a helper is available, he can hold the aircraft until the engine is started and you are ready to taxi away. If no helper is available then the aircraft should be suitably restrained and not released until you are seated. Release in this case can be made by releasing a rope which is threaded through a fitting or around a strut. If it is necessary to allow the aircraft to drift away from its mooring, then surrounding obstructions such as other aircraft, trees, rocks, and piers will dictate the procedure to be followed. If you face this situation with a clear plan of what to do if the engine fails to start, such as releasing an anchor, or paddling, there is less likelihood of damaging the aircraft.

If the engine has to be started by hand, the propeller must be swung from behind. This is done by standing on the right float with a firm grip taken on a convenient strut; however, usually only the smaller engines can be started in this manner. The Air Regulation governing engine starting and engines left running applies to floatplanes as well as landplanes. Since a floatplane has no brakes it will begin to move immediately the engine starts, unless suitably restrained.

Water Currents

Special operating considerations may be necessary when water currents, such as may occur in a river or in tidal action, exceed 5 miles per hour, especially in areas where obstructions or other hazards are present.

(1) When turning from downwind to upwind for take-off:
   (a) if taxiing against the current, begin the turn beyond the intended take-off point; or
   (b) if taxiing with the current, begin the turn before the intended take-off point.
(2) The best conditions for take-off occur when the take-off is made with the current (in the direction the current is moving) and into the wind.
(3) The best conditions for landing occur when the landing is made against the current and into wind.

The Flight

Pre-Flight Inspection

In addition to the usual items inspected in a landplane during a pre-flight line inspection, some important items in a floatplane warrant careful attention. The float compartments must be inspected for water and pumped out. The load penalty from water leaking into the floats can mean increased take-off distance, which could produce an accident. The condition of the float struts, brace wires, attachments, fittings, cables, water rudders, and paddle attachments should be ascertained.

Passengers

Unless a passenger is a qualified crewman or float pilot, he should, as a general rule, never be permitted out of the cabin while the propeller is turning. Many a passenger has been hit by the idling propeller or fallen into the water while trying to assist a pilot to secure or unsecure a line. Therefore, ensure that passengers stay seated until the aircraft is secured when docking or departing a dock.

Taxiing

The proposed taxi path should be planned in advance if obstructions exist, and wind strength, river current, tidal action, or a combination of these factors will dictate your actions while proceeding to the take-off area. When preparing to land at an unknown area, select the taxi path from the air when underwater hazards can be seen and other obstructions can be noted.

To aid in turning while taxiing at slow speeds, floatplanes have water rudders, hinged to the transom of one or both floats. They are linked to the normal rudder control system and may be retracted or lowered by the pilot from the cockpit. Water rudders are most effective at low speeds in comparatively calm water; at high speeds the pressure of the water tends to kick them up into the retracted position.

A floatplane has three taxiing modes, known as *idling, sailing,* and *planing.* In the first mode the elevator control should be held all the way back so that the propeller does not strike spray developed by the bows of the floats or wave action, since water striking a rotating propeller can inflict severe damage to the propeller and its components. Except when special wind and water conditions prevail, or there are other extenuating circumstances, experienced floatplane pilots consider it normal practice to taxi by means of a combination of the idling mode and sailing.

In the idling mode (Fig 2-100), the speed of the aircraft through the water is approximately 8 mph or below and the aircraft's attitude is about the same as when it is at rest on the water. Spend as much time as possible initially taxiing in the idling mode to familiarize yourself with the action of both water and aerodynamic rudders. This practice is best conducted when the wind speed is below 10 mph and the water relatively calm.

Great care must be taken when making turns on the water, especially at high speeds or in a strong wind. Floatplanes constantly endeavour to turn into the wind (weathercock) when being taxied across wind or downwind. Consequently, when countering control pressures are relaxed, the aircraft will swing abruptly into wind. Centrifugal force tends to make the aircraft roll toward the outside of the turn and the wind striking the side of the aircraft further aggravates the rolling tendency. If you turn abruptly when taxiing downwind, the combined action of the two forces can be sufficient to overturn the aircraft. Additionally, the more the aircraft heels over the greater the lifting effect of the wing exposed to the wind on the windward side and the less on the wing on the leeward side.

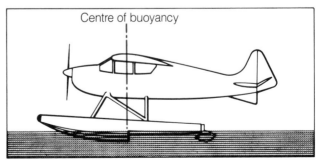

Centre of buoyancy

Figure 2-100   Idle Taxi

To make a turn into wind, simply neutralize the rudder, unless you are taxiing directly downwind. When taxiing directly downwind, a slight amount of rudder should be applied in the direction in which a turn is desired. As soon as the turn begins, neutralize the rudder. If the wind is strong, apply opposite rudder to slow the turn down.

Sailing

Sailing is a procedure used to position or manoeuvre a floatplane in, or to, an area where normal manoeuvring is inadvisable because of congestion or unfavourable wind or water conditions. With even the lightest breeze, a floatplane may be sailed into a very cramped space. If there is absolutely no wind the aircraft can easily be manoeuvred with a paddle, with which every floatplane should be equipped. Water rudders must be retracted when sailing.

In a light wind with the engine stopped, a floatplane moves backward in the direction the tail is pointed. In a stronger wind with the engine idling, movement is usually backward and toward the side the nose is pointed. Move the tail or nose in the desired direction by coarse application of rudder. Additional assistance can be acquired by full-scale deflection of the ailerons. When sailing with engine on, use the air rudder and aileron drag to steer the aircraft. A floatplane can travel as much as 45 degrees to the wind in this manner.

To sail directly backward, merely centralize all controls. Additional "sail" effect may be acquired by lowering flaps, lowering elevators, and opening cabin doors.

Care should be exercised and relative effects assessed where strong water currents or tidal action are present, since it is quite possible that these forces may offset the effect of the wind to varying degrees. When sailing near obstructions with the engine stopped, it is important to be able to restart the engine instantly, so that backward motion of the aircraft may be arrested immediately to avoid collision.

In the case of an engine that may not restart readily and must be left running should it be needed to arrest backward motion, its forward thrust while sailing may be reduced by allowing it to run on one magneto only. Do not operate the engine this way for too long a period at any one time. Once moored or docked, allow it to run on both magnetos for a short while before shutting it down. Carburettor heat may also be used to reduce idling thrust.

Taxiing on the Step

Due to the higher speeds and other considerations involved, taxiing on the step requires considerable skill and experience, together with a good knowledge of water obstructions or other hazards in the locality. To gain solo experience, carry out your initial practice on smooth water with light winds and in areas you know well.

The aircraft is placed on the step by holding the elevator control fully back and applying full power. As the power is applied the nose will begin to pitch up and the aircraft will begin accelerating. You will notice that at some point the nose will rise no further and there will be no further acceleration. When this point is reached, ease the control column forward and place the nose of the aircraft in an attitude slightly above the attitude the aircraft would be in at rest on the water. As this is done the aircraft will begin to accelerate noticeably again.

As the acceleration will be fairly rapid, the power must be reduced in order to prevent the aircraft from becoming airborne. About 65 per cent power should be sufficient for the procedure.

Should the nose of the aircraft begin to pitch up and down (a motion referred to as *porpoising*), it must be stopped immediately, as the oscillation will increase rapidly and the aircraft may become uncontrollable. The safest course of action is to close the throttle and hold the control column fully back, allowing the aircraft to return to idle taxi. Providing you recognize the porpoising action in the early stages, you can stop it by applying a back pressure on the control column as the nose pitches up.

Turns may be made on the step but they should be very gentle, and only a few degrees at a time, until you are thoroughly familiar with a particular floatplane. The aircraft is moving in excess of 30 mph over the water and the centrifugal force in too sharp a turn can easily capsize it. With certain wind and water conditions it is unsafe to execute a step turn under any circumstances. For example, if the wind speed is considerable, say over 25 mph, and the waves high, as the aircraft turns broadside to the wind the upwind float may be lifted by the crest of a wave while the downwind float is in a trough between waves. Under these conditions, if a turn is well established the aircraft is in danger of capsizing. Hence, if tendencies to heel over are evident at or near the start of the turn, throttle right back and apply rudder to stop weathercocking. Turns beyond 45 degrees on the step require a high degree of skill and experienced

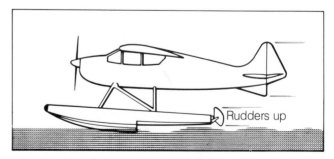

Figure 2-101 Taxiing on the Step

assessment of all existing circumstances and conditions. If any doubt exists as to the safety of this type of turn for a given condition, manoeuvre the aircraft by some other less spectacular method, such as sailing. (The water rudders must be in the "up" position while taxiing on the step.)

In addition to the three methods of taxiing previously discussed, it is possible to taxi the aircraft in what is called the nose-up mode. It must be clearly understood, however, that except for engine run-up, any nose-up taxiing should only be attempted by highly qualified seaplane pilots, due to the danger of upset. A general rule of thumb is that if the nose-up mode is necessary to turn downwind while taxiing in a high wind, then the average seaplane pilot should not be out there in the first place. If you are faced with such a situation, sailing backwards is recommended.

To enter this mode hold the elevator control fully back and apply about half maximum RPM for the aircraft. Be careful to hold the control column fully back during this procedure, to keep the propeller from being damaged from the spray should the nose get too low. Taxiing in this mode may be necessary when taxiing in rough water and when turning downwind in high wind conditions.

There is considerably more float "side area" ahead of the centre of buoyancy than aft of it. Therefore, when taxiing cross-wind in the nose-up mode, many aircraft tend to turn downwind instead of following the normal tendency to turn into the wind. This is why it is often necessary to adopt the nose-up mode when attempting to turn out of a high wind. It is possible to use power to augment rudder in this mode, since opening the throttle increases the speed of the aircraft, causing the nose to rise higher, which exposes more float area and thereby increases the tendency to turn downwind. Conversely, reducing power decreases speed, lowers the nose, and allows the aircraft to turn into wind.

Taxiing with the nose up should be limited to short periods of time, as the engine can very quickly become overheated. In addition, because of the relatively high speed and limited forward view, be very careful to ensure that the path ahead is clear.

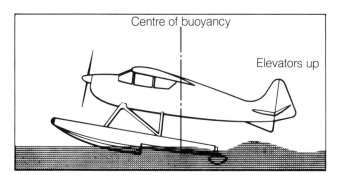

Figure 2-102   Nose-up Taxiing

Mooring and Docking

When approaching a dock or mooring point, observe it closely for obstructions and study the possible effects of wind and water currents. Left to its own devices, a floatplane will always point into wind, and it can always be turned into wind without difficulty. Therefore, it is safe to pass close to an object if the aircraft is on its windward side, since if any clearance doubt exists the aircraft may be easily swung into wind and manoeuvred away from the object. However, when passing on the leeward side of an obstacle leave plenty of room, for if the wind is strong and the aircraft swings it may swing into the obstacle.

Always have a suitable line ready when approaching a dock or other mooring if no shore assistance is available. Taxi speed can be reduced by operating the engine on one magneto, and/or using carburettor heat. Open the doors and release the seat belts. Brief the passengers on what is planned, and if necessary place them for easy pilot exit. As the aircraft nears the dock and it appears that inertia will carry the aircraft the remaining distance, shut the engine down, leave the aircraft, secure a line to a strut, and when sufficiently close, step off with rope in hand. At the time the engine is shut down, be prepared for weathercocking due to loss of slipstream. Protect the aircraft from damage by using one foot to cushion the contact with the dock, and secure the line. In high wind conditions, if the line cannot be secured quickly enough be prepared to jump back on to the float, restart the engine, and try again.

A seaplane ramp is a wide sloping surface, often of wood, with its lower extremity under the water. It is used for bringing seaplanes out of the water for sundry reasons, including routine docking. Other docking forms include piers, rafts, and buoys. The technique for approaching any of these varies, but if possible all of them should be approached into wind at a slow speed, since under this condition you have maximum control.

In the case of a raft (float) moored some distance from shore, even if the wind is blowing shoreward it is sometimes possible to taxi past the raft, turn, and then approach into wind. The same is true of a pier, since three sides are available for approach.

When "docking" an aircraft on a natural beach, ascertain the nature of the shore before contact is made. If it is rocky there is danger of damaging the floats, especially if the waves are such that they cause the aircraft to rock up and down. Sandy beaches are the best, but even these will wear off paint and protective coatings if there is wave action. With an on-shore wind the best approach to a beach is to sail the aircraft backwards to it with the water rudders up. This has the added advantage of not having to wade into the water and manhandle the aircraft around for departure.

If the wind is off-shore, approach slowly, checking for submerged obstructions, or obstacles which could damage the wings or tail. If the wind is on-shore and very light, the same type of approach can be made. However, if the wind strength dictates, raise the water rudders and sail backwards, watching for possible damage from obstacles on the shore. If the wind is parallel to the shore, taxi close until opposite the beaching point, then use the engine to turn the nose into shore and beach as soon as possible. Alternatively, taxi downwind and close the throttle when in a position where the weathercock action will face the aircraft for a close approach to the ramp. In high winds, always use a helper on shore.

Anchoring to a Buoy

Approach the buoy from into wind at minimal speed. When inertia will carry the aircraft to the buoy, shut down the engine and exit the aircraft with rope in hand. Secure the aircraft with a bridle or two ropes, one to each bow cleat.

Using an Anchor

Select a location, taking into account other aircraft or boat traffic, river currents, tide, wind speed, wave size, and depth of water. As a general rule, the anchor line should allow for 10 feet of length for every 1 foot of water. Always ensure that the anchor is holding before leaving the aircraft, and if wind speed increases, return to the aircraft to ensure its safety.

Leaving a Dock or Mooring

Departing from a pier or raft (float) presents no real problem. It is desirable to have an assistant hold the aircraft pointed towards open water until you start the engine. If no assistance is available and the bows of the floats are headed against the pier or raft, cast off and allow the aircraft to drift back far enough to make a turn without striking the pier or raft before starting the engine. When an aircraft is cast off and allowed to drift the engine may not start readily, so always keep in mind the possibility of drifting into obstructions or obstacles.

Departing from a Buoy

In calm conditions it is possible for a float to be directly over a buoy anchor. Damage could result if the aircraft is in shallow water and you step on to the float. The buoy anchor could also do damage when moving away, so always exercise care in shallow water. Always position the buoy for departure so that it is at the side rather than between the floats.

Departing from a Beach

Depending on the strength of the wind and its direction, push the aircraft out from shore with a paddle or sail backwards. Alternatively, face the aircraft towards the open water, start the engine, and put the water rudders down as soon as possible.

Taking Off

Take-off training should begin when there is enough breeze to make small waves but not enough to produce white caps. At the take-off position the water rudders should be placed in the "up" position, and the intended take-off path carefully studied to make sure that it is clear and will remain clear. Operators of pleasure boats, not being aware of the operating requirements of aircraft, are likely to move directly into the path of a floatplane while it is taking off.

Unlike the landplane, the floatplane ordinarily takes off and lands in public areas. It therefore always faces the possibility of encountering semi-submerged floating objects, and swimmers, which are difficult to see, as well as various types of watercraft. When taxiing into take-off position it is often advisable to taxi along the intended take-off path and check for floating obstacles and obstructions.

The take-off on floats is similar to a soft-field take-off in a landplane. When the aircraft is settled into wind, hold the control column hard back and smoothly apply take-off power, then allow the aircraft to progress through the nose-up mode into the planing mode according to the procedures already discussed. When the aircraft is in the planing mode (on the step) at full power, back pressure should be exerted on the control column. Too much back pressure will cause the heels of the floats to dig into the water and create a drag which will impede the take-off. Conversely, if insufficient pressure is exerted, the forward part of the bottom of the float will remain in the water and create undesirable drag. A common error is attempting to "drag" the aircraft out of the water, without realizing that the heels of the floats will be forced down into the water at a much lower angle than is required to put the tail wheel of a landplane on the ground. Experience will determine the best take-off attitude for each aircraft. If held at this attitude, the aircraft will take to the air smoothly and with adequate flying speed.

The importance of the proper use of flaps cannot be ignored. As a general rule in selecting the take-off path, when you feel you have sufficient distance, double it. The climb-out path must be planned prior to starting the take-off, with hills, valleys, and downdrafts being taken into account.

Rough Water Take-offs

When taking off on rough water, apply take-off power as the bows of the floats are rising on a wave. This prevents the nose of the floats from digging into the water and helps keep spray away from the propeller. Throughout a rough water take-off, hold the controls somewhat further back than in smooth water, so as to hold the bows of the floats well up above the surface. Once in the planing mode, the aircraft will begin to bounce from wave to wave and each time it strikes a wave the bows will tend to rise. If nothing is done to correct this, each successive wave will be hit with a severer impact. As the nose starts rising, exert forward pressure on the controls, then apply back pressure just before the aircraft strikes the next wave. It is important to exert back pressure at the correct instant, otherwise the bows of the floats may be pushed underwater, capsizing the aircraft, nose first. Accurate timing and quick reactions are essential. Fortunately, it usually follows that if there is wind enough to cause waves the aircraft will become airborne quickly.

The worst rough-water condition occurs when a strong current runs against the wind. For example, if the current is running at 10 knots and the wind speed is 15 knots, the relative speed between wind and the water is 25 knots. The waves will be as high as those produced in still water by a wind of 25 knots. In other words there will be the disadvantage of 25 knot waves without the advantage of a 25 knot wind to get the aircraft into the air quickly.

Just how rough the water may be before a take-off is inadvisable depends on the size of the aircraft, the wing loadings, the power loading, and your skill as a pilot. As a rule of thumb, if there are less than 2.5 waves along the length of the floats, take-offs should not be attempted except by the most expert and experienced pilots.

Effect of Winds

Besides the obvious effects on taxiing, high winds can impose limitations on float operations, depending on the size of the aircraft and the experience of the pilot. Take-off and landing paths in sheltered areas are desirable,

as open water can be rendered unusable by high winds. Learn to "read" the wind strength from the air by observing wave action, wind lanes, and other indications, before selecting a landing area.

Glassy Water Take-off

The take-off condition which may require more skill than any other occurs with the combination of a hot sultry day, calm wind, glassy water, and a fully loaded aircraft. Such a condition calls for timing, co-ordination of controls, and practice. The take-off run required will be longer and it will take longer to get the aircraft on the step than under normal conditions. Once the throttle is opened with the control column held back, and you are quite sure that the nose of the aircraft has come up to as high an attitude as possible, ease the control column forward to roll the aircraft onto the step. Make sure that it is on the step and is accelerating and planing at the correct attitude. Glassy water is "sticky." When aileron control is effective, one float is gently lifted out of the water (thereby reducing water resistance); at the same time the nose is raised slightly, held there for one or two seconds and the aircraft brought to level flight position. You will then find the aircraft is airborne. Delicate handling is necessary for the first few seconds as the nose may assume too high an attitude, due to the sudden unsticking from the water. If the nose of the aircraft is levelled too soon it will contact the water again. It is impossible to judge vertical distance from glassy water. Leave the flaps until plenty of height is gained, then raise them slowly.

Rocking onto the Step

There may be occasions, with a heavily loaded aircraft, hot weather or high altitude, and water and wind dead calm, that it is necessary to rock the aircraft onto the step. *This should only be attempted if it is absolutely necessary.* Rocking the aircraft is in fact a controlled porpoise started by pulling the control column right back and then releasing it. The nose of the aircraft rises and falls immediately the control column is pulled back again. This procedure is repeated until the nose of the aircraft reaches a maximum height. If the control column is then pushed well ahead and held there, the aircraft is jumped onto the step. The best planing attitude is then carefully controlled with the control column. Allow the speed to build up as much as possible and follow glassy water take-off procedure.

It is difficult to give a written explanation of the proper timing for rocking an aircraft onto the step in this manner. To become expert requires considerable practice and knowledge of the limitations of the aircraft being handled. It should be emphasized that if the nose refuses to come up progressively higher and the aircraft will not start to rock, it will be impossible to put the aircraft on the step. In order to avoid overheating and causing serious damage to the engine, throttle right back, taxi slowly, and lighten the load or wait for a breeze to spring up. Inexperienced pilots have been known to run a heavily loaded aircraft up and down a take-off area in an endeavour to put it on the step, possibly doing considerable damage to the engine. Through ignorance they are pleased if eventually they do succeed, due in all likelihood to using up enough gas to lessen the load. No further thought is given to possible damage caused by an overheated engine.

Cross-Wind Take-offs

Provided the wind is not too strong, cross-wind take-offs are entirely practicable. The procedure is identical to that for landplanes. The aileron control is held to the windward side and appropriate rudder pressure applied to maintain the desired direction. When the aircraft leaves the surface of the water, a gentle turn is made into wind, if possible.

Downwind Take-offs

Downwind take-offs are possible and may even be preferred when the wind is light, if obstructions or other circumstances do not favour a take-off into the wind. Hold the control column further back than when taking off into wind, otherwise the procedure is the same. Much more room is needed for a downwind take-off. In a small body of water completely surrounded by land, an excellent procedure is to begin to take-off downwind and finish it into wind. This is done by starting the take-off downwind and when in the planing mode doing a turn into wind in this mode, thus bringing the aircraft into the take-off configuration near the downwind shore. A reduction of power may be necessary to avoid upset, or for control during the turn in the planing mode; therefore, do not neglect to apply take-off power again immediately the aircraft is pointed into wind.

Landings

Landing a floatplane presents some problems that are unfamiliar to the landplane pilot. An airport, except possibly during the winter, always presents the same general surface, whereas the surface of the water is continually changing.

An airport is restricted to air traffic only and is as free as possible of obstructions and obstacles, whereas boats, floating debris, and submerged obstructions are everyday hazards to the floatplane pilot, which he must assess carefully before every landing. It is therefore wise to fly all around a proposed water landing area to examine it thoroughly for obstructions such as floating logs and mooring buoys and to note the position and direction of motion of any watercraft.

When a windsock is not present at a landing site, there are several methods for determining wind direction. If there are no strong tides or currents, boats lying at anchor point into wind. Seagulls and other water fowl invariably land facing the wind. Sails on boats give a fair approximation of the wind; smoke and flags are other indicators. If the wind has appreciable velocity its path is shown by streaks on the water, which in a strong wind become distinct white lines. The direction of the wind cannot be determined by these alone, but if there are whitecaps on the waves there is no difficulty. The foam appears to move into wind, an illusion caused by the fact that the waves move under the foam.

Landing Attitudes

Because of the continually changing properties of the water's surface, a pilot has to adapt to a wide variation of touchdown attitudes. When the water surface is reasonably smooth, the best touchdown attitude is at an angle such that the steps and the heels of the floats touch at the same time. A nose-high, power-off landing is safe, but it is not as smooth nor as pretty to look at as a "step-heel" landing. It is also liable to be a little disconcerting at first to the landplane pilot as the aircraft rocks forward almost to the level attitude immediately after contact. This is due to the heels of the floats striking the water first, causing a pronounced drag which tips the aircraft abruptly forward. However, remember that a smooth landing may be made in any attitude between the "step-heel" and nose-high attitude, provided the control column is moving steadily back at the instant the aircraft contacts the water and is held back after initial contact to prevent the floats from digging in.

Landing Run

Upon contact, the aircraft will progressively slow down through the three taxiing modes in reverse order to take-off — i.e., planing, nose-up, and idling. If the landing is made some distance from the docking or mooring point and water conditions are satisfactory, open the throttle sufficiently again while the aircraft is in the planing mode and taxi in "on the step." Taxiing in the planing mode is much easier on the engine than taxiing in the nose-up mode. With the latter mode, the engine RPM is the same, but as the forward speed is much lower engine cooling may be inadequate if long distances are involved. In any case, the last few minutes of taxiing should be done at idling RPM to cool the engine and prevent afterfiring when it is shut down.

Landing in Rough Water

When the waves are high select the best suitable sheltered location and land with a "positive angle" attitude, equivalent to the attitude of the aircraft in slow flight configuration, and plan to touch down on top of the wave. If the aircraft starts to porpoise after touchdown, carry out a missed approach. When landing in rough water, the aircraft will slow down appreciably when it strikes the first wave but not enough to keep it from slamming into the next one. The shock of this second contact can be greatly lessened by judicious use of throttle during the bounce. After landing exercise caution while taxiing. This may be an occasion to use nose-up taxiing to turn downwind to proceed to shore or an anchorage.

Glassy Water Landing

Landing on glassy water can be hazardous unless you follow proper procedures. It is absolutely impossible to determine the height of the aircraft above the water in glassy water conditions; without special procedures it may be flown into the water or stalled at a considerable height during the "float" after the aircraft has been flared for landing. Either situation can be extremely dangerous.

Power assisted approaches and landings must be used on glassy water. While it may not always be possible, it is desirable to set up a normal approach over the terrain preceding the leeward shoreline and land parallel to a shoreline. If these aids are not available, objects in the water should be used to judge altitude.

When approximately 200 feet above the surface (300 to 400 feet where visual aids for judgement of height are not available) reduce the rate of descent and apply more power. The objective is to produce a safe airspeed and power combination which will result in a nose-up attitude sufficient to prevent the floats from digging in on touch down. The descent should be established at 200 feet per minute or less by the time the shoreline is crossed. Provided the attitude and airspeed are correct, you need not alter the power until touchdown. Care must be taken to trim the aircraft properly to ensure that there is no slip or skid at the point of contact.

The flight instruments, particularly the airspeed and vertical speed indicators, should be adequately scanned during the final approach, while using peripheral or forward vision for clues of the height above the surface. If the rate of descent increases, apply more power until the desired rate of descent is regained while maintaining the correct attitude and airspeed. Make no attempt to round out or "feel for the surface". At the point of contact, which should be gentle with the steps and heels of the floats touching simultaneously, the throttle should be eased off gently while maintaining the back pressure on the control column to prevent the floats from digging in as the aircraft settles into the water. Remember, considerable space is required for this type of powered approach and landing.

The approach speed necessary to achieve the correct attitude and the amount of power used to control the rate of descent will vary with each type of aircraft. Procedures and airspeeds recommended by the aircraft manufacturer must be followed. In the absence of manufacturer's data, the approach speed should be determined by experimentation long before you attempt glassy water landings. While figures of 15 to 30 per cent above the calibrated stall speed are often quoted for approach speeds, each type of aircraft has to be dealt with individually. If during your seaplane endorsement training no glassy water experience is possible, you must receive dual instruction on the procedure from a qualified instructor before you attempt a glassy water landing as pilot-in-command.

The same landing procedures may be used if failing daylight, deteriorating weather, or other conditions affect depth perception over a landing area.

Should a pilot be forced to land on glassy water after the engine has failed, a landing should be effected as close to the shoreline as possible and parallel to it, the height of the aircraft above the surface being judged from observation of the shore. Floating objects, weeds and weed beds can also be used for judgement of height.

Landing in a Cross-Wind

The procedure for landing a floatplane in a cross-wind is much the same as for landplanes. Lower the water rudders as soon as possible after landing but not while in the planing mode. Do not attempt cross-wind landings in high waves because of the possibility of one float landing in a trough and the other on a crest, with the risk of capsizing the aircraft.

Downwind Landing

Avoid downwind landings if it is possible to do so. The excessively high "ground speeds" cause an undesirable forward pitching of the aircraft as the floats make contact with the water. Also, a much longer landing run ensues in a downwind landing; allow plenty of room and use the soft field technique in the approach and landing so that the floats touch the water at the minimum controllable airspeed. Engine power should be left on at point of touchdown only long enough to check the tendency for the aircraft to pitch forward.

Landing at Other than Regular Operating Areas

Before landing, check the intended landing surface and the subsequent proposed take-off path for rocks, sand bars, debris, or other obstructions, deciding on the taxi path if necessary and the method of beaching. In marginal areas, it is also wise to select a prominent reference point, from which you can carry out a missed approach if you are not already on the water, or, on take-off, from which you can discontinue the take-off if you are not airborne by that point.

Landing on Land

If it becomes necessary to land a floatplane on land, due to an engine failure or other extreme emergency, plan the approach and execute the subsequent landing so as to contact the ground with the keel of the floats as nearly parallel to the ground as possible. Immediately after touchdown pull the control column hard back.

Summary

At the completion of a float endorsement training course, remember that unless a course is lengthened to cover all the possible situations a float pilot might encounter, then an endorsement is merely a licence to learn. Approach situations you have not met during training with caution and the assistance of an experienced instructor or float pilot.

Float flying can, under normal conditions, be extremely rewarding and pleasurable. Otherwise inaccessible areas are opened up, and provided you pace your learning and confront new situations with respect and discretion, much is to be gained. Seasoned float pilots, who usually are most willing to share their knowledge, have little respect for pilots who attempt manoeuvres beyond their capabilities and knowledge.

Skiplanes

In those areas of Canada which afford a reasonably long winter season, an aircraft equipped with skis takes on a versatility, as a mode of transportation or sport, that no ordinary landplane has. As soon as the snow cover reaches a depth of 2 to 3 inches, practically every open expanse of flat land becomes landing surface. When the ice on sheltered lakes becomes thick enough, these too offer inviting wide open places for taking off and landing. It is an exciting experience to have take-off and landing areas on all sides practically as far as you can see. It is also a pleasant novelty to be relatively free of the other air traffic normally associated with aerodromes and airports.

Like any other endeavour in the field of aviation, operating an aircraft on skis must be kept within the bounds of certain guidelines. These guidelines require the exercising of basic common sense throughout the many and varied circumstances that may occur in a new and sometimes sensitive operational environment.

In this chapter we will discuss only those operational areas peculiar to skiplanes. The subject aircraft will be a typical tail wheel-style single-engined light aircraft equipped with fixed skis (as opposed to a retractable ski wheel arrangement). It should be pointed out that certain nose wheel aircraft may be equipped with skis, but most light skiplanes are of the tail wheel style.

Properties of Snow

Studies carried out by various agencies disclose many interesting aspects of the properties of snow and ice, but one point stands out in explaining why a skiplane may perform differently nearly every time there is even the slightest rise or fall of the ambient temperature or change in the texture of the snow. The pressure of the skis as they move on the frozen surface creates an extremely thin film of water between the ski and the surface, even at subzero temperatures. The film of water, depending on the type and temperature of the surface, acts either to lubricate the ski and assist its forward progress or to clog the bottom surface of the ski and impede it. For example, since a skiplane has no mechanical braking system, if it is landed on the bare ice surface of a lake in even the slightest tail wind, this minute film of water could mean practically no friction between the ski and the surface, so that the aircraft would slide unhampered until it collided with something or some action was taken to redirect its heading. On the other hand, this same film of water between dampish snow and the skis of an aircraft attempting take-off could create a surface tension which would drastically restrict acceleration and lengthen the take-off run considerably.

Types of Skis

Aircraft ski construction varies widely, from brass-trimmed laminated "boards" to sophisticated hydraulically operated wheel-ski combinations. Most skis are attached to the wheel axle when the wheel is removed, while others are a "roll-on" variety, using the cushioning effect of the tire, with the tire fitting in a channel built into the top of the ski.

Manoeuvring on the Ground

A skiplane in flight operates almost exactly like a landplane. The additional weight and the aerodynamic properties of the skis may affect the stalling speed and over-all performance of the aircraft, but to a degree that is usually negligible. However, on the ground and especially during the landing roll, the lack of brakes on normal skiplanes calls for special techniques and certain special precautions. Unlike the floats of a floatplane, the "heels" of aircraft skis cannot be forced

187

down into the snow or ice by elevator action to arrest forward motion. The steering effectiveness of steerable tail skis fluctuates from good to nil according to the type of snow or ice the aircraft is manoeuvring upon. Even with normally good conditions, the steering effectiveness of the tail ski may deteriorate considerably in a cross-wind. In any case, with no braking system at all, let alone no differential braking capability, sharp taxiing turns are more difficult to execute than with wheeled aircraft. This is especially important in congested areas. In strong cross-winds that would be difficult but not impossible for landplanes to taxi and manoeuvre in, the skiplane may have to depend on outside manhandling for directional guidance. A great many turns on the ground are done by "blowing" the tail around with bursts of engine power while applying full rudder in the direction of the turn desired.

Most of the problems associated with manoeuvring skiplanes on the ground occur in congested areas if there are strong winds. Offsetting this is the fact that skiplanes usually operate away from airports and are seldom required to manoeuvre in congested or confined areas. Almost invariably, the take-off and landing can be made directly into wind (there being no defined runway system); therefore, cross-wind taxiing is usually reduced to a minimum.

Slide

The strength with which skis will adhere to the snow comes as a considerable surprise to most pilots operating a skiplane for the first time. Sometimes even full engine power will not cause the aircraft to move. Between adhesion and the surface tension previously mentioned, the length of the take-off run and landing roll varies greatly with the condition and type of the snow surface. The weight of the aircraft also has more effect on this performance under poor snow conditions than in the same aircraft on wheels, to the extent that it may be necessary to lighten the load in order to get off the ground.

A skiplane attains its best take-off performance when the surface affords as much *slide* as possible. This is not a profound statement in itself, but it achieves importance when you consider that the surface condition which affords the most ideal landing run, since no brakes are available, could be one that produces as little slide as possible. Bear this in mind when contemplating an operation into and back out of confined space.

The best sliding conditions for skiplane take-offs can occur when the ambient temperature is relatively low or relatively high. At temperatures of -5 degrees Celsius and below, the film of water caused by compression between the ski and the snow surface is extremely thin, producing good lubrication but very little surface tension. When ambient temperatures rise to the point at which the snow cover becomes watersoaked and slushy on top of a sound surface, lubrication is good and the "smack" of the ski on the slush as it progresses forward breaks the surface tension. Although the sliding qualities of the higher temperature conditions are good, performance itself is not quite as good as at the lower temperatures, due to drag. Drag in this case is caused by the ski sinking slightly into the soft surface and having to push against the slush ahead of it; in a way it could be likened to the skis trying to ride up over a tiny but everpresent hill. Figure 2-103 offers a slightly exaggerated illustration of this.

Surprisingly enough, new snow even at fairly low temperatures does not provide a good slide factor, and if deep enough and new enough can affect the take-off performance of a light skiplane very seriously. The reason for this is a combination of drag (Fig 2-103) and lack of lubrication. New snow contains a great deal of air, which allows the skis to sink in deeply and at the same time acts like a blotter, absorbing the thin layer of water instead of allowing it to lubricate the skis. New snow of reasonable depth on top of older snow provides ideal landing conditions. A thin layer of new snow over ice could be somewhat less than ideal, because of the lack of braking action.

When planning a take-off on new snow, or any snow condition which allows the skis to sink into it to any depth, compact a take-off path by taxiing the aircraft up and down the proposed take-off area. Do this before loading the aircraft, to avoid overheating the engine and to make the aircraft easier to manoeuvre during the compacting process. If for any reason the take-off must be discontinued during the ground run, change the heading of the aircraft so that it leaves the compacted area. This will help bring the aircraft to a stop in a shorter distance, through the aid of drag.

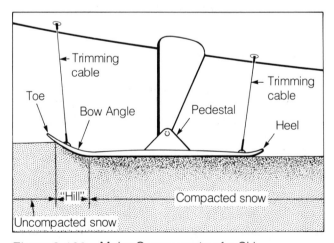

Figure 2-103   Major Components of a Ski

Take-off

The procedures for taking off and landing a skiplane are basically the same as a soft field take-off for a landplane. It is good practice, once the tail of a skiplane has been lifted on take-off, to hold the nose slightly higher than is customary with a landplane. This will tend to allow the toes of the skis to ride up over snow "ripples" instead of digging into them, and will transfer the weight from the skis to the wings as quickly as possible.

On a landplane the tires absorb a great deal of the shock and iron out bumps and other irregularities on the manoeuvring surface. A skiplane has only the suspension system to absorb shock, and it is not generally designed to counteract anything but minor irregularities. You must get used to a very high noise and vibration factor, and often quite rude bumps and shocks not experienced with wheeled aircraft. However, this does not mean that a skiplane has some special quality for accepting shocks that a landplane does not. There are many surfaces that would have to be considered operationally unacceptable for skiplane operations, except in an emergency. Under most circumstances, though, there is reasonable scope for selectivity and you should exploit it fully.

Landing

Most skiplane landings can be made into wind. However, if a landing is made in a cross-wind it must be executed in the usual manner, with the appropriate control action taken to counteract drift. There are many snow and ice surface conditions which can exert more side load on a skiplane's landing structure, if drift is present at touchdown, than the same amount of drift would exert on a landplane's landing-gear. Here again, the landplane's tire absorbs a great deal of the side-loading. A ski is long and a touchdown with drift in a rutted, icy, or hard-packed snow surface can twist the landing struts beyond the point of return to proper alignment. Ideally a skiplane should be landed in the three-point attitude.

Cross-Wind

It has already been said that because of the large off-airport manoeuvring areas usually available to skiplanes, landings and take-offs can be executed into wind at most times. But on a normal snow surface, which allows the skis to sink into the surface slightly, cross-winds may be handled in the same manner as with landplanes. However, you may have to land a skiplane (or take off) in an area limited in width, such as a river or a narrow serviceable area on a frozen lake. If the ice surface is relatively smooth, the influence of a cross-wind must be counteracted in a manner that is quite contrary to everything said thus far on the subject of cross-wind landings or take-offs. The cross-wind landing and take-off techniques for landplanes (and skiplanes under normal snow conditions) depend largely on a ground surface which will hold the wheels or skis firmly aligned in a desired direction while they are on the surface. A skiplane on ice does not have this advantage. When landing on an icy surface which freely allows lateral movement of the aircraft, a skiplane must come to touchdown by counteracting cross-wind drift in the normal manner. At touchdown the aircraft must be immediately crabbed into wind to maintain the desired direction of travel until it comes to rest. In other words, the aircraft is actually sliding sideways throughout the landing run. More and more crab is required as speed diminishes. On take-off, apply crab immediately and maintain it throughout the take-off run. Less and less crab is required as speed increases. Execute this procedure with great care and if possible only with a first-hand knowledge of surface conditions, since hazards exist when crabbing a skiplane on an icy surface in a strong cross-wind. Should the skis encounter a rough spot or a soft area while most of the weight is still on the skis, the aircraft may suffer considerable side-loading. The severity of the side-loading depends on speed, amount of weight still on the skis, and the extent and degree of the rough or soft area. The side-loading would ordinarily be least severe just after touchdown or immediately prior to take-off, since at these points much of the aircraft's weight is on the wings, and the crab angle is smallest.

In normal recreational flying avoid this type of operation, because of the possibility of damage to the aircraft, or select an alternative surface which will permit landings and take-offs into the wind with no side drift.

Snow is at its worst for slide when it is at its best for making snowballs. Skiplanes manoeuvring in this type of snow have difficulty making anything but large radius taxiing turns without severe blasting of the tail. The skis are also liable to stick to the surface, so that a lot of engine power is needed to get the aircraft moving. A peculiarity of skis, however, is that once moving, even at a snail's pace, they will continue to move even in adverse snow conditions. Once the aircraft has broken clear, keep it moving rather than continuously stopping and starting to avoid abusing the engine. This type of snow can be misleading since if the aircraft encounters an area compacted by other traffic the slide qualities will suddenly improve. Therefore, approach these areas cautiously to avoid unexpected forward progress.

Sticking

The skis of a skiplane parked for any length of time on any snow or ice surface will adhere to the surface. The adhesion will vary in degree, according to weather and other conditions, from one in which reasonable engine power will start the aircraft moving to a condition where no amount of power will get it under way. A skiplane which is stuck fast may sometimes be broken clear by judicious use of simultaneous engine power and movement of the rudder and elevator controls. The wiggle induced will unstick reasonable adhesion, but under no circumstances use this method without ascertaining that the tail ski is free. Forward movement of the elevator control may unstick an adhered tail ski so suddenly that it will be almost impossible to prevent the nose from dropping too far and possibly damaging the propeller.

By far the best way to unstick a skiplane is manually, by the careful use of strategically placed wooden levers. If the skis are so submerged in ice that you must chop them free, make sure that any lumps of ice are removed before attempting to taxi. If the snow condition is such that the aircraft sticks fast each time it stops, unload it and compact the area to be used by taxiing up and down until the surface slide improves.

If the aircraft is to be parked for any amount of time over two hours, under most conditions you should taxi it up on to something that will limit the degree of surface adhesion and allow the aircraft to easily break itself clear when it is next used. Spruce boughs, or the trunks of small trees, or 2 by 4 inch lengths of lumber laid out at right angles to the skis, will serve this purpose.

The main function of the trimming and restraining cables with which aircraft skis are equipped is to flexibly maintain and secure the skis in a correct attitude during flight. In the walk-around inspection prior to flight include a careful examination of these cables, to ensure that they are in good condition and that all their locking and securing devices are intact. Should a rear cable fail during flight the aircraft would become asymmetrically trimmed and awkward to fly, but if a front cable failed, a very dangerous flight condition and landing problem would exist. The affected ski would drop down, more or less at a 45 degree angle, and create extreme drag on one side of the aircraft. Landing in this condition carries the risk of the toe of the ski digging into the snow upon touchdown, tearing off both the ski and its landing strut. Because these cables are subject to minute inspection by most skiplane pilots, a failure is extremely rare. However, should a failure occur, search for a landing area with a surface that offers no opportunity for the ski to dig in, such as the snow-free ice on a lake or a river. Use a power assisted approach and landing to keep the nose high. Just before touchdown, enter a forward slip with bank toward the affected ski and gradually allow that ski to settle onto the ice, then remove the slip and complete the landing.

If during a refuelling operation fuel is spilled directly on to the snow or ice surface, move the aircraft a safe distance from the spill area before starting the engine. Gasoline lying on a cold surface does not evaporate as quickly as usual and could be accidentally ignited by the engine exhaust flame.

Common Hazards

White-out

Each winter there are a number of aircraft accidents as a result of pilots flying into white-out conditions and becoming disoriented due to the reduction in visibility, the lack of distinguishable features on the ground, and the loss of a visual horizon. The causes and effect of the phenomenon known as white-out may be described as follows:

(1) Overcast White-out. A product of a uniform layer of cloud over a snow-covered surface. The rays from the sun are scattered and diffused as they pass through the cloud and are then reflected back from the snow surface in all directions. As a result, the space between the ground and cloud appears to be filled with a diffused light with a uniform white glow. Depth perception is completely lacking as the sky blends imperceptibly with the ground at the horizon line, causing disorientation.

(2) Water Fog White-out. Produced by the clouds containing supercooled water droplets with the cloud base usually in contact with the cold snow surface. Visibility both horizontally and vertically is affected by the size and distribution of the water droplets suspended in the air.

(3) Blowing Snow White-out. Produced by fine blowing snow plucked from the snow surface and suspended in the air by winds of 20 knots or more. The suspended grains of snow reflect and diffuse sunlight and reduce visibility.

(4) Precipitation White-out. Although all falling snow reduces visibility, small wind-driven snow crystals falling from low clouds above which the sun is shining

produce a white-out condition. The multiple reflection of light between the snow-covered surface and the cloud base is further complicated by the spectral reflection from the snowflakes and the obscuring of the landmarks by the falling snow.

White-out conditions are most commonly encountered when flying over large lakes at some distance from the shoreline. Never proceed into areas where, due to white-out, it is not possible to distinguish between ground and sky, unless you are sufficiently experienced, and capable of instrument flight.

If it should be necessary to land during these conditions follow the procedure used for glassy water landings (see the section, "Glassy Water Landings," in Exercise 26). The heels of the skis should make contact with the surface first. As soon as this occurs, close the throttle immediately since, unlike floatplanes, the skiplane will have no tendency to pitch forward upon contact with the snow or ice surface. Due to the lack of visual clues the instruments must be used for altitude, airspeed, and descent reference throughout the approach.

Suitability of Snow Surface for Landings

When selecting a landing area under conditions of restricted visibility or bright sun it is often impossible to determine the condition of the surface. Extreme caution is advised. Ice ridges, hummocks, and windrows of snow are often impossible to see, and any one of these can cause serious damage to a skiplane. The annual toll of aircraft damaged due to "selecting unsuitable terrain for a landing" is a forcible reminder of the need for discretion when deciding to fly under such conditions, and once committed to it, when selecting a landing area.

Unlike water surface conditions, there is no relationship between wind conditions and ground conditions. High snowdrifts could exist in a no-wind condition and snowdrifts could be parallel as well as at an angle to the existing wind.

Ice or Snow on Aerofoils

The winter environment in which a skiplane operates makes one of the cardinal rules for cold weather flying even more important: never attempt a take-off with any snow, ice or frost on any part of the wings, horizontal stabilizer, propeller, or control surfaces. Even a film of ice or frost so thin that it almost defies measurement can very effectively destroy the lift qualities of an aerofoil. Insofar as snow, ice, or frost on other parts of the aircraft are concerned, consideration must be given to additional load and the possibility of controls becoming immovable due to dislodging or refreezing of the precipitation.

Thin Ice

When operating skiplanes on ice-covered lakes, or other ice areas with a water base, there are various rules of thumb to determine the thickness of ice required to support a certain aircraft weight. However, none of these will safely cover all situations. For complete knowledge on this phase of skiplane operations refer to the Transport Canada publication, *Recommended Minimum Ice Thickness for Aircraft Operations.* This publication may be obtained free of charge on request from:

Transport Canada
AISP / A
Ottawa, Canada
K1A 0N8

Operations

Avoid slush conditions whenever possible. Besides adding extra weight, the loss of lift due to disturbance of the airflow over the lifting surface can be substantial. Also, due to the possibility of extending the take-off run, it is important to remove dirt, sod, ice, etc. adhering to the undersurface of the skis before attempting a take-off. When operating off an ice surface remember that ice near the shoreline will bear greater loads in early winter, but should be used with great caution in the late winter and spring. In rivers, avoid areas of undercurrents resulting in thin ice. Points where creeks or rivers flow into or out of lakes should also be avoided, along with air holes, fissures, and deep snow.

Survival

While winter operations should automatically include survival equipment, the very nature of ski flying demands extra precautions. Carry ropes, axe, shovel, blow pot, snow shoes, tent, engine and wing covers, and a receptacle for draining and heating the engine oil, where applicable. Other survival equipment such as food, sleeping bag, clothing, and footwear should also be considered if you are operating away from home base.

Type Conversion

One side effect of improving the performance of any medium is, more often than not, complexity of operation. The manual change six-speed gearboxes in transport trucks and buses afford more efficiency and flexibility than the transmissions in conventional automobiles, but to operate them effectively requires much greater skill than the average car driver normally possesses. And so it is with aircraft. One which requires only basic skill and a minimum of professionalism to operate safely usually lacks the overall performance of the more complex.

For our purposes, in addition to flaps, carburettor heat, and mixture control, an advanced-type aircraft in the middle range of complexity is equipped with retractable landing-gear, a constant speed propeller, and a multicell fuel selection system. It invariably has a higher wing loading than an initial trainer; therefore, it also has a higher stalling speed. Extra cockpit equipment will include a propeller pitch control, a landing-gear position indicator, a landing-gear position selector, an engine manifold pressure gauge, and quite often engine cylinder head temperature, exhaust gas temperature, or carburettor heat gauges.

The pilot's visual inspection of a complex aircraft is similar to the inspection of a basic aircraft. To begin with, when you enter the cockpit to check that magneto and master switches are off, also check that the landing-gear up-down selector is in the "down" position.

When checking the tires and other standard items of the landing-gear, also look for hydraulic fluid leaks in the lines and actuating cylinders of the landing-gear retracting system. If the system is electrically operated, look for loose electric wires and switches. The exposed threads of the screw-type jack of an electro-mechanical retracting system should be bright and free of accumulations of oil and dirt sludge.

The weight and balance of a complex aircraft is usually more critical than that of a basic aircraft. The complex aircraft, with its greater length, fore-and-aft baggage compartments, and greater load carrying capacity, can easily be improperly loaded. Pay strict attention, therefore, to weight and balance prior to flight.

Complex aircraft, with their greater efficiency of operation, offer the flexibility of carrying a limited payload a great distance with full tanks, or a heavy payload a short distance with limited fuel. This calls for very careful payload and fuel load planning on the part of the pilot-in-command.

Complex aircraft often have separate baggage compartments with their own doors. These doors must be securely closed prior to take-off. Besides other obvious consequences, a door that opens in flight and cannot be reached and closed may change the aerodynamic characteristics of the aircraft and produce serious difficulties in control. The security of baggage doors is the pilot's responsibility, a responsibility that should never be passed on to unqualified persons.

Retractable landing-gear gives the recurring advantage of a gain in airspeed, due to a reduction in parasite drag. For all practical applications, the ratio of the advantage increases as airspeed increases.

Another distinct advantage of retractable landing-gear is that it extends the safe operating speed between stalling and normal cruising speed. This gives you a wider choice of speeds for fuel economy. Under normal circumstances, an aircraft with retractable landing-gear will climb faster than its counterpart with fixed landing-gear.

An aircraft with its landing-gear retracted has a shallower glide angle than a similar aircraft with fixed landing-gear. The gear may be left in the retracted position to gain distance and extended at the right moment to reduce speed or increase the glide angle.

A constant speed propeller allows the pilot to match the operational performance requirement of an aircraft more readily with its available engine power at a certain throttle setting. Most internal combustion engines attain their maximum horsepower at a point somewhere near their maximum allowable revolutions per minute (RPM), but the power requirement for economical cruising is usually found at considerably less than maximum RPM.

When listing the performance figures in an aircraft flight manual, the manufacturer usually begins the list with the distance, in feet, that the aircraft requires for its take-off run. Being able to accelerate from a stopped to an airborne condition in as short a distance as possible, and then climb out initially at a good rate, is a prime performance requirment of most aircraft. To accomplish this the engine must be allowed to develop the RPM which produces its maximum power output. This is done by setting the pitch angle of the propeller blades small enough to allow the engine to rotate freely up to the desired RPM. When the pitch angle is small the propeller takes a smaller bite of the air it is rotating in, but it takes many more bites because it is turning faster. This is much like the need to use a lower gear in an automobile for acceleration, or to climb a steep hill at low speed. Once the aircraft is in cruise climb or cruising flight, the air is coming through the propeller at such a speed that if its blades are left at the smaller pitch angle, it cannot take a sufficient number of small bites to efficiently chew its way forward. (This is like leaving an automobile in low gear while trying to maintain highway speed.) At this point the propeller pitch angle must be increased so that a bigger bite of air can be taken for each engine revolution.

Thus, to use the available horsepower of an aircraft engine effectively, for a given flight configuration, you must be able to control the pitch angle of the propeller blades. The fixed pitch propeller used on an initial training aircraft is carefully calculated to provide the best compromise between take-off performance and cruising speed, but it is only a compromise.

An internal combustion engine can be operationally damaged, even to the point of failure, by sustained overspeeding and/or subjection to high internal pressures for lengthy periods of time. To use a familiar parallel again, when an automobile is forced up a steep hill at relatively low speed in high gear with the accelerator depressed to the floor, severe and damaging pressures are being generated within the combustion chamber of the engine. This condition could be remedied by selecting a lower gear. Because it is air-cooled, an aircraft engine is even more susceptible to damage by similar engine abuse. In an aircraft with a fixed pitch propeller, the pilot cannot, under normal circumstances, subject the engine to abnormal internal pressures nor is it likely that he will allow engine overspeeding to occur for too long a time. This is not so in the case of aircraft equipped with constant speed propellers. The pilot has control over internal engine pressures and can also overspeed the engine very easily. Should the engine be equipped with a supercharger, "overboosting" of the engine can occur during the take-off.

To assist in maintaining acceptable engine pressures, in addition to the familiar tachometer the complex aircraft is equipped with an instrument called a manifold pressure gauge and quite often also a cylinder head temperature gauge. The engine handling procedure for take-off and climb in most initial training aircraft is to apply full engine power and maintain this power setting until the altitude selected for cruising is reached. To do this with most constant speed propeller equipped aircraft would subject the engine to severe and unnecessary abuse. If the engine is unsupercharged, take off with full throttle and the propeller pitch control fully forward in the high RPM position. However, as soon as the aircraft is established in the normal climb attitude at a safe altitude throttle back to reduce the power, until the recommended climb pressure is indicated on the manifold pressure gauge. Then bring back the propeller pitch control until the recommended engine RPM for the climb is indicated on the tachometer. Recommended pressures and RPM are found in the owner's handbook, or the flight manual for the aircraft being flown. (Supercharged engines do not normally use full throttle for take-off; recommended manifold pressures are shown in the owner's handbook.)

When cruising altitude is reached, bring back the throttle to the manifold pressure recommended for the speed desired at the selected altitude. Then bring back the propeller pitch control until the corresponding recommended engine RPM is indicated on the tachometer.

When the pilot selects a specific RPM setting, the governing mechanism of a constant speed propeller will maintain it regardless of reasonable variations in throttle setting and aircraft attitude. With this type of propeller, reasonable movement of the throttle will change readings on the manifold pressure gauge but will not alter the engine RPM. However, movement of the propeller pitch lever affects both RPM and manifold pressure. When the pitch lever is brought back, the RPM will decrease and the manifold pressure will increase. Conversely, ease forward on the pitch lever to increase the RPM and the manifold pressure will decrease. An increase of manifold pressure by movement of the pitch lever alone is undesirable. Therefore, remember the rule: to increase engine power, first increase RPM; to decrease engine power, first decrease manifold pressure. Or: to increase power: (1) pitch forward; (2) throttle forward; to decrease power: (1) throttle back, (2) pitch back.

There may be mechanical reasons for starting the engine with the propeller pitch lever in the fully forward position, but the most important reason is operational. To start the engine of an aircraft in the class under discussion, it must be cranked at about 250 RPM. To crank the engine at this speed the starter must produce a specific amount of power with the propeller pitch at its smallest angle (smallest bite). If the pitch level is not fully forward, the blade angle will be greater and the starter may not be able to crank the engine fast enough to cause it to start, or if it does start there may be an undue strain on the starter and battery.

We have said that when the propeller pitch lever is fully forward, the propeller blade pitch angle is at its smallest, and when the lever is pulled right back, the pitch angle is at its greatest. In the aviation community there are various terms to describe the position of the propeller pitch lever in relation to the blade angle, but perhaps the most descriptive and least confusing is:

(1) Pitch lever forward   high RPM
(2) Pitch lever back   low RPM

Carburettor icing will be indicated in the case of an aircraft with a fixed pitch propeller by a decrease in RPM. This is not the case in aircraft with constant speed propellers. The propeller will continue to maintain its RPM setting until the carburettor is so choked with ice the engine will not have the power to maintain RPM, even at the smallest propeller blade pitch angle. The instrument that will indicate that carburettor ice is present is the manifold pressure gauge. If the altitude and the throttle setting have been constantly maintained, a decrease in manifold pressure may indicate that carburettor ice is present. We say "may" since other factors can cause fluctuations in manifold pressure. The manifold pressure gauge is a pressure instrument and is influenced by the atmosphere; therefore flight from a high pressure area into a low would cause the manifold pressure to drop, and vice versa. A drop in manifold pressure may also indicate an engine malfunction. In any case apply carburettor heat in the manner prescribed by the manufacturer. If there is a momentary drop and then a rise in manifold pressure, carburettor ice is most likely present.

When the aircraft has a multicell, multiselection fuel storage system, study the relevant section of the operator's handbook very carefully, since there may be a certain fuel tank (or tanks) which cannot be selected for take-off or landing. When so specified there are various technical reasons for this precaution. It is not always the case of course, but generally the fuel tanks which are specified as not to be used for take-off or landing are designated as "auxiliary" and those that may be used as "main." It is good practice to start and warm up the engine on an auxiliary fuel tank to check the system, then select a main tank prior to the engine run-up and ground check. This confirms that no fuel flow problems exist, and that an adequate supply of fuel is available to the engines for take-off. Auxiliary fuel tanks should not be selected until cruising altitude is reached and the aircraft is in a level attitude. Prior to landing, the main fuel supply should be selected as part

of the downwind check, at the latest. Many pilots select the main supply at the beginning of the descent from altitude and then recheck the item during the downwind check.

The complex aircraft under discussion is most likely somewhat larger than the initial trainer; therefore it may be presumed that considerably more fuel is being carried in each wing. In order to keep the aircraft in good lateral trim, the fuel should be used alternately from each side of the aircraft. If, for example, an aircraft is carrying 4 hours of fuel on board (2 hours on each side), fly for 45 minutes on one side initially, switch over to the other side, for 1½ hours, then return to the original side, which now has 1 hour and 15 minutes of fuel remaining.

It is never considered good practice to run a fuel tank dry unless a fuel shortage warrants doing so. When a tank is sucked dry there is a possibility of sediment or water being drawn into the carburettor or fuel injection system, but probably more important still, an air lock may be introduced into the fuel system. The best procedure for fuel management when full use must be made of the available supply is to calculate fuel consumption and accurately time each tank, using the fuel gauges as monitors. When the fuel state requires running a tank dry, try to do so at altitude in level flight while at cruising speed. If there is a fuel warning light, select a new tank when it begins to flicker, avoiding an empty tank position, and switch on the fuel booster pump, as quickly as possible in that order. In running a tank dry, if you must wait until the engine falters through lack of fuel, select a new tank and then move the throttle lever back to a position half-way between the idle and normal cruise setting until the engine is running evenly again.

You will recall that early in training you were warned against abrupt applications of power, and adequate reasons for such a warning were given. In the case of supercharged engines there is another important reason. Some superchargers are exhaust operated but most are mechanically driven by the engine through a gear train which rotates the supercharger impeller as high as 10 times engine speed. An abrupt application of power may demand that the engine RPM be increased from 1,000 up to 3,000 RPM in a split second. This means that the supercharger impeller is being forced to accelerate from 10,000 RPM to 30,000 RPM in the same split second, or conversely, to decelerate the same amount in a split second. Whereas the supercharger is designed and constructed to accept some abuse, it is obvious that changes in power applied to a supercharged engine must be progressive and smooth with the degree of rapidity warranted by the situation.

When you are climbing an aircraft with a constant speed propeller at the recommended manifold pressure and engine RPM, the manifold pressure will decrease as the aircraft ascends. This will require constant forward adjustments to the throttle to maintain the correct manifold pressure. When you reach an altitude where the throttle will no longer cause the manifold pressure to increase, open fully until the desired cruising altitude is reached. On descent from altitude, you will have to constantly adjust the throttle backwards to maintain a desired manifold pressure.

Several principles are used to effect the change in blade pitch angle of the various makes of constant speed propellers, but in the majority of cases engine oil at engine pressure provides the moving force. The propeller must be "exercised" from its high RPM to low RPM range through at least 2 cycles prior to take-off. This is ususally carried out during the warm-up and engine ground check. The main reason for doing this, of course, is to assure that the propeller mechanism is functioning properly, but it is also for the purpose of circulating warm engine oil through the propeller actuating system.

When checking the magnetos for drop in RPM during the engine ground check, make sure that the propeller pitch lever is in the "full high" RPM position. Being a constant speed propeller, it will automatically adjust the RPM to compensate for power loss due to a magneto drop if the lever is in some intermediate position. In other words, the drop will be there but the tachometer will not show it.

In the early days of constant speed propellers, it was considered good practice to place the propeller pitch control into the "full high" RPM position somewhere in the traffic circuit, prior to landing. Primarily, this assured that full power was available should the landing have to be aborted with both landing-gear and flaps extended. Gradually this practice has been modified to the point where most operators leave the pitch control at the normal cruise setting during the approach and then place the pitch lever into the "full high" RPM position (forward) after passing the threshold of the runway. This increases propeller drag and serves to shorten the landing roll, besides ensuring that adequate engine power is immediately available in an emergency.

The handling and performance characteristics of a complex aircraft may differ from those of a basic aircraft as follows:

(1) The take-off run may be longer.
(2) Greater torque and thrust may require coarser rudder movements to keep the aircraft straight during the initial stages of the take-off run.
(3) It is more difficult to regain control if directional control is lost during the take-off run.
(4) There may be poorer forward visibility in the climb attitude.
(5) Climb will be faster, requiring more vigilance for slower aircraft ahead or in the vicinity of the airport traffic circuit.
(6) Stalling speed is higher.
(7) The radius of a standard rate turn is usually larger.
(8) The majority of complex aircraft have a low wing; therefore, other aircraft at a lower altitude are obscured at certain angles of vision.
(9) A substantial reduction in airspeed occurs when the landing-gear is lowered.
(10) More foot pressure may be required to operate the rudder of nose wheel aircraft when the landing-gear is lowered.
(11) The approach and landing speeds are higher.
(12) The landing roll may be longer.
(13) The brakes may not bring the aircraft to a stop as quickly.

Although there are aircraft with manually operated landing-gear, most are operated hydraulically, electrically, or by a mixture of both, with an emergency method of extending the gear manually. Since the systems are remarkably trouble free, pilots are apt to ignore the procedure for manually extending the landing-gear, resulting in delay and confusion should a landing-gear emergency arise. It is good practice to allow a few seconds to review the procedure for manual extension of landing-gear, as part of the pre-taxi geographical check of the cockpit.

The climb performance of a complex aircraft is greatly enhanced when the landing-gear is retracted. Therefore, in the case of short field take-offs, especially over obstacles, retraction should occur as soon as possible and consistent with safety. Some aircraft flight manuals recommend a delay in this procedure, as the drag of gear-door opening and the retraction process may exceed the drag when the gear is down. Aircraft with devices which protect against accidental retraction of the landing-gear may require special procedures for retraction below a certain airspeed. Before contemplating a short take-off procedure review the subject carefully in the aircraft's flight manual or owner's handbook.

It is not good enough to presume that the actual position of the landing-gear automatically corresponds with the position of the "up-down" selector. An aircraft may be flown for miles while the pilot searches for the reason for a poor performance, eventually to find that the landing-gear is still extended due to a popped circuit breaker or a blown fuse. The landing-gear position lights should be rechecked when power is reduced for the climb or as part of the after take-off check. Nearly all systems incorporate an arrangement of green lights to indicate that the gear is down and locked. Red lights warn that the landing-gear is up and they remain on when the gear is not down and locked. During the training period, the landing-gear will most likely be lowered during the cockpit check on the downwind leg prior to landing. However, there may be advantages to lowering it at a point more suitable to the operation. Therefore, it is important to set up a procedure to treat this action as an independent or additional check item, to be carried out on final approach. At controlled airports the control tower may add the words "check gear down and locked." The green and red gear position indicator lights in some aircraft are automatically dimmed when the position lights are switched on. This has caused more than one pilot to believe he did not have a "gear down" indication while flying at dusk, when the cockpit was not sufficiently dark to show that the lights were on. Switching the position lights off momentarily will confirm that the lights are functioning. If a light does not illuminate as expected, it may be burned out. Disconnecting a light that is functioning, and inserting it in the place of the suspected defective light will remove all doubt from your mind.

Taxiing

When the outside air temperature is below freezing, refrain from splashing through puddles of water or accumulations of slush to avoid the possibility of the landing-gear freezing in the "up" position after it has been retracted following take-off. If it is suspected that the landing-gear is wet or slush covered, delay retraction for a short period after take-off to allow freezing, and the possibility of a related mechanical malfunction to occur while the wheels are in a desirable "down" position.

Most aircraft manufacturers publish airspeed restrictions concerning the raising and lowering of the landing-gear of a specific aircraft. There is a maximum airspeed above which the landing-gear should not be retracted. In the case of some aircraft, above this maximum speed it will refuse to retract. There are often aerodynamic and control reasons for these speed restrictions: it is important to commit them to memory and placard them conspicuously in the cockpit.

Epilogue

The preceding pages of this Manual have outlined background knowledge and techniques which are time proven and have been formulated through the years by the learning experiences of others. It is impossible to put in print solutions to every possible situation which might arise, but the common sense application of the messages that this Manual has tried to transmit to you should leave you well prepared to face the world of aviation. Receipt of a new licence or endorsement is an acknowledgement that you have reached a certain level of competency and knowledge — you now have a licence to learn. Exercise the new privileges you have earned with care and responsibility. Keep an open mind,

and do not be afraid to ask questions or question the validity of ideas which have been accepted for many years as being gospel. Several "sacred cows" and "old wives' tales" have been laid to rest in the Manual, and only a questioning mind will find more effective solutions to problems and tabulate information which can be passed on to future generations of pilots by means of manuals such as this. Those of us who have put this Manual together are fully aware of the responsibility we bear and appreciate the opportunity we have been provided to pass on to you, the reader, the lessons learned from thousands of hours of collective experience as flight instructors.